Listen to Leaders in

MEDICINE

Listen to Leaders SERIES:

Listen to Leaders in BUSINESS
Listen to Leaders in LAW
Listen to Leaders in MEDICINE

In Preparation
Listen to Leaders in SCIENCE
Listen to Leaders in ENGINEERING

Listen to Leaders in

MEDICINE

Edited by

ALBERT LOVE and

JAMES SAXON CHILDERS

TUPPER AND LOVE / *Atlanta*

HOLT, RINEHART AND WINSTON / *New York · Chicago · San Francisco*

Designer: Ernst Reichl
85336–0313
Printed in the United States of America

Contents

Listen to Leaders in

MEDICINE

How This Series of Books
Came About

ONE SUNDAY AFTERNOON, a group of college students were sitting around talking and the talk drifted to what they wanted to do with their lives, the careers they wanted. Some wanted to be lawyers, but admitted they didn't know much about the law. Some were interested in medicine. Others spoke of business. They kept saying they wished they could talk with the "big men" in medicine, in business, law, and other professions.

We two older men—who have turned out to be the editors of this series of books—happened to be hearing all this and we decided that here was where we came in. The students wanted to be in touch with the top men (and hundreds of thousands of other young people want this same privilege), and so we decided we would see what could be done about it.

Since they had asked for top men, and since we were planning this whole series of books, we thought of various top men to write for each volume—medicine, law, business, and all the other books that are to come later—and we began by one of us going to see Mr. Justice Felix Frankfurter. He thought it a great idea, wonderful for the young people of the nation to have these men tell their experiences, answer questions, and give the advice and guidance that is so much wanted. Here was *really* something worth while. But a book! He was continuously busy on the Supreme Court—for this was before his retirement—and he had no possible time to write a book or any part of a book.

This was the way it was with everyone. None of the men or women we visited for any of these books could take time from work as a Justice of the Supreme Court, or a lawyer with a demanding practice; as Chairman of the Board, or President of some huge corporation; as a surgeon, a psychiatrist, or a doctor directing the work of some great hospital staff. Yet, each did take the time to write for young people, telling about business and the professions, telling how to make a career in whatever direction a young person wants to go.

In doing what they set out to do—to write their experiences and to advise and teach young people—these men and women have done a great deal more than that. As they related facts, both of the past and of the present, they unintentionally, unknowingly perhaps, disclosed their own philosophies of medicine, of law, of business, and so on. They not only shared their experiences but also their beliefs in an open and uncommon way. The books, therefore, are far more than books for young people only. They are of professional use to doctors, to lawyers, businessmen; they are of personal use and value to anyone.

To thank these writers is impossible. What they have done puts them beyond the province of thanks and establishes only the obligation of the editors and of the readers.

Each of the authors has written his chapter in his own way, in his own style, and they have not all exchanged chapters to compare them. For this reason there are some diversities of thinking and writing; actually, at times, disagreements, some of them sharp and important, and this is because each writer is talking solely for himself, telling what he himself has learned, what *he* believes. Yet one will notice that a few basic beliefs are repeated —some of them repeated again and again—and this is because these beliefs are common to the various writers; they are fundamentals in the study and practice of medicine. It is finally true, however, and unmistakably true that, as one reads the book, he recognizes that what they all say, when it is put together, can suggest to a person how to make a career, or to improve a career, and build a worth-while life for himself.

—A. L. and J. S. C.

1 *Medicine:*

AN INTRODUCTION

BY EDWARD D. CHURCHILL, M.D.

JOHN HOMANS PROFESSOR OF SURGERY, EMERITUS
The Harvard Medical School and

FORMER CHIEF OF GENERAL SURGICAL SERVICES
Massachusetts General Hospital

DR. EDWARD D. CHURCHILL

Born: 1895, Chenoa, Illinois

Northwestern University: B.S., 1916
                        A.M., 1917
Harvard Medical School: M.D., 1920
University of Algiers: Dr. Hon. Causa, 1944
Princeton University: D.Sc., 1947
Queen's University: LL.D., 1954
University of Alabama: D.Sc., 1959
Harvard University: D.Sc., 1961

Colonel, M.C., AUS: Surgical Consultant North African and Mediterranean
    Theaters, 1943–46
    Distinguished Service Medal
    Legion of Merit
    Chevalier Legion of Honor; Order British Empire; Comdr. Order
        Crown, Italy; War Medal of Brazil; Ordre du Cédre, Lebanon

John Homans Professor of Surgery, Harvard, 1931–62
    Emeritus since 1962
Chief General Surgical Services, Massachusetts General Hospital, 1948–62

Fellow American College of Surgeons
Fellow Royal College of Surgeons, England (Hon)
Fellow Royal College of University Surgeons of Denmark (Hon)
Member: American Surgical Association: President, 1946
    American Association for Thoracic Surgery: President, 1948
    Society Clinical Surgery: President, 1949
    Other U.S. and Foreign Surgical Societies

Alpha Omega Alpha
Sigma Xi
Delta Tau Delta

FROM THE point of view of an individual, medicine is a profession—perhaps "his" profession. From the vantage point of society, medicine is a social institution performing a truly important function in our civilization. By going into medicine one commits himself to carry forward the function or commitment of the profession with respect to society. I say "carry forward" because medicine would not have been accepted generation after generation by a changing society if its central tradition were a static one. It has not only survived but grown in stature because its commitment is to change—to the untiring quest for more effective ways to preserve health by the elimination of disease, and for more humane and effective methods to care for the sick and the suffering. Only as the profession restlessly seeks to unburden society of the need for the very function it performs does medicine truly meet its commitment.

Of the many professions open to young men and women today, three ancient ones bear the distinction of being called "learned" professions. These are: Law, Divinity, and Physic (Medicine). A quick glance at Law and Divinity will help to highlight some of the distinguishing features of Medicine.

The great tradition of the law in the United States lies in the judicial function which maintains government under the law. By the built-in mechanism of appeal to the Supreme Court, the Constitution itself, which was "designed for a developing nation," is constantly under study and subject to reinterpretation. The law thus responds to the changing circumstances of human society as pressures of conflicting interests reveal themselves. A judicial decision between conflicting interests which may even slightly alter the interpretation of the law is rendered only on the basis of an actual "case" heard by the court. Like medicine, the law is committed to gradual change and learns from experience with concrete circumstances that arise in the lives of the people. It can follow changes in their way of life that require new guidelines, or require review or repeal of the old, and it is committed to evolve with the profound social and economic changes that permeate twentieth-century society. In its history and in its growth, the law, like medicine, must be accepted by the people to be effective. It relies on the habit of the citizen to hold respect for the law. As expounded by the Supreme Court, law depends upon the confidence of the people in this Court as an institution.

In addition to the judicial function there is also a vast area of activity that reaches into our individual lives and within which a lawyer may and does give advice to his client and acts in his behalf. This has been called "lawyer's law." In a similar manner a physician advises and works for his patient. This could be called "doctor's medicine"—if not confused with some mixture in a bottle. One may lose confidence in a lawyer, but not in the law; in a doctor or in what is in the bottle, but not in medicine as an institution. Were we to renounce our confidence in government under law, our society would revert to anarchy or totalitarian dictatorship; loss of confidence in medicine as an institution would expose us to the plagues and pestilence of the Middle Ages and very likely carry us back to some primitive tribal way of life.

The clergy center on quite a different attribute of man than do either lawyers or physicians. Their commitment is toward the spiritual life of man, his striving to raise himself from the level of the beasts toward his God. The particular God or gods he identifies for himself are a matter of theological belief and doctrine, usually based on divine revelation. As such, theology is resistant to reinterpretation or change by the force of logic or reason.

It is difficult to envision a mechanism within the sphere of Divinity which might bring about gradual adaptive change. The clergy have been splintered into independent sects each with its own theology, its own interpretation of divinely revealed truth. Change takes place it is true, but typically by the emergence of a new sect associated with the teachings of some celebrated divine who shows the courage to dissent and expound a new system of theology which those who become his followers are ready to accept. In the same manner over centuries, changes came about in medicine through the capacity of some celebrated physician to move ahead, to seek more effective ways to cope with the problems of the sick and suffering who came to his door. Neither Medicine nor Divinity has built into itself a central mechanism such as the United States Supreme Court. A democratic government calls for the collective action and consent of people, but Divinity and Medicine (except for Public Health which is incorporated in government) typically deal with the individual person.

The medical profession, with its commitment to change, is a *learning* as well as a learned profession. For centuries, medicine, like the law, relied on the careful observation of actual "cases," and the cautious trial of new methods to see whether they might "work." Advance was agonizingly slow with this "trial and error" learning method; but more recently, medicine, along with other useful arts, has based its learning on a changed scientific approach to its problems. Because of this new approach, and in order to understand contemporary medicine more clearly, it is necessary for us to pause here for a moment and glance at Science—the moving force in the modern world which, in the present century, has reached a stature justifying its identification as the fourth learned profession.

It is, of course, beyond the scope of this chapter to provide even an outline of the origins of scientific thought. We can, however, come down through the annals of science to the sixteenth and seventeenth centuries when the vigor and speed shown by changes in scientific thought led to this period being called the era of the Scientific Revolution. Science, at this time, was making a new world—and the astounding and radical changes in the ways by which man sought an understanding of nature came from the application of mathematics to mechanics and the introduction of the experimental method.

The subject matter of physics and chemistry was most amenable to measurement and experimentation and in consequence these sciences developed most rapidly. In fact, chemistry soon branched off from medicine and became a science in its own right. Biology and human biology lagged somewhat behind because of the complexity of living organisms and the need for prior development of chemical and mechanical concepts. (A separate and later Biological Revolution, dating from about 1830 to 1870, has been recognized.)

Prior to the Scientific Revolution, medicine had already long been grounded on the descriptive and observational sciences, and subjects such as anatomy had become a well-developed study as early as the sixteenth century. Indeed, in 1628, William Harvey, anticipating the introduction of experiment into human biology, announced a discovery that united structure and function—the heart acts as a pump and the blood moves in continuous circulation through the body. Perhaps looking at the valves in the heart started Harvey thinking and soon he began simple experiments with the valves in his own veins. Measurement also played an important part in this discovery, for Harvey measured the capacity of the heart and found that in a single hour it pumped a much larger quantity of blood than the amount present in the whole body.

Later, with the Biological Revolution of the nineteenth century, medicine began rapidly to supplement the observational methods of its older descriptive sciences with the new science of experiment and precise measurement. A new medical science of physiology developed to carry onward the work of Harvey. Disease itself came to be regarded as an experiment conducted by nature and, when the preceding normal state was known, the results of nature's experiments were observed, measured when feasible, and interpreted. What I have called the central tradition of medicine and its commitments to society—that it must seek constantly for more effective ways to preserve health and eliminate disease—became based on the new science.

Science now underlies all technological activities of today's world. But the rate of increase in scientific activity cannot be realized until one considers the estimate that this activity has doubled every ten years since the time of Harvey's great discovery. It has been calculated that there are about ten times as many scientists living in the world today as the total number, prior to our immediate time, in all recorded history. And yet the goal of our society is to increase even this number. Our scientists today live in the well-protected environment of universities and institutes, the expenses of their higher education are paid, and their laboratories are built and equipped for them. Like a nest of ants caring for their aphid "cows," our society cares for its scientists with great affection, hoping that from time to time a drop of ambrosial nectar will be exuded which can be lapped up to the benefit of the nest as a whole.

Science, the fourth learned profession, is by its very nature a learning profession, and scientists are committed to factual and theoretical inquiry concerning the nature of the world. The so-called "Laws" of science (Newton's and Kepler's are familiar examples) are constantly subjected to study, reformulation, and specification as they are applied under new conditions. A scientist becomes celebrated when he discovers a new and revolutionary fact or law, the acceptance of which transforms the activities of the scientific community like an accepted judicial decision transforms the political realm. Between such revolutionary discoveries scientists carry on their practice of science within the conceptual framework of past achievements, not unlike practitioners of medicine, or lawyers practicing "lawyer's law."

After this thumbnail sketch of these four great professions, it is of interest to see what attribute they have in common. What quality distinguishes a profession from a vocation or a trade? Society grants professions a high order of autonomy and self-regulation and at times may provide them with solicitous care. The medal has two sides, however, and by unwritten contract, as I have already suggested, society expects something in return.

Of the Law, society expects government-under-law; of Divinity, nurture of the spiritual life of man; of Medicine, health; and, of Science, advance in knowledge. The people look to the three secular learning professions for changes which keep pace with their own changing worldly expectations and needs; to Divinity they look for guidance toward transcendent and eternal values.

Early in my course in medical school an educator of renown was invited to talk to the class. He was Charles W. Eliot, President Emeritus of Harvard University, then a very elderly man. "Gentlemen," he said, "a lasting regret of my life comes from not having been a member of the medical profession. I have worked with doctors and for doctors during the greater part of my life, but have always been aware of being an outsider. Medicine is more than a profession—it is a fraternity."

While all professions, and indeed many trades, bear certain earmarks of a fraternity, in no instance are they more evident than with medicine, except perhaps with those branches of the clergy which wear distinctive dress. One other occupation, or profession if you will, can be regarded as a fraternity, not because of distinctive dress, but because its members are bound with vows not to reveal their secrets—the society of magicians.

It is no happenstance that doctors, clergy, and magicians have in common the trait of making outsiders aware of being outsiders. In the early days of history, these three activities—magic, religion, and healing—were combined, and Egyptian, Babylonian, and Greek temples often took on many aspects of a hospital, along with those of a sanctuary dedicated to some god or goddess. Healing of illness of both body and mind was sought by prayer, votive offerings, and sacrifice to appease the gods, and by magic potions prepared from herbs and other strange mixtures.

The Greeks showed a great fondness for games and sports and today we carry on the Olympic championships in this tradition. It was natural then, as now, to place emphasis on personal hygiene and sane and healthy ways of living. Hippocrates, called the Father of Medicine, lived in Greece in the fifth century B.C. and taught simple rules of health, as well as an equally direct and common-sense approach to illness. Instead of believing, as the sick man did, that a pain in the side came from being struck by an arrow from the quiver of Apollo, Hippocrates made careful inquiry about the pain, when it started, and about

other symptoms that might have accompanied it. He also refused to fool the patient by giving him some magic charm to
protect him from an enemy or witch who was bringing about the
"stitch" in his side by sorcery.

Hippocrates and his followers thus began the separation of
the art of healing from magic trickery, and also from the belief
that illness was a manifestation of the anger or displeasure of a
supernatural being. Students were taught to look at a sick man to
see what changes in his appearance might have taken place because of illness, to listen to him and find out what he could tell
the doctor about his illness and, most important, to examine the
sick man by feeling for swellings, lumps, or painful places in the
body. And yet, to this very day primitive folk mix healing, magic,
and religion together. The doctor is expected to know, without
asking, when and where a pain started if he possesses the magic
power to heal. Even our own phrase "miracle drug" likens the
action of a powerful antibiotic to a cure attributed in olden times
to supernatural or Divine power.

The famous Oath of Hippocrates bound his students to a way
of life and conduct in their relations with those who sought help.
This code is commonly repeated today by classes of students as
they receive the academic M.D. degree. It is no longer looked
upon as an oath or vow, but serves as an historical reminder of
the responsibilities of a physician. It is symbolic of the fraternal
nature of the medical profession concerning which President
Eliot spoke. The wording of the Oath of Hippocrates is quaint,
and the meaning of certain phrases is not understood by scholars.
However, by obligating physicians to certain rules of conduct, it
stands as the cornerstone of the ethics of the profession. This is a
subject which will now be examined.

Many people are confused and at times annoyed by the behavior of a doctor because of his adherence to "professional
ethics." For example, a doctor will rarely if ever criticize a course
of treatment prescribed by another doctor, although if a patient
shifts the responsibility of his care from Doctor A to Doctor B,
the latter is then perfectly free to change the line of treatment if
he thinks it best for the patient.

Why, as a matter of professional ethics, not merely politeness, do doctors refrain from criticizing the methods of treatment advised by other doctors? To begin with, it should be recognized that the profession has no means by which it can compel its members to treat a patient in any particular manner. It has, therefore, no means by which it can criticize the methods used by an individual physician, so long as the treatment does no harm either directly or indirectly.

The careful observance of critical restraint is a fortunate custom among physicians. If criticism among them were common, the relationship between a doctor and his patient might be seriously, and most unfortunately, affected. A doctor has no authority or power to compel an individual patient to accept his advice in regard to treatment or an operation. A doctor's role with respect to his patient, with respect to other doctors, and in the society of which he is a part, is solely that of an adviser. His influence depends only on the faith which his patients, his fellow doctors, and his community have in him.

It is well known that many of the complaints which patients pour out to a doctor can be dispelled by his assurance that they are not signs of a serious disease. It is also known that faith in the doctor may reinforce the effectiveness of some remedy he may advise.

Let us look more closely at this word *faith*. In its early usage, faith referred to a relationship between two individuals, and meant trust by one human being in another. Later, particularly in theology, the term faith was held as the basis for belief in a statement or doctrine even though one could not fully understand its meaning. Converts to a religious sect, for example, might be asked to accept certain teachings by faith. Faith also plays its part in medicine: a sick man may have confidence in the doctor's advice or his prescriptions, but the patient's greater faith is in the doctor himself.

To use criticism—unless rightfully aimed at harmful practice—and thereby undermine a relationship of faith between two human beings, whether they be patient and doctor, man and wife, or parent and child, is not an act to be taken lightly. So far as a doctor and his patient are concerned, faith may be more decisive in bringing help than any medicine that could be prescribed. This is one reason for the belief of the medical profession that every patient should be free to choose his own doctor. The voluntary act of placing oneself under the guidance of a physician in itself engenders faith in him.

I have dealt with the question of why doctors refrain from criticism of each other at greater length than perhaps the subject deserves, but it has an additional merit for us in that it serves as an illustration of the roots, the very deep roots, of professional ethics. A doctor is licensed to practice under the law of his state, not by the profession or by the attainment of an M.D. degree; but laws are not sufficient, or even suitable, to shape and maintain such a relationship as that existing between a doctor and his patient. Beyond laws, a code of ethics is required, and the acceptance of such a code is the duty of any profession granted a high order of autonomy by society.

The need for autonomy by the medical profession, and for its self-regulation by a code of ethics, lies in the complexities of the services a doctor provides. A wide range of freedom of action must be permitted because no two situations are likely to be precisely similar. In one set of circumstances immediate operation, following a diagnosis of acute appendicitis, is urged; in other circumstances, the best interests of the patient is served by a calculated postponement of surgery. Limits exist, of course, beyond which the doctor cannot go in the exercise of his own judgment and such limits are firmly set by criminal law. The freedom given doctors is in fact an expression of public faith in the profession itself, similar to the faith that the individual patient holds in his personal doctor.

Looked at broadly, professional ethics are little more than a conventional behavior pattern to which members of the profession adhere. They strive to be "gentlemen of honor," of good taste, and to observe the norms of their society. This general ethic has been of particular significance in those countries in which social evolution has permitted the male physician to examine the disrobed female patient and to serve as obstetrician.

In addition to the intangible ethical generalities found in medicine, often as concepts of the Golden Rule, there are special ethics pertaining to the profession. Many of them were hammered out in eighteenth-century England, a period of wrangling and bitter disputes arising from jealousies, economic rivalries, pride, and a desire for prestige. That these controversies developed out of the socio-economic background of guild organizations is evidenced by the open hostilities displayed at that time between the three major guilds of physicians, apothecaries, and surgeons. The rivalries finally called forth explicit rules of conduct, or regulatory codes, which brought order into the various activities of the profession.

Without the quiet acceptance of self-regulation, primarily focused on what is best for the people, the development of skills within the complex structure of the various medical specialties could not have taken place. There have been other developments which could not possibly have been covered by the phrasing of a law. It is, therefore, beyond the limit of law that the self-regulation of professional ethics takes over. Without a code of ethics, in cases where no actual law has been violated, it would be next to impossible to protect the interests of the public.

It has been the experience of the medical profession that statements of ideals of conduct, examples set by recognized leaders, exhortations, and the glorification of past leaders, are insufficient measures. It is necessary for a group to codify its rules of behavior. Beginning with the Oath of Hippocrates, a code of ethics has, therefore, constantly served the medical profession as a guideline to self-regulation. Admittedly without the "teeth" of a legal regulation, the code nevertheless has protected a society which has been unable, or unwilling, to confine by law the complex acts that a physician must perform for the benefit of his patient.

Alert to changing modes of thought, medicine has shared and contributed greatly to the magnificent rise of science and to the development and skilled use of powerful tools so essential in maintaining or restoring the health of the people.

In these evolutionary changes medicine has kept ahead of the people. Hundreds of thousands, perhaps millions, of citizens in this supposedly enlightened nation are still immersed in a fog of ignorance and superstition with respect to the structure and functions of their own bodies. They fall victims to the twentieth-century magic of quacks and charlatans. A religious sect with deep conviction refuses to accept blood transfusion on the basis of ancient scriptural writings set down thousands of years ago, and wandering evangelists perform momentary "miracles" of divine healing by the laying on of hands after what has become known as the "pulpit pitch" to arouse emotional fervor.

The stories about doctors who strayed from ethical practice to become quacks might be amusing were it not for the tragic consequences of such deceptions. The ability to believe in the untrue and absurd seems boundless. "There is nothing," wrote Oliver Wendell Holmes, "men will not do, there is nothing they have not done, to recover their health and save lives. They have submitted to be half-drowned in water and half-choked with gases, to be buried up to their chins in earth, to be scarred with hot irons like galley slaves, to be crimped with knives like cod-fish, to have needles thrust into their flesh, and bonfires kindled in their skins, to swallow all sorts of abominations, and to pay for all this, as if to be singed and scalded were a costly privilege, as if blistering were a blessing and leeches a luxury."

The medical profession itself can have little influence on the gullibility of the public because, in exposing quacks, it is immediately suspected of furthering its own selfish interests. Dr. Holmes, however, in writing the above paragraph in the middle of the last century, was crying out not merely against the outrageous methods of quacks; he deliberately included some of the remedies prescribed by leaders of the regular profession in his day.

In sharp contrast with such practices, I come to tangible endeavors on the part of the medical profession for the benefit of the people of the United States. The most important and basic of these has been the establishment and maintenance of high standards in the education of the doctors who serve them.

It is not an easy task to raise the standards of medical education in a nation faced by the opening up of vast new geographical areas, with a rapidly expanding population, and with the rapid growth of large industrial cities calling for more and more doctors. Also the things a doctor must know have been changing constantly and multiplying in pace with advancing scientific discoveries. Further, medical education is only a four-year course tacked on to some fifteen years of preliminary preparation about which the profession has no voice.

The license to practice, as has been said, is under control of state governments; but the legislators are advised, with respect to educational requirements, by State Boards of Registration, made up of physicians. These Boards determine the number of years required in the study of medicine; they also set forth a broad designation of subjects held essential to the proper instruction of the would-be doctor. Furthermore, it is the Board's examination that finally tests the learning of the student. In all this, however, it must be recognized that State Boards are concerned primarily with registration, examination and licensure of those prepared to practice and not with the educational process itself. The standards they set are minimum ones.

Over the past fifty years, the action of the profession to raise educational standards has been exerted largely through the American Medical Association and its Council on Medical Education. As these standards have been raised, they have been invested with legal authority, yet kept sufficiently flexible by the State Boards to permit a desired slow and steady elevation. In this century, scores of fly-by-night proprietary medical schools have been closed by refusal to grant licenses to their graduates. These schools, known as "diploma mills," extracted tuition from unsuspecting students and gave little worth-while instruction in return. Similar exploits on foreign soil, that in no way met USA standards, were discouraged by warning young Americans that licensure could not be granted on the basis of "degrees" from certain specified sources.

In its educational endeavor the profession was aided by American universities as these institutions increased in number and developed graduate schools. Large foundations, notably The Rockefeller, The Commonwealth Fund and more recently, The Ford Foundation, have given support to both medical schools and teaching hospitals. Gifts of private philanthropy have been many and generous.

It must be remembered that this reform in medical education

began in the last century when it became apparent to farseeing
educators that the rising tide of science was destined to have a
profound effect in the world of medicine. Courses in medical science were added to the curriculum until nearly two full years of
science studies came to precede the clinical instruction. Previously a high-school boy could spend two years reading medical
texts, attending lectures, and serving time as an apprentice to
a practicing doctor. Then he could open his own office and start
to practice. Little wonder that he blistered his patients, applied
leeches, and dosed them with "abominations" as his predeces-
sors had done!

Doctors of older generations, trained in the older ways, remained largely unaware of the tidal wave of biological science
and it is not surprising that many took a firm stand *against* the
intrusion of science. They felt that there was something mysteri-
ous about it, possibly a return to magic, certainly a puzzling de-
viation from the ordinary practical way of doctoring. Every effort
to measure with accuracy those aspects of disease with which
they were fumbling in daily routine met with opposition. The
measurement of body temperature with a thermometer, the determination of blood pressure in millimeters of mercury, the
scrubbing of the hands and putting on of rubber gloves before
operating—all were ridiculed and scorned in turn. Even to this
day, the introduction of a new laboratory measurement will pro-
voke remarks from oldsters about overemphasis on laboratory
findings, with an expression of nostalgia for the days when the
severity of a disease and its response to treatment were guessed
at, rather than precisely measured. Hospital treasurers who formerly protested the number of leeches that had to be supplied,
began to grumble about the expense of laboratory examinations
and X-ray films.

Despite the inertia and bewilderment of large numbers of the
profession, the educators had their way, strongly supported by
the leaders of the profession. The grandfathers of doctors practicing today found it necessary to spend two or more years in
Europe if they were to secure an education that prepared them
for their times. The fathers of these same doctors found it essential to go to Europe to get training as specialists. But today, the
medical education available in the United States to young men

and women who will be responsible for the health of the American people of tomorrow is second to none in the world.

Beyond the need for better general education in medicine, there arose in past decades the need for higher educational and training standards for the various medical specialists. The solution called for the co-operation of the thousands of hospitals in the nation, rather than that of the universities, for specialist skills are largely acquired in hospitals after the M.D. degree.

In raising the standards and requirements that lead to a certification of specialists, the medical profession has retained the responsibility in its own hands. Moreover, the Specialty Boards, which examine a candidate and issue a certification, are responsible only to professional associations and societies. Since the field of the specialties is too complex, and too changing, to attempt to freeze it by any form of legal regulation, a Specialty Board has restricted authority only.

The Board can say: "Dr. John Does has met the requirements and passed the examination of this Board as of this date." The Board does not have a negative authority and it cannot say: "Dr. John Doesn't shall *not* undertake surgical operations or identify himself as a specialist in this or that field." Yet, while the Board has no denying authority, an individual hospital can say, and some do, that only certified specialists may practice their specialty within its walls.

In 1940, residency training programs in one or more specialties were approved in 587 hospitals in the United States and these hospitals offered 5,118 residency positions. By 1960, the number of hospitals with approved specialty programs had grown to 1,307, and the number of residencies to 31,733. During this same period the number of internships increased from 7,998 in 736 hospitals, to 12,580 in 865. Also, the number of medical-school graduates since 1940 has increased about 40 per cent, and yet has not kept pace with the internships offered.

The subject of specialist training penetrates to the very core of a question that is being asked today. If, as is said, careless, inept, or unnecessary surgical operations are being performed, why doesn't the medical profession do something about it?

The nation is rightly proud of its system of community hospitals. Fund-raising drives are launched, matching funds for construction flow from the Federal Government under the Hill-Burton Act, and a new hospital is built or a shiny new surgical wing added. Such a hospital is "owned" by the people of the community and run by a lay Board of Managers. It is they who decide if Dr. Doesn't, whose name is not listed in a published Directory of American Specialists, shall perform surgical operations in their hospital. Actually, when hospital Boards have faced up to their responsibilities, and, if necessary, have sought outside advice from leading members of the profession, it has been demonstrated repeatedly that high-class surgery can be established in a community.

During the rapid growth of the hospital system in the nation, there have been other questions involving standards in patient care. For example, hospitals require licenses in most, if not all states, and legal regulations deal with such matters as fireproofing, sanitation, and food handling.

Despite these and all other legal regulations, the American College of Surgeons many years ago saw that if the public's need for safe surgery was to be met, professional standards far beyond measures that a state could specify would be needed. Surgery must be safeguarded by foolproof measures for sterilization, by written records of a patient's illness, his care, and many other safety controls. The establishment of this program was accomplished by rewarding a hospital which met the standards, publicly announced by the College of Surgeons, with a certificate that it had done so. Furthermore, inspections were conducted at intervals by invitation of the Board of Managers and the certificate could be withdrawn, if the requirements were no longer met. In recent years, the surgeons broadened the base of control by joining with the American Medical Association and the American Hospital Association in an accreditation board that now carries on this important service to the public. And yet, across the nation, some communities still patronize hospitals which have not attempted to meet these reasonable standards.

There are many other ways in which the medical profession has endeavored to justify the faith expressed by the public and fulfill its obligation to regulate itself. This matter of regulation raises the question of what is meant by "organized" medicine, and I should like briefly to explain the term.

The medical profession is not "organized" in the same sense that labor is organized into unions for the purpose of collective bargaining with employers. A doctor must rely for his living on payments for the services he provides his patients, and collective bargaining is impossible. The American Medical Association is not a union, but, as its name indicates, an *association*. It provides a forum for myriads of small, usually solo-conducted, businesses.

The view is commonly expressed that the profession should regulate its internal affairs more vigorously, using controls to govern the actions and behavior of its individual members. "Organized" medicine has none of the devices of the modern tight organizations in industry that are equipped with the authority to hire and fire; nor does it have any control mechanism with the power of exerting sanctions. The profession holds no police power over its members and, furthermore, this country is not a totalitarian nation that would tolerate practices amounting to a secret police force probing into relationships between doctors and their patients.

It should be pointed out, too, that withdrawal of a labor-union membership card carries a threat of unemployment because of the "closed shops." Withdrawal of membership in the American Medical Association and the State Medical Society may bar some individual doctors from admitting their patients to certain hospitals because of locally accepted hospital rules; but thousands of doctors and other types of practitioners, including notorious quacks and cults, carry on practice in this country without membership in the societies of "organized" medicine.

The difference between *external regulation by law,* and *self-regulation* in conformity to a code of ethics, must be kept clearly in mind. While the profession has no legal or organizational teeth to enforce sanctions against an erring member, there are committees set up by state medical societies to provide hearings for dissatisfied patients, to carry out investigations, and, when indicated, to present evidence to state licensing boards which may suspend or repeal licenses to practice.

At this time, I think that we should consider the posture assumed by "organized" medicine—that is, the American Medical Association—with respect to those subjects that become issues in the arena of national politics.

The profound social and economic changes due to industrialization, to urbanization, to recessions and depressions; the increase in the number of citizens over sixty-five years of age; the falling value of the dollar; the rising expectation of man himself to enjoy a way of life unknown amid the hardships endured by past generations—all these forces, and many others, directly affect the doctor, affect the availability of the tools with which he works, and his own standard of living.

Ideally, of course, he should express his political convictions not as a doctor but as a citizen through the established political party system. Practically, when an issue arises that directly affects medicine, he is likely to amplify his individual voice by speaking through his fraternal associates who constitute the State Medical Society or the American Medical Association.

It has been pointed out that doctors who make their living in the practice of medicine, and the vast majority of them do, are, from the economic standpoint, independent small businessmen. On the political spectrum, they are with other small businessmen and to the right of center. That is, the average doctor is a conservative. More than he realizes, a doctor has certain chameleonlike qualities which lead him to take on the protective coloration of his environment. Texas doctors talk like Texans, may wear ten-gallon hats (outside of Texas) and more important, *think* like Texans; doctors in the Deep South may collect, as a hobby, paper money of the Confederacy—and so on. Outside of his office the average doctor fades into the landscape of the upper middle class, from which his patients come, and spends his precious hours of relaxation at the country club, on the golf links, on fishing or hunting expeditions, or other recreational pursuits of his clientele. His primary task is to influence people with respect to their health affairs; to do this, he seeks to make friends with them and frequently is in accord with their national and community political views.

In further regard to politics, these physicians, as I have described them, are aware of changing conditions and find justification for political action because the rising cost of medical care is being laid at their door. They are ever fearful lest some ill-informed politician, on the prowl for votes, should seize on medical care as a "political football," promising to reduce costs by increasing government control of what is called the "distribution of medical care"—that is, medical practice. Doctors rally to the alarm of "socialized medicine" just as other citizens are aroused to oppose foreign aid, the United Nations, a sales tax, or whatever political issues they view with enthusiasm or dismay according to their political convictions.

Another reason for medicine to step into the political scene is the greatly increased number of legislative bills—pertaining directly or indirectly to health, education, and welfare—that are being dropped into the hoppers of the national Congress. Some of these have no implication of political significance, either conservative or liberal; some gain support or encounter opposition in purely tactical political party maneuvers; while others rely for implementation on judgments and decisions that require the expert knowledge of physicians.

Doctors are constantly at work within this web of legislative technology, not necessarily seeking to protect their own interests, for there are left-wing doctors as well as right-wingers. They are summoned to legislative hearings and asked openly to advise legislative committees with respect to bills that have to do with medical research, animal experimentation, the drafting of doctors for service in the Armed Forces, financial aid to medical education, and many other measures that directly or indirectly have to do with the health of the American people.

It has frequently been charged that the AMA has opposed many forward steps in the economics of medical care which subsequently have proven to be of value and have been universally accepted. It might be worth while, at this moment, to recall that one of the most common techinques in the political realm is for one side to appropriate a high moral purpose—the higher the better—as their sole possession, and then to propose a means by which they intend to accomplish it. Anyone who attacks the means is then accused of opposing the end. Actually the high moral purpose—the health of the American people—is held in common by the profession as well as by the politician. Arguments about the means must never be confused with the desire to achieve an end. Peace, for example, is desired by every sane man in the world. Whether peace can best be achieved through armament or disarmament is an argument about means. It is not fair, in the rules of debate, to accuse the advocates of a strong defensive force of being warmongers. It is always wise to examine any charges regarding an end, when in reality only the means are being debated.

For better or worse, the American medical profession has become a participant in the political life of the nation. The price paid has been a high one, particularly when the profession is accused of opposing what appear to be constructive measures designed to meet socio-economic changes in our society. An unfortunate part of the price has been the possible changing (or, as some say, "tarnishing") of the "image" of the doctor in contemporary society.

Regardless of the "image" which people form about doctors, it should be admitted that the medical profession, like any other segment of the population, has its share of incompetents, loafers, phonies, dollar-minded tradesmen, and other ill-motivated persons. It is highly probable, however, that the efforts demanded in medical training, and in meeting the educational requirements for an M.D. degree, provide the medical profession with a higher proportion of idealistic and well-meaning citizens than is found in any random cross section of the population. Certainly, I am happy to express my faith in the competence and integrity of the young men and women I see going into medicine today. They are serious and hard-working, broadly concerned with the health and welfare of our society, and determined to do their best to meet the *needs* of the American people, although it can be predicted that great difficulty will be experienced in trying to satisfy all of their increasing *wants*.

Wants demand medical *service;* needs require medical *care.* At the first visit of a patient, the doctor assesses the need for medical care, and, if such need exists, provides for it, either directly or indirectly. Wants, on the other hand, may be deemed urgent by the client but interpreted otherwise by the doctor. Nevertheless, if they are not quickly met, the service is likely to be thought unsatisfactory.

The foreword to the Special Supplement of the October, 1960 issue of *Harper's* opened with two statements: "1. American medicine is the best in the world. 2. Millions of people are dissatisfied with the medical care they are getting." The paradox can be resolved by changing a single word in the second statement: "medical care" should read "medical service." Urbanized and industrialized American society makes service a keynote of satisfaction. The refrigerator, the TV set, the dishwasher, the washing machine, all must be serviced promptly on demand in the home or apartment. Hotels are rated on whether the service is poor or excellent, and if room service falters in meeting the wants of the guest, dissatisfaction is expressed immediately.

In the area of service, what does one hear about doctors today? Doctors are hard to get. They will not make house calls. They are too busy. A common criticism is, "We want doctors to listen more, to explain more. We want to talk to them more." An economist has said that when a society reaches the stage of affluence, wants are increasingly created by the very process by which they are satisfied. It is not too farfetched to believe that these mounting wants and demands for service, which harass the family doctors particularly in well-to-do suburban communities, are making this form of practice less attractive to young men. It is of more than passing interest to recall that in 1930 about 69 per cent of students chose the career of family doctor for their life work; in 1960 only 35 per cent expressed this choice.

Correlated with this is the increasing number of applicants for admission to medical schools who say they look forward to working in underdeveloped lands, where the needs for medical care crowd in from every side, but wants are few. Analysis of motivation in such a matter is admittedly complex, and today's young people are shy about expressing a simple desire to be of help to their fellow man. To do so might expose them to being told that they are corny or perhaps escapists. The fact remains that most doctors find their satisfaction in meeting the needs of sick and suffering people, and it is not difficult for me to understand why a student's Walter Mitty projection of his career is more attractive against a jungle background than in landscaped suburban America where wants are insistent, but needs are comparatively few.

It seems quite proper, at this time, to mention a fact which is of great significance to us—it is to be found in the social outlook which has converted health from a privilege of the favored few to the right of all. When this right is viewed against the predictions of the rise in population in this country, the reason for beginning to sift wants from needs becomes apparent. The magnitude of the task of medical service that lies ahead, if this screening is not done, lies basically in a characteristic of the American people underlined by De Tocqueville in 1832 and called by him a "passion for physical well-being." He found that "uppermost in every mind" was the desire "carefully to satisfy even the least wants of the body." If this desire is focused on momentary wants and minor ailments, the doctor's service work load will get dangerously out of hand.

Measures are already under way to increase the supply of doctors, but there are difficulties. "Even to maintain the present ratio of physicians and dentists" (to population), the President has said, "we must graduate 50 per cent more physicians and 90 per cent more dentists per year by 1970." This will require not only the expansion of existing schools, but also the construction of at least twenty new schools of medicine and the same number for dentistry. The administration's program for federal aid to education has taken this into account and includes grants for the construction of both medical and dental schools. Even with more new schools, however, many qualified young men and women could not afford the long and expensive training. President Kennedy, therefore, made a second point and proposed that four-year scholarships be provided for 25 per cent of medical and dental students.

It is fortunate that the standards of medical education had already been brought to a high level before such pressing urgency for expansion arose. The supply of physicians cannot be measured merely in its quantitative aspect. Quality is of paramount importance. One reason for this is that the profession, for the first time in its long history, has come into possession of powerful tools. These, as I have implied, have been developed in consequence of medicine's dependence on, and association with, science. Because these tools are of value only when applied with professional skill and learning, it may be said that the profession holds a monopoly on their use. The emphasis on the quality of medical education, and the competence of the physicians themselves, becomes understandable as one recognizes that the powerful tools of contemporary medicine must be used with expert skill, for they determine the issue between life and death; between hopeless crippling and useful life span.

More tools are coming, being forged in the laboratories of science, and less than first-rate medical care is expensive care— expensive in dollars if poorly educated doctors ineffectually prescribe costly remedies, and expensive in life and suffering if powerful tools are used incorrectly or not at all. In anticipation of the establishment of new schools, the Federal Government has already turned its attention, through its National Institutes of Health, to the scientific education of young physicians to prepare them for positions in the new faculties that must be formed. There is no thought of returning to diploma mills or horse-and-buggy doctoring which, at one time, may have comforted the frightened and anxious family, but could bring little more than courage and cheerfulness to the sick or disabled patient.

These measures to educate more doctors and to assure that they remain *learning* doctors will go a long way toward meeting the major problems confronting us. In addition, it appears inevitable that doctors themselves must find ways to make more effective use of their time. No one can envision replacing a doctor's service by automation; but the doctor himself must be ready, as soon as his patients are receptive, to move forward into the jet age. His methods of practice need revision to bring specialist skills into greater integration with general practice. His access to diagnostic tools as well as methods of treatment needs improvement. Practice in groups is increasing. Greater use of technical assistance by nonmedical personnel can be anticipated. Computers are already being introduced into hospitals as time-saving devices for the recall of information about patients seen previously.

The people may well have to accustom themselves to, and be willing to accept, a new type of medical service in order to obtain the benefit of a more effective form of medical care. Communities can bestir themselves and devise means of coping with problems that are now being unloaded onto the shoulders of doctors. The physician can and will act as expert adviser, but it is not really essential that he grapple personally with many of the complaints of old age, loneliness, unhappy marriage, juvenile delinquency, poverty, and malnutrition, to name only a few of the maladjustments of today.

When health becomes the right of all, medical care is no longer related to the patient's capacity to pay. Last summer two good Vermonters were giving my small cottage a much-needed coat of white paint. When they knocked off for lunch, I joined them and entered into their conversation. A few months earlier one of them had spent several days in a community hospital not far away having his hernia repaired. He was still smarting about the size of the *total* bill for his care. "If I had my way," he complained, "I'd shut those doctors up inside that hospital and tell them to go to work to bring down the cost."

"Jim," I said, "I am a citizen of this town just as you are. I pay taxes on this house, just as you pay taxes on yours. When there was a drive for funds to build the hospital, I helped out just as you did. If you were sick in your own house, you might want me to come in and take a look at you; but would you expect me to bring in groceries to feed you, supply clean sheets for your bed, and sit by to give you your medicine every hour or so? If you were in need, everyone in town would be chipping in to take care of you through the taxes we pay, and I would certainly be contributing my share. But just because I am a doctor is no reason to think that I should feed you, provide a bed for you, and come to your house and nurse you. The community built and maintains a hospital for this purpose, a place for people to go and be taken care of when they can't be taken care of at home. This hospital doesn't belong to the doctors and they don't profit from it. The cost that seems high to you is because the cost of daily hospital care has risen from $9.36 in 1946 to $32.23 in 1960."

This little incident is mentioned merely to illustrate how twisted even the elementary principles of medical economics can become in the minds of well-meaning people. One of the first breakdowns that should be made is to separate the cost of hospital care from the charge by the doctor for his professional services. It is quite true that certain doctors, particularly in the specialist groups, are guilty of charging excessive fees that bring discredit on themselves and on their profession; but it is not likely, now or in the future, that fortunes of any significant size will accrue from the practice of either medicine or surgery. The cost of medical care is an exceedingly complex problem and is being actively discussed and investigated at the present time, but it is beyond the scope of this chapter to do more than identify it.

A doctor is likely to express himself (which I did on one occasion) in the following manner: "A sound and healthy citizenry is the prime requisite to create, staff, and run a modern nation." An economist is likely to reverse the statement and declare: "A modern nation through its productivity accumulates wealth, part of which, if it so elects, can be expended to improve the health of its citizens." Here is the old problem of the hen and the egg. The doctor is exerting his energies to organize, educate for, and control an expansion which from his viewpoint is itself the end. The economist argues that health does not produce wealth, but that wealth provides for health.

The Minister of Health in England has wisely referred to expenditure upon the health services as "like all those other expenditures of which neither the purpose nor the outcome is economic benefit but which are the specific mark of a human society, and, in their elaboration and refinement, distinguish a civilized nation from an uncivilized, an advanced culture from a backward one."

Public health is provided through taxes. Medical care—that is, hospital expenses and doctors' services to individuals—is met in several ways: in part, through tax-financed governmental agencies (veterans, armed forces, tuberculosis, mental diseases, hospitals for the poor, and so on); in part, by spreading the cost through insurance; and, in part, by direct payment from patient or family.

Financing by taxation and by insurance are examples of collective action; the former by the taxpayers of a governmental unit, the latter by a group of voluntary insurance-premium payers. The trend for wage-earning and salaried people, a trend which extends into the foreseeable future, is to spread and prepay the cost of illness by insurance coverage.

Rising costs of all kinds increase tax and premium payments, and the various states already have their responsibilities to regulate insurance-premium rates. As the number of citizens covered by insurance increases, this supervision and control will inevitably increase. When government takes a dollar from the pay envelope of a wage earner, or permits an insurance agency to do so, it assumes a responsibility to provide competent medical care in return. This may be done directly by building hospitals and hiring doctors; or indirectly by subsidizing insurance plans. With the inevitability of this increased control in mind, it should now be apparent why doctors tend to be conservatives rather than liberals with respect to measures which increase the participation of government in fiscal aspects of medical care.

Against this background it is pertinent for us to return to the problem posed by society's wants and needs. Wants are aroused in a person by *symptoms,* real or imaginary; a symptom is a subjective experience related to the bodily functions and structure about which the average layman is so profoundly ignorant. Everyone has symptoms but not necessarily symptoms of disease. Having symptoms may be a perfectly normal state and their intensity and their frequency are known to increase with anxiety or rough stretches on the road of life. Headache, looseness or costiveness of bowels, indigestion, burping, cough, weakness, dizziness and many other symptoms can be normal experiences of healthy people. When medical service is "free," that is, made available to the individual through collective action of society by tax or insurance support, floodgates are opened to an endless flow of people wanting to be relieved of their symptoms, or at least assured that they mean nothing serious. Even with a direct cash payment as a barrier, it has been estimated that three patients out of five consulting their family doctor express such wants.

In passing, it is also important to recall, when we say that "health makes wealth," that doctor's medicine, sometimes called curative medicine, is one of the less important measures in the health of a nation. Housing, sanitation, pure water and milk, personal hygiene, recreation, exercise, food, working hours and conditions under which work is performed, as well as education itself—in other words, a sane way of life, as Hippocrates taught —go far toward maintaining a healthy citizenry.

As with politics, like it or not, the activities of the medical profession have taken their place as one of the dynamisms of the socio-economic life of the nation. Medicine is subject to scrutiny from all sides and, in the end, the limits of its extension and expansion will be determined by objective appraisal and measurement against the nonmedical wants and needs of the American people. Social engineering has replaced ideology in a modern democracy committed to solving social problems by organization, efficiency, and the general welfare. In health and illness, however, the roots of problems penetrate deeply into the subsoil of irrational man where they cannot be reached by the light of reason.

Cries of alarm about "socialized" medicine can at this point be more clearly understood. They are protests against looking on medicine purely as a utilitarian service. As brought to bear on the wants and needs of the people of a society, medicine is an applied social science—one of the oldest, in fact. Carried forward from the nineteenth century, "socialism" is a discredited word, identified today with communism by some persons of the extreme right political wing. Actually, a large segment of the medical care of the American people is already fiscally "socialized," that is financed in whole or in part by the collective mechanisms of insurance or taxation. It is that other portion of medical care covered in part by voluntary insurance, subject only to the light touch of state insurance commissioners, and that portion of individual care provided by direct arrangements between doctor and patient, which remain "unsocialized."

It is this "unsocialized" practice that the doctors and the American Medical Association are struggling to maintain in the so-called "free enterprise" sector. It is often said that doctors are fighting for their own selfish interests. Admittedly it is difficult to

separate self-interest from either person concerned in any interpersonal service. The doctor, however, knows full well that sickness, even imagined sickness, is a matter of alarm not of logic.
The care of the sick is a far more complicated matter, as I have
shown, than the provision of a utilitarian technical service. The
nonlogical experience of illness touches off a chain reaction of
emotions that extends beyond the patient to family, friends, and
sometimes to the community. The spectrum of fear ranges from
the negativism of ignorance to a pressing insistence that things
beyond all reason be provided or accomplished. A terrifying
sense of urgency may be real or imagined. Sickness brings loneliness and uncertainty—one's destination is clearly stamped on
an airline ticket, but not so on a card for hospital admission.

These emotional aspects of illness are faced by the doctor
many times a day. They cannot be quieted by reason. Faith, as I
have defined the term, in the doctor and in the profession, or in
some particular hospital or clinic, may introduce a harmless
touch of ancient magic or the scent of burning incense. The important issue is that the sacrifice shall not strip the man of his
flocks and that in return he receive the full benefit of scientific
technology if needed.

While a doctor may assent to these words, the economists
and social engineers cannot be expected to comprehend their full
significance. In estimating the circumstances that will surround
the practice activities of the medical profession of the future—
particularly its responsibility to make medical care available to
all the people—it is essential that reasons be given for preserving
a private sector of medical care based solely on the consideration of the long-range benefit to society itself. It is my personal
conviction that these reasons are so compelling that, barring a national catastrophe, a large segment of individual medical care
will continue in the foreseeable future to be provided by direct
fiscal arrangements between doctors and patients. To avoid the
use of the unpalatable and vague words "socialized medicine,"
let this be called the private sector as contrasted with the public
sector.

The learning functions of the profession, and therefore its ability to change in adaptive evolution with the American people,

will be threatened by entanglement in the web of democratic government. Democracies are becoming existential societies, quite different from societies with ten-year plans and directed futures. "We seem to be flexible," C. P. Snow is quoted in an editorial in *The Lancet* as having said, "but we haven't any model of the future before us. In the significant sense we can't change. And to change is what we have to do.

"Some of the most important choices about a nation's physical health," Snow continues, referring to the National Health Service of England, "are made, or not made, by a handful of men, in secret, and again in legal form, by men who normally are not able to comprehend the arguments in depth."

After having completed the quotation from Snow, the editorial itself declares, ". . . the history of the National Health Service since 1948 has shown again and again that major questions of policy vital to its development have been decided at Treasury or Cabinet level without any evidence that those taking the decision were 'able to comprehend the arguments in depth,' or, if they were, that they paid sufficient heed to them."

One thing should be made clear: It is not my intent to find fault with the National Health Act of England as a measure to meet the post-World War II needs of England in 1948 when the act was passed. As evidenced by the above extracts from a 1961 issue of their leading medical journal, the point at issue now is the lack of comprehension brought to bear on the problems of a social institution of the size and complexity of medicine when it is bound within a parliamentary governmental structure. Also, there is the lack of sensitivity to the constant needs for change.

A quotation from James Reston in the December 3, 1961, issue of the New York *Times* will show what I mean. "The big news in the world today," he writes, "is not what the politicians and statesmen are saying but what the people are doing. Almost everywhere the activities of Governments are running behind the activities of the people. Despite all the talk of the rising authority of government, it is the energy of the family, the creativity of the scientist and the engineer, and the willful purpose of millions of individuals in all the continents that are shaping the modern world."

It was with reluctance that I introduced this controversial semipolitical and philosophical discussion into a chapter to be read by young people considering medicine as a career. My reasons for doing so are based on evidence that the fears and gloom of some of the older doctors in the profession are being reflected in the attitude of young people at its threshold. "We do not want to hear what medicine *was*," they say; "we want to know what it is *going to be.*" And rightly so!

Let it be frankly admitted that the medical profession and society itself have been thrown off balance in the socio-medico-economics of medical care. Many more facts and carefully planned experiments are needed to clarify the issues involved and protect the long-range interest of the American people. Research and investigation in this area have lagged far behind the effort that an active industry exerts on its management problems. The Public Health Service is currently spending about $2,250,000 to support research on the administration of hospital and medical-care services. Voluntary agency and foundation spending in this area is probably somewhat less. This means that altogether perhaps four to five million dollars, or $\frac{1}{50}$ of 1 per cent of all health expenditures, is being invested in attempts to understand how a twenty-six-billion-dollar industry functions and how to improve its operations.[1] This investment of five million dollars is a minute amount in relation to the magnitude of the problem. Very few of the elements involved have received more than superficial attention.

My personal conviction is that American medicine will continue to have two sectors—public and private—and that from time to time as the population increases, and as needs arise for medical service beyond what the resources and manpower of the profession can supply, segments of medical care will be transferred to the public sector or will be heavily subsidized within the private sector by governmental fiscal support. Similar transfers have taken place in this nation for a century when needs for

---

[1] Of the $26.5 billion the nation spent in 1960 for health and medical care, about $20 billion was spent privately, including $5.3 billion for hospital care, $5.1 billion for physician services, and $3.9 billion for drugs, according to the 1962 edition of the "Statistical Abstract of the United States."

medical care, which include giving shelter to the sick, have exceeded the ability of the individual to pay for them. For the long-range benefit of the American people themselves, the following functions will remain in the private sector in the foreseeable future:

1. Medical service to economically privileged patients who seek physicians or physician-groups of their own choice in institutions of their own preference.

2. The establishment and maintenance of standards in health measures—with continuing and convincing demonstrations of their merits. (These standards must be reflected in the public sector.)

3. Constant adaptation of medical activities to socio-economic changes taking place regionally. Such changes are inevitable with industrialization and urban development.

4. The quick appraisal of new methods in making medical care available to the people, and the adaptation of these methods to regional community needs.

5. Advance and change in methods and tools that emerge from unhampered scientific endeavor. The time lag between scientific discovery and wide application will be reduced. In this area, university faculties can be expected to exert leadership, as they are now doing, because this function transcends the ability of the practicing doctor.

6. Standard setting and adaptive changes in medical education, shared by state-financed medical schools and privately endowed university schools—both aided by federal funds. Medical education is far from being a fixed pattern and must be viewed in continuity with preceding education and subsequent hospital training. The content will be shaped by scientific advance and applied community needs. Specialties will be shaped by the changing needs of the people and not by the projection of self-interested specialist guilds.

Medicine on this broad pattern will continue to offer incentive and inner satisfaction to young and old members of the profession, and, what is more important, continue to be acceptable to the American people, for it will be quickly responsive to their changing needs.

While I defend the need for a private sector on the above

grounds, and am confident that these or closely similar circumstances will prevail, one condition is essential. Doctors cannot exploit their position of power over human welfare as one of economic privilege rather than one of professional responsibility. To retain the desired freedoms of a private sector for selected functions, the profession by its own self-discipline must assure its status as a learned profession which merits the confidence of the people.

Careers within medicine are numerous and varied, in fact one of the major problems of medical education is to provide even a glimpse of these varied opportunities and varied ways of life so that a student may select a sphere of activity within which he will be able to develop his personal talents. While, for the sake of clarity, this chapter has centered on the practice of medicine, there are careers as family doctor, surgeon, internist, psychiatrist, obstetrician, and many others that differ greatly among themselves. Also, there is the medical teacher, the medical scientist, the clinical investigator, the medical administrator, and others, some of whom may participate in practice activities as well.

Specialism ranges from concentration on a number of disorders with certain features in common, to concentration on a single disease or organ. Then there is industrial medicine, military medicine, tropical medicine, medical jurisprudence, preventive medicine, and public health which calls for an added academic degree. All of these have within themselves a variety of sub-careers. Shortly after a student enters medical school, he begins to think about selecting a field—broad or narrow—and is amazed to find how many doors there are ahead, and how many stand open.

There is only one argument for selecting medicine as a career: that it seems at the time to be the desirable thing to do. Other arguments tend to persuade the young man or woman *not* to take up medicine. In his great book *The Wealth of Nations*, Adam Smith, in 1776, wrote: "The contempt of risk and the presumptuous hope of success, are in no period of life more active than at the age at which young people chuse their professions." His book celebrated the appearance of a new kind of man—the economic man who was destined to shape the modern world by participation in the industrial revolution. The "success" Adam Smith envisioned came to be measured in terms of economic achievement and ultimately in the building of individual fortunes.

One can speak about such success in any kind of career, including the professions; and, in an age of economic materialism, it is remarkable that so many men continue to enter medicine, a field in which opportunities for fortune do not exist. The best to be said is that by reasonable effort they will make a comfortable living, be able to raise a family and educate the children. The very fact that the profession has lagged behind in solving its socio-economic problems, yet forged ahead in other activities, is good evidence that it is not dominated by men with a "presumptuous hope of success" measured in terms of wealth. Clever businessmen would have solved their economic problems to their own advantage long ago.

The reason medicine "appeals" to a man, the reason the decision to enter it may seem "desirable" or "right," often is far from clear to the man who makes it. When asked why he "wants" to go into medicine, an applicant for admission to a school can rarely give a meaningful answer. It is later, once he becomes a part of medicine, that he can find reasons, or at least rationalizations, for continuing. These usually center on the inner satisfaction or elation his daily work provides.

My forty years of close contacts with medical students, interns, residents, and physicians leave me as inarticulate as the applicant for admission, when I attempt to identify the intangibles which make medicine "appeal" to men. What is it that leads a young surgeon, during those long and lean training years of economic hardship, to say that he has never worked so hard and never enjoyed life more?

Perhaps it is that little streak of magic that still clings to his achievements. Magic has ever expressed a craving to transcend the pursuits of ordinary humanity, and the magician is a primitive symbol of superhuman achievement. Perhaps it is the mystical aura of the priest and the faint tinkling of a bell when a miracle takes place. Then, too, if he has had a Christian bringing up, perhaps it is the story of the healing of the sick by Jesus and the numbering of St. Luke among the disciples.

One explanation is far too simple, I believe: that is saying that a young man was influenced by the "image" of some doctor. Into the mundane "image," he may have projected his own childhood phantasies of some day doing something important. Also, if one must speak of "image," the influence may have taken the form of a greatly enlarged and highly colored projection of the doctor as magician-priest-healer, such as once loomed in the mind of primitive man.

As for doctors themselves, they deal in such an important service, that they are little concerned with the "image" of a doctor in the Madison Avenue sense. This sort of image changes so quickly with changing situations. The most vocal cocktail-party critic of doctors, regaining consciousness later that evening in a hospital bed, and learning that he has narrowly escaped death in an automobile crack-up, will never again engage in loose and critical talk about doctors. He will remember that it was a real doctor who took care of him—not some "image" of a doctor. He will have learned the lesson contained in that verse of Ecclesiastes, which has an alternative reading, "Honor a Physician before thou hast need of him."

Sometime after the accident there may be another episode which we should mention here: the erstwhile critic may seek compensation by legal action based on residual disability. Now, perhaps, the "image" of the doctor may once more change. Family, friends, and lawyer of the claimant take up the cry, proclaiming the injury and saying, "He never complained of a lame back before. Yet the doctor can find no cause for this newly developed lameness." The experienced doctor knows that there is no effective remedy for "compensation neurosis." Time passes, and the claim is acted on. Once it is settled, whether in or out of court, the miracle takes place: the lame back disappears and the man goes back to work. His complaint was not an illness in a medical sense; it was a politico-socio-economic ailment.

One of the rewards which brings satisfaction in medicine is the sense of doing something of importance. Rudyard Kipling, in an address to medical students in 1908 reached the heights of oratory in the passage: "If you fly a yellow flag over a centre of population you can turn it into a desert. If you choose to fly a Red

Cross flag over a desert you can turn it into a centre of population toward which, as I have seen, men will crawl on hands and knees." Young men today are too factual-minded to be stirred by such phantasies. But Kipling continued: "You remain now perhaps the only class that dares to tell the world that we can get no more out of a machine than we put into it; that if the fathers have eaten forbidden fruit the children's teeth are very liable to be affected. Your training shows you daily and directly that things are what they are, and that their consequences will be what they will be and that we deceive no one but ourselves when we pretend otherwise. Better still you can prove what you have learned." Even the Generals in World War II had to be taught that a GI, like the barrel of a howitzer, had to be replaced after so many rounds.

There is no doubt that elation may come to the doctor from the applause and response of an audience. This may lead him, like the prima donna on the stage, to exert himself to the utmost. But such applause is rare, usually reserved for some winner of the Nobel Prize, and even he knows that this signal honor is shared by hundreds of others on whose shoulders he stands. The inner satisfaction of the doctor today, as of the doctor of yesterday, is derived from the quiet gratitude of individual patients, a gratitude that cannot be expressed in words.

Robert Louis Stevenson was a patient for years of his short life and finally died of tuberculosis. His contacts with doctors were numerous, including a sojourn at Davos, the Magic Mountain of Thomas Mann. To prescribe a regimen of rest was the only weapon against his disease available to a nineteenth-century physician, and, while rest usually prolonged life, it was an inadequate measure in comparison with the powerful tools available in this century, for it rarely restored health. Stevenson's illness deprived the world of a promising engineer, but it produced a famous essayist and novelist. Out of his experience with doctors, and out of his gratitude to them, he wrote: "There are men and classes of men who stand above the common herd, the soldier, the sailor, the shepherd not infrequently; the artist rarely; the physician almost as a rule. He is the flower of our civilization and, when the stage of man is done and only to be marveled at in history, he will be thought to have shared as little as any in the defects of the period and most nobly exhibited virtues of the race. Generosity he has, such as is possible to those that practice an art, never to those who drive a trade. Discretion, tested by a hundred secrets, tact tried in a thousand embarrassments, and, what is most important, Herculean cheerfulness and courage."

This, of course, is the honored physician described by the eloquence of a patient-essayist at a time when the best weapon to be brought to bear against tuberculosis was to instill "cheerfulness and courage." What would Stevenson have written today if his life had been spared by specific remedies, or by the surgical operations which had their day of usefulness and now have been practically displaced?

The rewards which come to the doctor in expressions of gratitude by mature and articulate patients are muted today because of the robust state of health that prevails in the adult population. This circumstance also is at the bottom of many of the criticisms of doctors. An increasing number of young and middle-aged adults of both sexes (for childbirth with modern obstetrics has removed the dread of its complications from women), have personally experienced little more than the transient nuisances of short-term illness. The tragedies of disease that formerly cut down men and women in the prime of life, wrecked homes and families, and brought hardship and poverty to surviving dependents, are now relatively little known among upper-class and middle-class citizens. An increasing number of these healthy people have never experienced a want or a need for a doctor, and, in consequence, they, like the cocktail-party critic, may be hostile toward all doctors, identifying them with illness or injury that may interfere with a desired program of work and play. Such men, often driving themselves to the limit of their capacity, do not relish being told that they "can get no more out of a machine than is put into it." The generals, smelling the smoke of battle, were furious with the psychiatrists when told there was a breaking point beyond which men's brains turned to water. "You have been, and always will be exposed to the contempt of the gifted amateur—the gentleman who knows by intuition everything that it has taken you years to learn," is another line from the Kipling address.

The gifted amateur still enters medical discussions with his opinions supported by charts, graphs, and statistics. A Canadian Professor of Social and Preventive Medicine has recently written: "Such data can only be obtained from a variety of unrelated sources. The sources used, and the information obtained, frequently reflect the bias and prejudice of the investigator. It is quite understandable, under the circumstances, that an infinite number of judgemental pronouncements on psychosocial economic topics are made by innumerable self-appointed experts. These experts may be heads-of-States, sociologists, economists, playwrights, novelists, psychiatrists, columnists, and even ordinary physicians." Frustrated in their well-meaning efforts to correct socio-economic evils and neglects, the indignation of these "experts" becomes centered on the doctors for their seeming "indifference." Thus the "hard-faced" doctor emerges, as did the "hard-faced" industrialist, as a popular target of abuse.

So far as the "hard-faced" doctor is concerned, I rarely lose an opportunity, when talking with junior medical students, to paraphrase a remark made by Trudeau, undoubtedly one of those physicians who instilled "cheerfulness and courage" in Robert Louis Stevenson during his stay in the Adirondacks. "In the physician," Trudeau said, "Pity as an Emotion passes; Pity as a Motive remains."

Centuries ago the only institutions that resembled hospitals were known as Houses of Pity. They were staffed by groups living under monastic rule and bound by vow to care for the sick and others who needed aid. By this single inadequate institution society sought to provide for the upbringing of orphans; to provide a hostelry for beggars; to give shelter to illegitimate mothers; to offer asylum to the insane and domicile to the aged, the infirm and the blind; to bring correction to vagabonds and punishment to criminals. These varied efforts were oftentimes housed under one roof, and they remained there until finally the sick were rescued from the medley, then the insane. Others remain today in the slums, skid rows, poor farms, and jails waiting for some free and learned professions to take their difficulties to heart, study the nature and cause of their ailments, and demonstrate how to deal with their ills.

As one considers the aged and the hopelessly ill, there come to mind still further words of Rudyard Kipling. He once told a group of surgeons that their days were filled with a "piteous procession of men and women, begging them for leave to be allowed to live a little longer, upon whatever terms." This is all too true and it has become easy for the young and the physically sound to accuse the doctor of prolonging life at the cost of suffering. Such talk, the arguing of the matter intellectually, has increased as our institutions for the aged and our nursing homes have become filled with helpless old people whose minds have died before their frail bodies, but who linger on as "human vegetables." It is frequently asked: Why should the doctor give penicillin to halt their pneumonia, once known as "the old man's friend"? Why should he not go one step further and mercifully administer a narcotic quietly to end an existence that has no possible future?

The issues raised, though they may appear simple on the surface, are in reality very profound ones, involving the norms of society, its ethics and its morals, its religious beliefs and its laws. The medical profession cannot move ahead of society in these grave matters. If and when society desires to face up to such problems, it is not difficult to envision a physician serving as an expert witness; but the law and the clergy, as well as medicine, must be there to share responsibility and give assent. The family, under emotional and economic pressures, may be the least dependable witness. Should such solemn judgment finally be made, the physician must never assume the role of the executioner merely because he has the technical know-how. The situation is similar to that of the judge, who, having passed sentence, does not go to the prison to throw the switch on the electric chair. The physician's is the healing, the life-giving profession, and if there is to be an ending of life, decreed by society, then there must be others to accomplish it. Many doctors are deeply religious men; all respect the law. Even under the ruthless authoritarian command of Nazi Germany, only the disreputable fringe of the profession participated in the crimes against humanity.

The decreasing number of students entering medical schools from the state of Maine (only 16 entered in 1959) led to exploration of the causes. It was established that two basic reasons were a lack of proper information on the subject of a medical career and an abundance of misinformation. This applied not only to the students, but also to those from whom the students were getting the information—presumably their instructors and advisers. Also, it is commonly true that the student who displays talent and enthusiasm in his scientific studies is likely to encounter excessive encouragement to pursue science as a life career. I refer not only to scholarship awards but also to a conviction instilled in able students that they are in some way exceptional and uniquely adapted to research undertakings.

Biologists are familiar with the tendency for living creatures (man included) to arrange themselves in a hierarchical pattern which expresses some inner sense of relative importance. In the poultry yard this hierarchy has been described as a "pecking order": Hen A pecks Hen B and C, Hen B in turn pecks Hen C but never A, and so on. In a democratic society of human beings, however, he who gets pecked is likely to peck back.

The structure of one man-made pecking order, which spreads between scientist and doctor, became noticeable after World War II when it was evident that golden corn in the form of federal money was to be tossed into the human poultry yard. Without trying to include all categories, the pecking order (with everyone pecking back) was: Theoretical Physicist—Physicist—Physical Chemist—Organic Chemist—The Life Scientists—The Medical Scientists—The Physician Scientist—The Physician—The Surgeon—and the "ordinary" practicing doctor.

A young man, once aware of this hierarchy, will realize the need for a grain of salt when hearing some comments which are intended to be flattering, such as: "You have too brilliant a mind to go into medicine." Or, "You shouldn't prostitute your talents by going into surgical practice; surgeons are interested only in making money." And, in reverse, the young man may be asked, "Why spend so much time studying science? Come with me and I will show you the practical way to take care of sick folks."

Despite the contradiction and possible confusion in this varied advice, surveys have shown that young men are likely to make their decision to go into medicine at a far earlier age than men choosing other careers. And what of those who actually do make this decision while still in college, perhaps in the very early years of college, or possibly even before? What happens to them?

In the first place, they have a tendency, I believe, to take unto themselves certain attributes of a professional fraternity all too soon for their own good. They tend to eat together, talk shop together, and to concentrate with a compelling intensity on making high grades in those subjects required for admission to medical schools. By doing so, they deprive themselves of many of the values of a liberal education which might well be assets to them as doctors later on. An instructor in biology has told me that even a few premedical students can ruin his section work by the intensity of their concentration on the acquirement of facts which may increase their chances to pass the examination. Broader, more theoretical concepts of far greater significance are ignored.

This attitude is quickly sensed, and rightly resented, by a student who is holding his own choice of career open and is seeking a broad base for whatever he may ultimately decide to do. "If that is the kind of man going into medicine," he may think, "I do not care to join him." As a matter of fact, admission committees at medical schools are coming to realize that placing too great emphasis on grades and requirements in science may ultimately react to the detriment of the medical profession; perhaps it has already done so.

Again, the very content and rigid systematic instruction in some college course, required or deemed desirable for premedical consumption, can be misleading. I am thinking of one famous course in organic chemistry that has made able young men turn away from a decision to enter medicine. "If this is what medicine is like, it is not for me," they have said. This, in fact, is an excellent course; but it is designed for would-be chemists, not would-be doctors. While it is desirable that some doctors have the flair necessary to enjoy this course, such a flair by no means provides an index to the talents and interests that usually find expression in medicine. Apart from this particular course, however, it should be made clear that there are so many and such varied careers in medicine that there are bound to be some unpleasant, possibly even unnecessary steps in any required educational program.

Most young men going into medicine today base their decision on a feeling that they want to do something, or discover something, or teach something, important to other human beings. If you feel this desire yourself, come on in. It may be impossible to put into words the elation and the inner satisfaction that will come from the experience of doing something that you want to do (provided you and others feel that it is important); but it will be, I believe, like learning to play a musical instrument really well, winning a case at law, or perhaps riding the nose cone of a rocket.

At the risk of being accused of writing an apologia in behalf of doctors and of medicine itself, I have tried to look behind some of the many arguments that might persuade you not to enter on its studies. One of these is the contention that studying medicine will mean traversing a stretch of highway that seemingly prepares you for life, but that really offers scant opportunity to experience life itself. Actually, and on the contrary, each day on this highway of medical education brings new and deeper experiences—an intimate share in the joys of people, and, what is far more, the privilege of standing by their side to face with them events that are commonly shunned as too difficult to bear. You as a student will become familiar with fear, anxiety, despair, and death itself. The familiarity achieved will be a vicarious one it is true; but to experience these things even indirectly, through people who look to you for help, will lead to the realization that the unpleasant things are also a part of life and can be escaped only by a retreat from life itself in an attempt to deny their existence.

Only if it seems to you that going into medicine is a desirable thing to do, that life at the far end of the road will be "worth" the effort, should you undertake it. But how can you know?

Do not expect your decision to appear entirely comprehensible; it is certain to have components that seem illogical and irrational. The actual reasons may not be clear and specific; but this, within itself, is no cause to doubt that you are admirably suited to be a doctor. The decision may have come about within you as a whole man, and not solely on the basis of some one, or even several reasons, that you have found to explain your decision to your friends. By the "whole" man I do not mean the "well-rounded" man so frequently referred to, but the man who has within himself the capacity to come face to face with the evils and the despairs of the darker side of life. It is commonly said that a doctor must prepare himself to care for the "whole" man. If, indeed, he is to achieve this goal he must first himself become a whole man.

2 *Medical School—*

AND YOUR STUDY

OF MEDICINE

BY PERRY J. CULVER, M.D.

CLINICAL ASSOCIATE IN MEDICINE AND
ASSISTANT DEAN OF THE FACULTY OF MEDICINE

The Harvard Medical School

and GEORGE PACKER BERRY, M.D.

PROFESSOR OF BACTERIOLOGY AND
DEAN OF THE FACULTY OF MEDICINE

The Harvard Medical School

DR. PERRY J. CULVER

Born: 1915, Stillwater, Minnesota

Phillips Exeter Academy
Harvard University: A.B., 1937
Harvard Medical School: M.D., 1941

United States Air Force Medical Corps
    Active duty, 1942–46

Massachusetts General Hospital:
    Clinical and Research Fellow in Medicine, 1946–48
    Assistant in Medicine, 1948–50
    Assistant Physician, 1950–60
    Associate Physician, 1960—
Harvard Medical School:
    Research Fellow in Medicine, 1946–47
    Milton Fellow in Medicine, 1947–48
    Instructor in Medicine, 1948–49
    Associate in Medicine at Massachusetts General Hospital, 1949–58
    Clinical Associate in Medicine, 1958—
    Assistant Dean for Admission, 1960—
Consultant to Plasma Fractionation Commission, 1952—
Consultant in Gastroenterology, United States Public Health Service
    Hospital, Brighton, Mass., 1952—
Consulting Physician: Massachusetts Eye & Ear Infirmary, 1954

Harvard Medical School Admission Committee, 1957
    Chairman, 1960—
Massachusetts General Hospital: Staff Clinic Committee, Chairman
    Storrow House Committee, Chairman
    Student Health Committee
    Infectious Disease Committee
New England Postgraduate Assembly Program Committee, Co-Chairman:
    1953 and 1954
Member, American Association for the Advancement of Science
American Board of Gastroenterology, Diplomate, 1957
American Board of Internal Medicine, Diplomate, 1950
American College of Physicians, 1956—
American Federation for Clinical Research
American Gastroenterological Association
Trustee, Concord Academy, 1962

DR. GEORGE PACKER BERRY

Born: 1898, Troy, New York

The Hill School, Pottstown, Pennsylvania
Princeton University: A.B., 1921
Johns Hopkins University: M.D., 1925
Hobart and William Smith College: LL.D., 1949
Harvard University: A.M. (hon), 1949
Union College: S.D., 1950
Princeton University: S.D., 1951
Tufts College: Litt. D., 1952
Harvard University: S.D., 1954
New York University: S.D., 1955
University of Rochester: S.D., 1955
Jefferson Medical College of Philadelphia: LHD, 1955

United States Naval Reserve, 1941–53

Johns Hopkins University School of Medicine:
  Assistant in Medicine, 1927–28
  Instructor in Medicine. 1928–29
Hospital of the Rockefeller Institute for Medical Research:
  Assistant Resident Physician, 1929–32
Rockefeller Institute for Medical Research:
  Assistant, 1929–31
  Associate, 1931–32
University of Rochester School of Medicine and Dentistry:
  Professor of Bacteriology, Head of the Department of Bacteriology,
  and Associate Professor of Medicine, 1932–49
  Assistant Dean, 1941–47
  Associate Dean, 1947–49
Harvard Medical School:
  Dean of the Faculty of Medicine and Professor of Bacteriology, 1949—
Harvard Medical Center:
  President, 1956—

Association of American Medical Colleges
  Executive Council: 1947–52
  Vice-president: 1947–48
  President: 1951–52
Department of Health, Education and Welfare:
  Consultant, Medical Research and Education, 1957—
  United States Navy: Honorary Civilian Consultant to the Surgeon
  General, 1952–56
Arthritis and Rheumatism Foundation, Massachusetts Chapter: Trustee,
  1950
President's Committee on Education Beyond the High School, 1956–57
Committee on Medical Education, Massachusetts Medical Society,
  1956—
Trustee: American University of Beirut, 1952—
Charter Trustee: Princeton University, 1956—

THE PERIOD of formal graduate study that is pursued in medical school is devoted to a scholarly approach to the medical sciences and an introduction to their clinical application. Here the young doctor begins a fusion of the scientist's power of analysis with the healer's intuitive art, a fusion that will develop and guide him for the rest of his days.

"Life is short, and the Art long," Hippocrates has written, and true it is that one of the most difficult and challenging goals in the world is in learning the art of medicine and becoming a good doctor. Planning for a career in medicine should begin early, hopefully in secondary school, and continue during the years of undergraduate study in college. Because the physician of the future will function at the focus of the natural sciences, the social sciences, and the humanities, it is necessary that the prospective medical student gain educational experience in each of these areas.

There are many careers open to the doctor upon the completion of his years of professional education in medical school. He may choose to serve his fellow man as a family physician or as a practitioner in one of the more specialized fields. He may direct his attention to research, an important field, for his ability to provide continually improving medical care is dependent upon the advancement of knowledge in the basic sciences and clinical areas. Such research is accomplished most successfully by those who have imagination, intelligence, curiosity, and an ability for hard and persistent work. Those whose talents tend toward teaching will find this a rewarding career, for medical education is the wellspring from which both research and practice arise.

46

Administrative aptitudes, qualities of statesmanship, and an interest in social problems will draw others into the fields of public health and hospital and medical-school administration. The need for better communication of medical knowledge will attract individuals with writing skill.

It is obvious that qualified students with wide ranges of interests and backgrounds will be entering medical school and that all their experiences, whether in the classroom or in extracurricular activities, should be considered as contributing to their medical education and the development of the "complete physician." Irrespective of a physician's career, however, his education does not cease upon graduation from medical school. The good doctor enters a lifetime of continuing study, from which he will derive constant satisfaction in scholarly achievements and dedicated service.

When you begin to plan for a career in medicine, there are various sources of information and counsel available. The family physician possesses firsthand knowledge concerning the life of medical students and physicians. Also, friends who have started their medical education can share their experiences and perhaps give advice. In secondary schools, the guidance counselors may be of assistance, though unfortunately there has often been an absence of communication between medical schools and high-school advisers, and the latter sometimes lack accurate information about requirements for admission to medical school.

Most colleges have faculty members who are designated as "premedical advisers." Knowing you personally, and with an objective knowledge of your academic performance, intellectual ability, interests, and personality, they can be most helpful in advising you about appropriate medical schools. These college premedical advisers have been handicapped in many instances by inadequate information about what the medical school will require of you; but, during recent years, a remedy for this situation has been sought in conferences which bring together medical-school admission officers and premedical advisers.

Reading about the many varied careers possible in medicine is another way to gain understanding that will aid you in deciding about the study of medicine. In the Admission Requirements handbook, published annually by the Association of American Medical Colleges, there are listed books covering such broad categories as the physician, biography, fiction, history, reminiscenses, and so on.

The most reliable help may come from a visit to a medical-school faculty member who is active on the admission committee of a medical school. You can be sure that you will be warmly welcomed. The visit should be planned in such advance of your anticipated application to the medical school that, should you decide to go there, you will have time in college to complete the requirements for admission. Also, the intervening time will permit you to test the strength of your conviction that you wish to make medicine your career.

In selecting specific subjects for study, a student should view his educational experience in secondary school, college, and medical school as a whole. At the secondary-school level, development of basic skills is more important than the accumulation of factual knowledge. In college, these skills should be applied to obtaining a broad education in the liberal arts as well as to the scholarly pursuit of depth in some field of special interest. In medical school, the student, now equipped with the basic skills and started toward a good general education, is expected to learn how to think more effectively and to develop within himself the discipline for continuing self-education.

With these general principles in mind, you would be well advised to study English, a foreign language, mathematics, and science in secondary school. Inability to read with speed and comprehension is often a major obstacle to success in medical school. You should endeavor to develop facility in the English language, including the ability to think clearly and express yourself lucidly in both the written and spoken medium. At least four years' study of English literature and composition are desirable. Futher development of the art of communication, as well as increased understanding of language itself, is provided by the study of a foreign language, either modern or classical. Four years of experience with one language are preferable to two years' study of two languages.

Mathematics is becoming more and more an essential tool of

science, and inadequacy in this skill is a major cause of academic failure in medical school. You should study as much mathematics as your high school offers, if possible taking an introduction to calculus. The weaker your aptitude in dealing with quantitative material, the more important it is that you study mathematics.

Because your success in any career in medicine is dependent upon your aptitude in and familiarity with science, you should try to take at least three years of science in high school. This work is basic preparation for more advanced study in college. It is hoped that your high-school science courses will teach you concepts and help to develop in you a scientific attitude. One may characterize this as curiosity and an ability to ask a question, to plan an experiment, to analyze data, and to formulate a hypothesis. Science courses that are taught by the experimental method are successful in stimulating an inquiring mind.

In college, the selection of courses can be more varied. Choice should depend on the individual interests of the student. A rigid premedical curriculum is not desirable and inflexibility may stifle your full growth.

There are, on the other hand, certain minimal requirements in science for admission to all medical schools. In general, these consist of two years of chemistry, including one year of organic, a year of physics and a year of biology. Additional courses in science are suggested by some medical schools and required by others. Such subjects include physical chemistry, qualitative and quantitative analysis, comparative anatomy, embryology, and genetics. You should consult the handbook previously mentioned, *Admission Requirements of American Medical Colleges*, to determine the specific courses required by the medical school or schools of your choice.

Should you desire to concentrate in one of the fields of natural science or plan to take more than the minimal requirement, you should not take, in college, those courses that will be repeated in medical school, for example, biochemistry, histology or physiology. To do so not only deprives you of the opportunity to study in the fields of the arts, humanities, and social sciences, but also may create a false sense of security about your knowledge of the subjects when you repeat them in medical school.

When you are deciding which courses to study in college, you should consider the depth, breadth and quality of each course, rather than the number of semester-hour credits. Do not take an elementary course for the sole purpose of earning a high grade with the mistaken idea that it will make you a more desirable candidate for medical school. If your aptitudes and previous educational experiences make it possible to enter more advanced courses, do so. You will gain educational growth. Also, the admission committees of medical schools are well aware of the degree of difficulty of the subjects you have studied.

With improvement in the quality of education in secondary schools, more and more students are able to enter college with advanced placement in one or more subjects. This poses two questions:

First, should the student who is given credit for advanced placement in science subjects, and who wishes to major in a non-science field, use such credits to meet the medical-school science requirements without taking additional science courses in college? If he chooses to do this, he may find that he will be in difficulty with some state boards of registration in medicine, which rigidly require that science courses be taken at the college level. Of more importance, the opportunity to take some advanced science courses and still major in a nonscience field will prepare you to become a better doctor.

The second question is whether to let advanced standing shorten your period in college. Your decision about this matter will depend in part upon your age, your maturity, and your desire for a broad experience in the liberal arts. It is a question to be considered most seriously before accepting the shortened time.

The study of mathematics should be pursued in college through at least a year of integral calculus. Here we wish to repeat the advice we gave about the study of mathematics in high school: the less your aptitude for this subject—which you can estimate by your scores on tests for the College Entrance Examination Board—the more it is desirable to study it. The teaching of basic sciences in medical school is becoming more and more mathematically oriented, and your comprehension of these sciences will be greatly improved by the study of college mathematics.

Thus far in our recommendations for courses to study in college, we appear to be as inflexible as the so-called "premedical curriculum" previously deplored. For the sake of clarity, we hasten to point out that if a student has had good secondary-school preparation in science, and then chooses to take a minimum of four whole courses in natural science and one in mathematics in college, he will have devoted to these subjects only 30 per cent of the four-year curriculum of his college study. This leaves ample time for him to major in depth in the area that he finds most interesting in the humanities or elsewhere.

Courses in the social sciences and psychology have value for increasing understanding of human behavior, including your own. Familiarity with human activity is also to be gained by the study of history, literature, art, and religion. Moreover, through these studies, you will become an educated person in the liberal sense. Even if you choose a science major, you should devote at least 50 per cent of your undergraduate curriculum to nonscience areas.

Irrespective of your college major, you should take advantage of honors courses, advanced courses, and opportunities for research and periods of independent study.

More than diligent study of the formal college curriculum is required for the development of your personality. Participation in extracurricular activities is important to becoming a well-rounded person, one who is both interesting and interested. Athletics, campus publications, music, dramatics, student affairs, service organizations, recreational activities, and gainful employment can all contribute to the development of leadership and skill in interpersonal relations. They foster self-discipline. They may well evoke interests that will enrich your life. It is wiser to engage more fully in a few activities than to spread yourself too thinly among a great many.

Before concluding these comments on preparation for medical school, a word about summer vacation may be helpful. Travel or working with people in all types of job situations can foster growth and development. Spending one or more vacation periods in a hospital working as an orderly, volunteer, or laboratory assistant will give some firsthand information on careers in medicine and test your emotional reaction to the environment of sickness and death. Unless it is necessary for the completion of your college requirements, you would be well advised to forego summer-school study. Put another way, if you permit the increasing pressure of academic competition to lead you to focus all your attention on books, you may well shortchange yourself. The most desirable candidates for medical school are good scholars who have also experienced life in nonacademic ways.

The Medical College Admission Test (MCAT) is required for admission to most medical schools. (Six medical schools currently do not require the test; they only recommend it. However, 94 to 100 per cent of the applicants to these six schools take the test.) The Psychological Corporation of New York City administers the MCAT for the Association of American Medical Colleges. This test is given in the spring and fall of each year at many conveniently located testing centers. For information, write to the Psychological Corporation, 304 East 45 Street, New York 17, New York.

The MCAT is a scholastic aptitude test that gives a fair indication of a student's intellectual capacity. The test is of the objective type with multiple-choice questions. There are four sections in the test: verbal, quantitative, general information, and science.

The verbal area measures a student's ability to read and to comprehend verbal relationships. The strength of his vocabulary is also tested. Verbal ability is an indicator of general intelligence.

Questions in the quantitative area are designed to measure aptitude for understanding concepts and relationships as well as an ability to reason. Questions in this part of the MCAT evaluate another facet of general intelligence and may predict the level of performance in the basic medical sciences. In general, there is good correlation between a high score on this section of the MCAT and the enjoyment of mathematics.

Breadth of interests is indicated by the questions on general information. You will be tested on factual knowledge of a number of nonscience areas such as history, literature, geography, art, music, philosophy, psychology, sociology, economics, government, and current events.

In the science area, your ability for perceiving and understanding scientific concepts is appraised. There are also problems to test factual knowledge gained from experience in the study of biology, chemistry, and physics. The science score of the MCAT is an indicator of both scientific aptitude and knowledge.

You should plan to take the MCAT in the spring of the year in which you apply for admission to medical school. The fall test is given for the benefit of those who are unable to take the test in the spring, but results of the fall test are not available to the medical schools until November. By then, admission procedure is already well underway and you may be at a disadvantage compared to applicants whose credentials have been completed earlier.

There is no special way to prepare for the MCAT because the test is a measure of general academic ability. A review of basic science concepts and of mathematics may have some value. You should plan your college curriculum so that you will have studied biology, chemistry, and physics before you take the MCAT.

A student is not permitted to take the test more than once in a twelve-month period unless a particular medical school specifically requests him to repeat it. Repetition of the test seldom improves the result, a fact well established by the study of the comparative scores of repeated tests. A minor exception has been observed when more science has been studied between the first and second trials.

By decision of the Association of American Medical Colleges, the results of the MCAT are not given to individual students or to undergraduate colleges. Instead, the scores are sent to those medical schools the applicant indicates when he takes the MCAT.

As mentioned, the MCAT provides a good estimate of intellectual capacity. As such, it is an important factor to be considered by admission committees along with academic records and personal attributes. At medical schools having a large number of highly qualified applicants, the MCAT may indicate candidates who will not be seriously considered for acceptance. The reason stems from the experience at these particular medical schools that academic failure has been associated with low MCAT scores. On the other hand, admission committees do not usually select candidates on their MCAT percentile rankings alone.

MCAT scores are also useful for making objective comparisons among students from colleges of varying academic standards. Admission officers know that the MCAT scores correlate to some extent with the quality of the high-school and college educational experience.

Marked discrepancy between college grades and MCAT scores is an indication for further testing and for special investigation of the student's particular problems—often to the student's ultimate advantage.

Recently, tests of scholastic aptitude and achievement have been coming under critical scrutiny, largely because these tests are no better than the people who use them. The specificity of a numerical score or percentile rank may give a false sense of reliability. The MCAT shares the limitations of other objective multiple-choice tests. They do not measure such important qualities as imagination, creativity, motivation, determination, responsibility, and compassion. These qualities are evaluated during the admission procedure by the study of academic records, extracurricular activities, letters of recommendation, and personal interviews.

There are eighty-five medical schools in the United States. Three of them are two-year schools, which teach only the basic medical sciences; from them students transfer to four-year schools for two years of clinical instruction. Clinical teaching facilities at most university hospitals are flexible and can be expanded; there are, consequently, many places available in the third- and fourth-year classes. Students who have performed satisfactorily in one of the two-year schools can easily transfer to a four-year school, for the bottleneck in medical teaching today is in the first and second year, where a limitation of faculty and of laboratory space restricts instruction in the basic medical sciences. To alleviate this situation, additional medical schools are being planned, some of them to be two-year schools.

In evaluating medical schools, one should realize that they, like men, are not all alike. In fact, each school has its own distinctive characteristics. In planning a medical education, therefore, it is important for a person to choose the medical school appropriate for him. Some schools have large classes, others small. At some, the students work in an intimate, noncompetitive atmosphere. Elsewhere, there is an attitude of intense intellectual drive and competition. Also, teaching techniques at one school may be strongly directed, didactic, and pragmatic. At another, the approach is experimental, emphasizing concepts and leaving the student to plan his own daily program. Although the general program of the curriculum is much the same in most schools—two years of basic science followed by two years of clinical teaching—there are many variations in the organization of the curriculum. At some schools, the curriculum is highly organized and all available time is carefully planned. At others, there is free time for reading, for elective courses and research. At still others, there are semesters when the curriculum is integrated or co-ordinated by interdepartmental teaching.

Competition for acceptance by medical schools varies from school to school. Some have large pools of highly endowed applicants, of whom only one in ten can be admitted. Elsewhere, at some state-owned schools, for example, where residential restrictions control acceptance, there may be only two candidates for each space available.

Beyond these differences, and after all basic requirements have been considered, the chances of acceptance at some medical school may be still further modified by an advanced degree, previous study at the institution, sex, or age. A realistic appraisal of the chance of being accepted may be based on the fact that, during the last decade, one out of every two applicants in the total national pool has gained admission to some medical school.

After reading this brief description of the differences in the character of medical schools, you may be in some confusion as to how to choose. To help you solve this problem, let us suggest that before you send an application to any school, or before you even request an application, you take the following steps:

First, obtain the handbook, *Admission Requirements of American Medical Colleges*. Read the brief description of each school and its requirements for admission. This will give you some background for selecting the schools to which you may wish to apply.

Next, write to those schools that interest you for their catalogues, which will give you much further information.

A visit to the schools of your choice during the year prior to your planned application, or during the summer before your application, can have great value. Write for an appointment. The members of the admission committees or designated faculty members will be glad to talk to you and to give you an understanding of the philosophy of the school. You should ask for a tour to obtain some idea of the laboratory and clinical facilities. If possible, talk to some of the students; such talks are most desirable.

By carefully planned and thoughtfully evaluated visits, you can develop a feeling for the atmosphere of the schools you are considering, in addition to learning specific facts about them.

If you take these steps before making application to any medical school, you will be on firmer ground in deciding which ones actually to apply to. It is important that you apply to the right ones and, in determining which are right for you, take into account your reaction to each school's curriculum and teaching methods. Consider the size and atmosphere of each. Which ones seem compatible with your likes and dislikes? In judging them, judge yourself also, and be certain to weigh your college performance and your competitive spirit.

On the basis of these considerations you should make application to those schools where your chances for acceptance are good. It is unwise to apply to one where you have practically no chance of being accepted. But do not underestimate yourself, or fail to apply because of lack of self-confidence.

The "admission season" for most medical schools begins in September and runs to the fifteenth of January—sometimes later into the spring of the year in which the class will enter. You should write for application blanks to the medical schools of your choice during the period from May to September of the year *before* you wish to enter medical school.

It is often difficult to decide how many medical schools to apply to. The average number of applications filed by most prospective medical students is from three to five. Some students feel so sure of acceptance by a single school that they apply only there. This is not usually advisable. No one can know the quality of the pool of applicants in any particular year, and the quality during the year of your application may be so high as to keep you out. On the other hand, if you feel so insecure that you make application to twenty or more schools, you should re-examine your situation, seeking advice from premedical advisers in college as to whether or not you are really well suited to enter upon the study of medicine.

The application forms of medical schools vary as to the information called for. These forms should be filled out carefully. Some medical schools require that you write a statement describing why you wish to enter medical school and what you hope to do with your medical education. These statements are seriously considered by admission committees. Here is a word of advice on these statements: Be yourself. Avoid a stilted style, large words, or "cute" phrases. Avoid broad generalizations and philosophizing about the role of medicine. Tell about yourself. Try to be completely honest as to why you wish to enter medicine. If you are idealistic and sincerely wish to help your fellow men, say so. If you have a strong interest in science, emphasize this fact. If you desire to be of service to backward nations, explain what you would like to do. Do not try to guess what will appeal most to the admission officers. Just be honest about yourself.

Some application forms ask you to list the extracurricular activities you have engaged in. It is not worth much to list a very large number of organizations you have joined but in which you have taken little active participation. It is always more helpful to mention the degree to which you have participated.

Many schools ask you to describe your plans for financing a medical education. Admission officers at any school are well aware of the financial burdens that such an education imposes on students and their families. Make a realistic appraisal of your finances and explain how you plan to support yourself and pay your expenses. You will not jeopardize your acceptance by pointing out your need for financial help, although some schools do not have much money available for student aid. On the other hand, it is dishonest to indicate that you have adequate financial support when you do not, in the hope that it will help you to be accepted. If you are admitted under such circumstances and then indicate that you are unable to finance yourself, the school may not have funds available for your needs, or may decide that your character is such that you are not suitable for a career in medicine.

It is also improper to underestimate your ability to support yourself in the hope of getting a "free ride" because you happen to be a student of high endowment. The funds available for financing medical education are so limited that it is completely unfair for some individual to receive unneeded financial assistance, when there are other well-qualified students who actually require such help.

In addition to the application form, the admission committees of the medical schools to which you apply will request a transcript of your college grades. Some schools also ask for a transcript of your record in secondary school.

Letters of recommendation are sought by most medical schools. These may come from the premedical committee of your college, where they often take the form of a composite appraisal of your personality, activities, academic performance, and a comparative rating with other students at your college. Such recommendations from premedical committees receive careful consideration by the admission officers of the medical schools. Oftentimes you are also asked for letters of recommendation from members of the faculty at your college. It is better and more helpful to your chances of being accepted to request letters from instructors or teachers who have known you well, rather than from a more distinguished professor who is personally unacquainted with you.

A word of warning about letters of recommendation. If a physician, especially an alumnus of the medical school to which you hope to go, knows you well, a letter from him will be very helpful to admission committees. On the other hand, letters from people of importance who may be acquainted with your family, but who do not know you personally, have little value in the eyes of admission officers. They may even create a negative reaction. You are strongly advised not to solicit such letters. Letters from your parents will not help either.

Some applicants believe that "pull" can exert a favorable effect on their chances of acceptance. Such an idea is almost universally false. Acceptance by medical schools is based on the merit of an applicant's record. What may be said by influential people concerning him will have little effect on his gaining acceptance to a medical school.

The interview is an important part of the admission procedure at many medical schools. You should not look upon it as an effort to put you under stress, but rather as an opportunity to present yourself to the school in as natural and as honest a way as possible, to the end that the admission officers can find out what you are like as a person. Try to be relaxed. Do not try to create an "impression." You are not on trial; the interviewer is simply looking for qualities deemed desirable in future physicians.

Consider the interview a "two-way street": you will not only answer questions, you should also ask them. Just as the interviewer needs to find out about you, so you need to find out about the school. Ask questions concerning whatever you want to know.

Your questions should be fully answered, but never with any suggestion of a sales talk. If the interviewer appears to be trying to persuade you to come to that school, then further questions should be raised in your mind. Ask him, openly and directly, why he feels he should try to lead you to his school instead of merely discussing the school's merits and liabilities, as well as your own.

After the interview, and with the application forms and all supplementary information in hand, the admission committees begin the process of choosing the medical class for the next year. The technical details of this selection vary from school to school, and the resulting decisions are often confusing to premedical advisers and to prospective students when they discover that a candidate is rated as highly desirable at one medical school, but not accepted at another. It is also confusing that a medical school may accept a student who is not considered promising by the premedical adviser or by his student peers. This situation is caused by differences in "personality" among the medical schools, as well as by variations in what admission committees seek when selecting a class. Such variations are consistent with the many careers available to those who enter the profession of medicine. Since many individuals of varying backgrounds and wide range of interests are necessary for supplying future generations of doctors for the nation, there is no single "ideal" medical student.

There are, however, many aspects of the admission procedure that are common to all medical schools. The scores of the Medical College Admission Test, academic performance, extracurricular activities, and personality are always considered. The relative weight given to any one of these factors will vary from school to school, or from candidate to candidate at a given school. Selection of medical students is a highly individual process, and it is the total picture of the applicant that is important.

Students frequently believe that certain grades or certain admission-test scores will insure acceptance. This is not so. At most medical schools, acceptance is made on a comparative basis and each admission committee tries to choose the applicants who seem best suited for the educational experience provided at that school. Do not fear that you will fail at any given school if you do not achieve an "A" in organic chemistry, or assume that you will necessarily be accepted if you are a Phi Beta Kappa, or the number one man in your class.

In these comments on how to prepare for medical school, we have indicated the need for broad academic preparation and have stressed the importance of extracurricular activities in developing a well-rounded personality. Now a further word on what the admission committees are looking for in the way of personality. Granted that there are individual variations, all medical schools are seeking evidence not only of intelligence, but also of strong motivation to excel at whatever you do. The reasons for wishing to study medicine are examined carefully. No one is unhappier than the student who finds himself in medical school because of pressure from parents, the desire for prestige, or the hope of financial gain. A student should study medicine because he enjoys the quest for scientific knowledge, for the truth, and because he wants to help people. Admission committees also hope to find evidence of skill in personal relations, compassion for and a love of people.

Since integrity is obviously important in the field of medicine, intellectual dishonesty and lack of moral courage are obviously detrimental. Regardless of what medical field you enter, you will need to develop a mature attitude, a sense of responsibility, and sound judgment. Emotional instability is a handicap. Aim at achieving poise and self-confidence without arrogance. Adaptability, creativity, imagination—these also are desirable attributes.

Just as there are certain qualities of personality highly valued by admission committees, so are there others that will weigh against you. Attempts to bluff, evidence of insecurity and insincerity, a withdrawn attitude, excessive aggressiveness, an argumentative attitude, inability to adjust to other people, selfishness, rigidity, narrowness of interest, a tendency to be "a grade grubber"—all these are clearly undesirable characteristics.

In the present chapter we have been writing briefly about what your medical school will require of you. We have discussed your academic background and your personal characteristics.

Now we can sum this up, very briefly, as follows: To accept you for medical study, a medical school will require of you a strong record from your past, evidence of character and ability, and proof of dedication to your ideals.

3 *You in Training*

AS AN INTERN AND
AS A RESIDENT

BY ROBERT BIGLEY, M.D.

INSTRUCTOR IN MEDICINE
University of Oregon Medical School

DR. ROBERT BIGLEY

Born: 1929, Auburn, Washington

University of Washington: B.S., 1951
University of Oregon Medical School: M.D., 1953

United States Naval Reserve Medical Officer, 1955–57

Internship: Bellevue Hospital, New York City, 1953–54
Residency: Bellevue Hospital, Internal Medicine, 1954–55
   University of Oregon Medical School Hospitals, Internal Medicine,
   1957–59

Fellowship: United States Public Health Service Postdoctoral Research
   Fellowship, in Coagulation Laboratory, University of Oregon Medical
   School

Appointments:
   University of Oregon Medical School, Instructor in Medicine
   Consulting Hematologist, Portland Veterans Administration Hospital

THE COURSE in human anatomy at one medical school is an interesting and practical study of the functional structure of the human body; at another it seems a tangle of bones and meat, memorizable but not comprehensible. One psychiatry professor introduces the study of human behavior in rational and exciting terms; another offers his students a glimpse of what seems an unreal approach to bizarre activity. Fortunately, most students see through such vagaries to the facts of medicine, which do not vary from school to school. So it is no surprise that there are few detectable differences among graduating classes of American medical schools.

After medical school, during another one to six years of training in intern and resident programs, young doctors become mature physicians. Such training programs differ greatly among institutions, yet equally effective physicians emerge from them. Some hospitals, for practical reasons, eschew certain types of problems, e.g., contagious diseases, acute traumatic injuries or obstetrics. An intern's experience may be limited by the few patients he sees, or he may have to care for so many patients that he has insufficient time to learn from them. Attending physician supervision and guidance may be inadequate, or so excessive that interns and residents have no responsibility for patient care and no opportunity to develop their own approach to the diagnosis and treatment of disease. That such differences are relatively unimportant is one reassuring sign that individuals control their environment. Your success as a physician and your experiences in training will depend mainly on you. For an example, let me tell you a little about my training.

Three years at a state university were taken up by premedical science courses. Large classes and succinct lectures allowed one to slip through without a great deal of thought or inquiry. I had planned a more strenuous fourth year of history, philosophy, and advanced chemistry, but lightly forgot it after acceptance to medical school. I often mourn that year.

More active thinking was encouraged at medical school; but the "memorize, understand if possible" method secured good grades for me during the first two years. During the third year, I tried to apply my well-arranged notes to patients. Somehow, the complaints and observable abnormalities of the man in the bed rarely matched the catalogue specifications for any disease on my list. My efforts were most often rewarded with my own sensations of rapid heart beat, dry mouth, and sweaty hands. I could recognize any anxiety reaction, and could fill in for the patient the symptoms he neglected to mention.

When I was getting ready to choose my life work, it had seemed to me that physicians were well respected and lived interesting lives, dealing with infinitely varied people and their problems that were anything but dull. Later, the physicians I saw at medical school did not disappoint me; they seemed the best-rounded, best-informed men alive. But sometimes I wondered whether I belonged with them! Old friends from college and earlier days occasionally came by to chat. They knew something of events outside physiology books and operating rooms, and obviously enjoyed responsibilities of family and community. They compared favorably with the only men I had thought to admire, and they appeared distressingly more mature than one medical student who lived on the paternal dole, did nothing for others, and contacted the nonmedical community mainly in taverns and on ski slopes. I looked more closely at my medical heroes, and wondered a little about my own motives and future.

One day, an instructor in the outpatient clinic gently led me from an exposition of a patient's complaints and his few detectable physical abnormalities through a discussion of the possible chemical, physiological, and pathological bases for these derangements, and of the clinical entities associated with such abnormalities, to the diagnosis. But this was not all—he led on. The diagnosis included pathologic name (an implied visualization of the pathology), description of deranged physiology and anatomy, description of the patient's current state of disability, and consideration of confirmatory diagnostic studies and treatment. I had been led this way before, skipping over easy parts, stumbling on infirm ground, and wandering when bored with pedantic exercise. This time I followed, and finally realized that the scientific method is a practical clinical tool, usable even with such inexact observations as subjective symptoms, unmeasurable changes in mobility of a joint, and abnormal appearance and texture of skin.

Among the fine qualities of that instructor and others equally impressive, I found a common motive, sufficient to justify the work of becoming a real physician: a wish humbly and scientifically to define and ease the problems of people.

As a fourth-year medical student soon to change title to intern, I was twenty-three, single, in considerable debt to my family for a long and costly education, and eager but barely aware of how to apply myself to the problems of sick people. Then an acquaintance described the training program he had recently left: an active teaching service in a New York City municipal hospital. The pay was poor, but room and board were free. At least I would live on my own income for the first time. I applied, and was accepted. I daydreamed of curing the pneumonias of bowery bums and opera singer—but *The New Yorker* lay on top of my medical books.

In 1953, airport limousines in Seattle called for passengers at comfortable hotel lobbies. In New York, the LaGuardia Airport bus dropped its passengers beneath a viaduct in front of Grand Central Terminal to test their agility against Forty-second Street traffic. Thinking the city might appear less menacing after a shower, I headed for the hospital. The taxi driver sat tight while I struggled into and out of his cab with my bags, then successfully bullied from me his unearned tip.

I took refuge in the hospital, hoping the city would seem less harsh in a few days. The very old buildings, with porous roofs and crippled elevators, were so connected that there were few one-floor passages between them. One-room wards accommodated forty patients. From their desks, the few nurses directed a wild traffic of aides, orderlies, and patients. The clinical laboratory seemed totally inadequate; interns drew blood for testing and did their own blood counts, urine examinations, and smears for bacteria. Interns took patients to and from X ray, then stole the films from the guardian of the X-ray files and carried them to the ward for inspection.

Out West (Why had I left?) interns were physicians, not messengers and technicians, and nurses were the cool-handed, human administrators of the physicians' intent.

My first new patient spoke Spanish; I didn't. No friends or family were with him and I couldn't find an interpreter. He was sick. After examining him thoroughly, I knew that his pulse and respirations were rapid and that he was hot, sweaty and *very* sick; nothing more. I felt scared, inadequate, and a little sick myself. I examined him again. His skin and oral membranes were blue. *Some unoxygenated blood was leaving his lungs.* His breathing was shallow, and appeared to cause him pain. *Some structure in his chest was painful when moved; perhaps a broken rib or inflamed covering membranes of lung and chest wall.* The right side of his chest moved less well than the left. *The disturbance was on the right.* The resonance induced in the right lower posterior chest when I tapped with my fingers was of shorter duration and higher pitch than elsewhere. The sounds of moving air heard through the stethoscope over the same part of his chest were high-pitched. *The natural frequency of resonance of the right lower lung had changed from the low frequency of porous lung to the high frequency of solid tissue or fluid-filled lung—consolidation.* The chest X ray was abnormally dense in the location of the right lower lung lobe. The patient coughed up rusty sputum. Smeared over a glass slide, stained, and examined with a microscope, it showed large blue dots arranged in pairs, some surrounded by a faint halo. *My patient had pneumococcal pneumonia in the right lower lobe.* The medical resident had reached this conclusion an hour before, but kindly waited until I had composed myself and the diagnosis before discussing the case with me. The patient was given oxygen and penicillin.

By morning he was dramatically improved, and I was ready to work! So what if the wards were big and packed? It would be convenient to see all my patients at once. The long corridors seemed to take on character and the sub-basement passage, the only one connecting all buildings on one quasi level, was my favorite. Cool in summer and closed to some of the elements in winter, it was an auxiliary storm sewer during rains. Under the pathology building, planks and bricks led over the floor to a narrow circular iron staircase on which one climbed to the third-floor autopsy room. There, a few naked bulbs lit a couple of rows of tables. At one or two tables post-mortem examinations were usually in progress. At another, a woman prepared bodies for return to the morgue. A tall, muscular, bleached blonde of indeterminate age with impassive face but kindly eyes, she supported a cigarette between her thin lips as she gently sutured abdominal incisions and scalp flaps. She uttered no sound in the dissecting room, but in my imagination I still picture her patting the heads of her charges and saying a tender, personal good-bye as she slid them back into their refrigerator compartments.

The nurses, who seemed officious at first, knew more about the patients than I most of the time, and they solved many problems for me. To care for a forty-bed ward, there were one or two nurses during the day; one for two wards in the evening; and one for four wards after midnight. Patients were well cared for, and doctors' needs were anticipated. With one of my favorites, I had a daily argument. Each mealtime she insisted, "Doctor, go eat! One minute of peace for the patients!" The same nurse, a strong believer in the evils of drink, yearly used the same tinsel for Christmas decorations; with the money allowed for such things, she bought wine for the patients' holiday meal.

My objections to the hospital and the system dwindled, and finally became hardly noticeable in the high spirits with which we went about our work. Each day, interns arrived early to see their patients and draw blood for laboratory tests. After eight o'clock, mornings were devoted to rounds; sometimes with the resident alone, sometimes with the chief resident, with medical students, with the physician attending the ward, or with specialty consultants.

Rounds and other activities were, of course, set aside when new patients were admitted to the ward or when patients urgently needed care. Most patients entered the hospital at night. By custom, all patients were "worked up" immediately after admission—complete examination; urinalysis; blood count; bacteriologic, X-ray, and blood-chemistry studies necessary for working diagnosis and urgent treatment; and a review of findings by the resident. At the patient's bedside the next morning, at the time of the rounds made by the ward staff (nurse, resident, interns), the examining intern related pertinent information about the patient to the others. Together the staff reexamined and discussed the patient, deciding on further diagnostic study and treatment.

Using selected patients, this process was repeated with medical students for reciprocally beneficial discussion; and with the chief resident, attending physician, and consulting staff for more of the same. So much walking and talking may seem excessive. There may be some discussion just for the sake of talking, and such discussion may wander far from the patient and his illness; but so long as all persons are interested, they think and learn.

The attending physician expects to learn and be stimulated as much as house officers or students. Few patients' problems are so clearly defined that didactic pronouncements characterize them and their management. Good interns and residents know this. Questioning intelligently, and inciting students and attending physicians to do the same, the intern and resident make rounds profitable for all concerned.

Afternoons usually were devoted to procedures such as thoracentesis (needle aspiration of fluid from the chest) and fluoroscopy, dictating summaries for patients about to be released from the hospital, and talking to patients' families. The ward library was always open and the contents of texts and journals, when related to current patients' problems, were far less abstract than they had seemed in medical school. These activities often went on into the night, but sooner or later the intern going off duty made another brief round of his patients with his co-intern, alerting him to problems which might arise during the night, and then left the ward to study, play, or sleep.

So passed an enjoyable year. I began to differentiate between medical facts and impressions. Early in the year, for example, I had staunchly stood by philosophies of treatment that I had learned in medical school and that I knew were held by experts in other places, but that were quite different from the approaches used by my co-workers. Most of these differences were unimportant; patients improved by either method. My medical provincialism might have lasted much longer had I not heard other, and differing, narrow views during internship.

I learned from nurses, other physicians, students, patients, and books. Patients' families also taught me some lessons. A gentle, quite-voiced man had far-advanced tuberculosis and a managing wife. He seemed to care little about how or where he was; but she was very concerned, and took more time than I could afford to express gratitude for her husband's care. When the man's acute problems were well controlled, he was sent to a sanatorium for prolonged treatment. In detail I explained to patient and wife that at least several months of sanatorium care would probably arrest his infection, leaving him moderately short of breath but able to enjoy much more activity than he had for some time, and that without such treatment he would endanger others and become progressively, perhaps untreatably, worse.

Two weeks later the wife telephoned. The doctors at the sanatorium had not been nearly so kind as we, and she had taken her husband home. Could I treat him at home? . . . No, but he might come to the outpatient clinic, where further treatment would be arranged. But what about his going to another sanatorium? . . . Couldn't do that. He must stay at home.

An hour of futile re-explanation followed, ending with a compromise arrangement for treatment by a visiting nurse, which might at least keep the patient's disease stable. Two weeks later, the patient arrived at the hospital, acutely ill.

The cycle was repeated four times during the next year, until I realized that my sympathy for the patient and his wife was being used to compromise their health and that of others and to make fruitless work for the visiting nurse, the hospital, and me. If the patient is still alive today, his wife may be teaching some other intern the same lesson.

A pale, tight-lipped, seventy-year-old Italian tailor arrived on the ward one afternoon surrounded by very vocal sons, each of whom insisted on telling the story. Papa picks mushrooms. We don't eat them; he does. One hour after lunch with lots of mushrooms, papa vomits, has pain, diarrhea. Here we are!

The patient averted his eyes and refused to speak. The membranes of his mouth were dry; his blood pressure, low; pulse, fast; bowel activity, increased; muscles, cramping. Careful fluid and salt replacement was started, and drugs were given to ease the painful cramps. There was no urine in his bladder two hours later. Urine formation had stopped either because of water and salt deficiency from vomiting and diarrhea, or from the effect of mushroom toxins on kidney cells. Water and salt replacement had to be sufficient to correct deficiencies but no more, since excesses of these are extremely dangerous when kidney function has stopped.

After six hours, urine began to drip from the tube in his bladder. As the drops came faster his physicians made undignified noises of great joy. The patient and his family were happy. A mycologist from the Bronx Botanical Gardens identified the mushroom as an unusual member of the genus *Amanita,* related to *A. Phalloides,* which probably contained both muscarine, causing vomiting, diarrhea, and cramps, and a cell toxin which in this case apparently produced little death of kidney cells. The patient, who had been picking and eating mushrooms for sixty-five years, promised to mend his ways. He mourned in gastronomic detail his pantry full of pickled and dried mushrooms, so *delizioso* with *risotto alla Milanese, scallopini,* etc., etc. (By this time, I could talk about bodily functions and distresses in Italian, Spanish, German, and Yiddish and was branching out.)

On the third day he had pain when urinating, chills and fever. The infection, a complication of the bladder tube, subsided slowly with treatment and he was improving when his family suddenly decided that he would be more comfortable in another hospital and moved him there. They took away not only our prize patient, who would soon have gone home well, but also for a time my desire to deal with people. Such experiences seem to be less frequent as time goes by—or, anyhow, I have learned to accept them with a *little* more equanimity.

I was pleased with my intern year, so stayed on as assistant resident in internal medicine. My duties and responsibilities changed, and the care of patients on one ward became my primary responsibility. I supervised the work of two interns, ordering diagnostic studies or therapy when necessary, but preferably stimulating them to work out problems by themselves. I assigned patients to students and tried to help them develop their own rational approaches to clinical problems. There is great temptation for residents to "take over" a ward, delegating routine work to students and interns, and giving them no chance to contribute to the study and treatment of patients. I succumbed several times, and I not only learned less at those times but also caused others on the ward to waste their time.

Still single, slightly better paid, and finally able to hold my own with New York taxi drivers and waiters, I took time to enjoy the city's food, pictures, music, and plays. This experience in a big city can be a valuable part of any man's growing up.

I left reluctantly after one year of resident training, sailing to Europe and Japan for two years as medical officer on a small Navy ship. The crew was young and healthy, and gave me little medical exercise. I read. I played the phonograph. I enjoyed brief acquaintance with several seaports and I had time to think about my training and my future.

I had seen a lot of disease in New York. Sometimes, though, there had been insufficient time to learn about it, or from it. Then, too, there were some types of disease which I had not seen, such as neurologic disease, because they were treated on special wards. I wanted to become an internist, a consulting physician for diagnostic and therapeutic problems of all kinds. So, for my remaining two years of residency, I chose another institution where I knew I would have well-guided and unhurried experience with all phases of medicine.

It was toward the end of this residency when I realized that answers were coming more easily. I no longer anxiously hunted symptoms and signs for clues to the cause of a patient's prostration. Instead, I listened and observed, reasoned inductively, considered all possibilities, and acted rationally on my conclusion. I no longer struggled with problems; I thought about them. Nearly every physician matures at some time during his training. Some mature in medical school; many are good physicians when they finish internship. I matured later and now see that the excellent programs at the hospitals where I trained would have been more valuable had I used them better.

My choice of a career has proved to be a happy one. I now attend rounds with other physicians, some younger, some older than I, seeing new patients and diseases, reading, and learning. I will be doing the same many years from now. Though medicine and internal medicine are special fields, they are not restricted, and I look forward to many interests.

I have written mostly about myself, though I could well have been writing about the experiences of any other young man in medical training. Now I would like to make some general comments about intern and resident training programs.

There are several kinds of intern training programs. In a "rotating" internship, the intern gains experience in all services of a hospital: medical, surgical, children's diseases, bone diseases, skin diseases, and so on. Some states require such experience for licensure. A rotating internship is necessary for a general practitioner and valuable for any physician, providing him with knowledge of diseases outside his specialty.

"Straight" internships offer more concentrated experience in such fields as medicine, surgery, or children's diseases. The economy of a straight internship is obvious, but to argue the relative merits of straight and rotating internships is futile. Neither need be limiting, since the principles of diagnosis and treatment are the same in all fields of medicine.

There are prejudices about the relative merits of internship and residency in private *vs.* charity, and medical-school *vs.* non-medical-school hospitals. The prospective intern cannot use these classifications. When he considers a hospital for internship, he must see for himself whether he will be allowed sufficient responsibility for development of his abilities in diagnosis and treatment, whether he will have sufficient staff guidance, and whether the number and kind of patients he will see will be adequate.

Salary is sometimes a prime consideration for prospective interns, especially those with families. The stresses of debts and less than comfortable living conditions can take most of the pleasure, and a good part of the educational value, out of a training program. But after eight expensive years of college and medical school, a tuition-free year of internship, no matter how low the pay, should not be impossible to finance. An internship or residency chosen solely for salary may be a sad experience.

About residency. This extra one to five years of training is a means of gaining concentrated experience, usually in a special field, guided by experienced physicians, with time for consideration of clinical problems in detail. All good physicians continue to learn throughout their careers, and some have become excellent specialist consultants through self-training while in practice. But most find, at least during the first several years of practice, that they miss greatly the number and variety of clinical problems seen in hospitals with teaching programs, and that the rush of practice interferes with detailed study. As an indication of the value of this additional training, many intending general practitioners take a year or two of general residency or some special training, such as surgery and obstetrics.

Should you decide to become a physician, internship and possibly residency will be a part of your education: a time to bring together and apply in practice the information you gathered in medical school, and also preparation for continued learning throughout your career. You will work hard and have a good time. You will not regret the time spent unless you waste it.

During your training you will decide—perhaps changing your mind several times—on the course of your future career. If your interests have been wide, your choice will be anything but restricted.

_4_ *Beginning Your*
MEDICAL PRACTICE

BY CHESTER W. MORSE, M.D.

Decatur, Georgia

DR. CHESTER W. MORSE

Born: 1915, Brockton, Massachusetts

Peddie School
Phillips Academy
Harvard: B.A., 1938
Harvard Medical School: M.D., 1942

United States Army, 1943–45
   Prisoner of War: France—Germany: 1944–45

Roosevelt Hospital, New York City, 1942–43
Grady Memorial Hospital, Atlanta, Georgia, 1945–46
Lawson Veterans Administration Hospital, 1946–47
Emory University: Physician to Students, 1946–47
Agnes Scott College: Student Physician, 1947–48
Private practice, Decatur, Georgia: Internal Medicine, 1947—

OCCUPYING a permanent place in the dreams and plans of every young intern, army medic, and resident is the day when he will hang out his shingle and begin the practice for which he has trained so long. I can share with you some of the ideas and experiences I had in arriving at this point.

When I was a boy, I had no thought of being a doctor. I was interested in flowers and animals and wanted to be a florist most of all. My father told me I might have a hard time making a living at it, so I said I would be a veterinarian. Then sometime, and I do not know exactly when or why this happened, I decided that if I were going to treat animals, I might as well go on and treat people. So I became a doctor.

I finished medical school in 1942, some six months after Pearl Harbor, and medical students could then get a year's deferment from the draft if they went on for training. I did this and went to Roosevelt Hospital in New York City as an intern. By this time I had married and we existed on my wife's pay as a secretary at $32.50 a week. In those days, as is true now, the better the educational facilities at any hospital, the less you were paid—and Roosevelt was the acme. We interns got no stipend; we even had to furnish our own white monkey suits. My wife and I lived in a one-room walk-up in the Hell's Kitchen district and we ate lots of macaroni, cheese, and beans, for they were cheap. But we had a wonderful time; we were young, healthy, in love, and had that stabilizing dream—it is not forever—that the day would come when we would be in practice.

At the end of the one year of training, I was drafted into the army. Pennsylvania. Louisiana. Texas. Fort Leonard Wood—the old army shuttle until one day we shipped out of Camp Kilmer in New Jersey. By this time I was a battalion aide surgeon. We landed at Omaha Beach on D plus 10 and moved on north through St. Lo, through flattened towns and burning villages.

Then one beautiful afternoon, bright and sunny with the smell of clover in the air, while we were working on two badly wounded men, bullets suddenly started whizzing over and around us and we thought that a sniper dogfight had started. But a few mortar shells dropped on us and to top it off a few concussion bombs. So we crawled back some two hundred yards, taking our patients with us, climbed over a wall and onto a sunken road. We worked on our patients for half an hour, crouched in the road with the leaves on the trees above us being shot off, and we supposed that we were in a pocket of resistance.

We waited for a while until things cooled off; then one of my men stuck his head over the hedge and said, "Look at those French bastards up there going through our medical supplies." This infuriated me and I came out of that sunken road in a hurry, determined to give those fellows a piece of my mind. I ran up to where they were plundering our medical supplies and asked them what they thought they were doing. "I can't speak French but . . ."

One of the men looked at me and grinned: "*Sprechen Sie deutsch?*" ("Do you speak German?") He pointed in one direction. He pointed in another. And still another. Everywhere he pointed was a tank, each one looking ten times bigger than any tank I had ever seen before. We medics hadn't been taught to spot German uniforms and we didn't recognize German soldiers, but I certainly recognized the giant Swastikas painted on the tanks and I saw their guns pointed at us.

This was the beginning of my time as a prisoner of war, an American doctor retreating across France and on into Germany with the SS troops of the German army. For eight months, as the Germans fell back before the American advance, we retreated with them, prisoners ourselves and yet continually setting up whatever medical facilities we could, first at one prison camp and then at the next in our line of retreat. At each of them, we received wounded Americans who had been captured and brought in.

Then in April, 1945, the Americans came on so fast that they overran our camp and we were liberated. Some of the men went out and kissed the tanks, for these had the white stars on them.

A few months later I was back in the United States, a civilian once more, and one summer day I began duty, almost casually, at a hospital in a small Southern city. That first night six babies had to be delivered—and I had to deliver them! Thanks to a cracker-jack surgical nurse, everything went all right; but she even had to tell me when to use the scissors to cut the umbilical cord. Next morning I took out five pairs of tonsils. These hair-raising experiences kept up for a week; then I gave up and left the hospital.

In France and in Germany, I had worked in dirty, filthy barns and shacks, the weather freezing. I had treated men with broken and maimed limbs, with amputated legs and withered arms, their bodies burned, and had worked with typhus in the room. I had almost no medicine and when surgery was required, I had used knives as dull and chipped as saws, clamps that flew open as soon as my hand came off them, no asepsis worth using, no gloves, no warm water, often no anesthetic. For bandages we folded toilet paper and packed it into a wound.

Disquieting, at times tormenting, was the realization, as I faced some medical problem, that I didn't know very much. Yet later, when I came back to the United States, I thought that, having been through so much in Europe, I was good enough to start on the staff of a small hospital, even though there was no super-vision or training program there. Then, right off, I was con-fronted with those six babies and the five pairs of tonsils. I knew then that I was not ready and I went back to a hospital at a big university, willing to work once more on a subsistence salary to get the training I needed. I stayed on in training for two years.

One of my old teachers used to say, "More training will not add a penny to your income, but whatever time you spend in training will repay you tenfold in the satisfaction you derive in your practice of good medicine."

It is right for you to dream about setting up your practice, but let me say—and emphasize: Don't be in too big a hurry. *Get all the training you can.* With what is going on in medicine today, with all the rapid changes and developments, unless you are thoroughly trained, and unless you have a determination to keep yourself up to the highest standards of medical study and practice, you will soon slip below even the level of mediocrity. I think back to my time in prison and realize the training I lacked. How much more useful I could have been. How much more useful any doctor could be if he only had more training.

It is wise, I think, to have your last years of training in a hospital located in the geographical area where you wish to practice. I did this, taking training at Grady Memorial Hospital, Atlanta's large charity hospital, operated by Emory University Medical School which is near Decatur, Georgia, the community where I intended to practice. This gives an opportunity to observe first-hand the type of practice in the community, the personalities of the other doctors with whom you will be associated, and the quality of work that each does. Also, you will get a chance to know something about the people of the community, for you will meet them in groups in churches, in little neighborhood and social gatherings, and you will come to know many of the individuals with whom you will live later on. This knowledge and these contacts can be of greatest help to you when you set up your practice.

Finally, after all your training, all your getting ready, you will be faced with the problem of actually beginning practice. The chances are that, a long time before this, you will have been asking yourself the same question every beginning doctor has always asked, "Just how does a man go about the mechanics of setting up in practice?"

If your father is a physician, and you are to follow in his footsteps, there is no problem of decision and probably none of finance. I was the first physician in my family, so that the decision of *how* to start—whether alone, or in a partnership, or in a group—was the all-important one that I had to settle for myself. The chances are that you, too, will have to make this same fundamental decision.

But before we go any further in considering how to start, I want to stop long enough to tell you about a situation that may very well confront you, and that you should thoroughly understand as early as you can. It is entirely possible that during your last year of training you will be approached by some older physician with whose patients you have worked in the hospital, assisting him in their care. Many of these older men are successful physicians and fine men who are honestly looking for a young, well-trained man whom they can take into partnership. Some of them, however, are tired and have worked long hours for many years; they want a fresh, eager young man to share or even to carry the load. I recall the story of one older physician saying to a new associate, "We are going to split the work load fifty-fifty. I have taken all the night calls for the last twenty years, you take them for the next twenty."

I also recall my own experience with an older physician. I was young, eager, in debt, confronted with a growing family and seriously feeling the responsibilities of fatherhood. It was at this time that I was approached by a pillar of the community, a leader in the church. Everyone in town, so it seemed, thought that I was fortunate to have such an offer from so fine a doctor and so eminent a Christian gentleman; and yet curiously, so I thought, two of my professors at the medical school kept suggesting that I was making a mistake. They said that I should take more training and continue in my residency program. I appreciated their advice, but they just didn't understand the economic pressure I was experiencing; nor did they recognize what a rare chance for me this was. So I thanked them, expressed my regrets in disagreeing with them, and went to nail down the details of this wonderful new partnership.

It wasn't until we entered a discussion of financial details that I realized what I was getting into. In anticipation of my coming, the older doctor had signed up more than enough obstetric cases to pay the very meager salary he offered me. I was to do all the obstetrics and all the night work. I was to pay all my automobile expenses from my salary, and, if I worked out successfully, I was to start my second year with him at 10 per cent of his net income. After that, there was to be an increment of 5 per cent a year and at the end of ten years I could become a 45-per-cent partner. From this point on there would be no further advance for me and the relationship would be stable. I looked at this generous gentleman who was offering me a real opportunity of peonage for ten years, told him I would have to consider it for a few days, then hurried home to tell my wife to tighten the belt, for we were going on in residency.

My friends at the medical school had tried to warn me, but I had to learn for myself. It cost me a few years of strained relationship with the older man, but better a temporary coolness than an intolerable situation.

A good senior-and-junior partnership should give the younger man a chance to share financially as rapidly as he produces. The older man may also profit from the association in many ways, but unfair financial advantage should not be one of them.

Such a partnership, I believe, is the ideal way to enter practice, but all details should be thoroughly spelled out in writing to avoid serious misunderstandings. A partnership has the especial advantage of offering continuous patient care, intellectual stimulation of an older and a younger physician working on mutual problems, and also makes possible those needed intervals of relaxation from the harassments of practice, giving each physician an occasional free Sunday and a short vacation. In a partnership it is recognized by everyone that a doctor is supposed to have a little time of his own now and then. He can thus avoid that disgruntled patient who, in the crowded vestibule of the church, approaches him and with a piteous moan announces: "I needed you last night but you were away somewhere."

Besides a partnership, a beginning doctor can start out on his own—or there is a third way, he can go into group practice. I was not approached by a group, nor was I attracted to group practice after the regimentation of military life. However, a group may be the right answer for a man who dislikes the idea of going out by himself, locating an area for his office, selecting the building that he wants to get into, choosing personnel, setting up records, files and bookkeeping.

He should take into account, though, the aspects of group practice which can detract from its appeal. Trying to work with a number of doctors, each with his own ideas and customs, opens the way for serious personality conflicts. Also, if the group is already established, it will not readily modify its policies and practices to accommodate some newcomer. Then, too, a fixed salary, paid from the income of the group, seems to lessen the incentive of the individual doctor. Certainly the doctor-patient relationship is less, since a patient is seen first by one doctor and then by another in the group. All these factors should be weighed before making a group affiliation because mistakes in an early start often can be just so much time wasted, costly in money and in personal and professional relationships.

After considering a partnership, investigating group practice, and also finding out the facts about practicing within an institution, I decided that solo practice best suited my needs and my personality. I committed myself to it with the hope that, if I made a success, I would someday make some young man an offer attractive enough to persuade him to practice with me. I vowed that should that day come, I would make so fair an offer and carry so much of the work load myself as to insure the success of the partnership.[1]

[1] After studying many partnership agreements, the one I have found to be the most equitable and likely to succeed is as follows:

Both prospective partners estimate the amount needed by the younger man to live on during the first year of the partnership. This amount is guaranteed him, and will be paid to him monthly as a salary.

Both prospective partners then study the senior partner's *net* income of the previous year. This amount will be his base pay for the first year of the partnership—provided there is a sufficient increase in the year's income to pay both the junior partner's salary, which must be paid, and also the base pay of the senior partner.

At the end of the first year, the two incomes are added together. Anything earned above the combined amounts is the "overage," and is split fifty-fifty.

At the beginning of the second year, the younger man gets an increase in his income. The amount of this increase will be three-fourths of the overage of the first year. (If at the end of the first year the overage of the partnership is $4,000, the younger man's salary is increased in the second year by $3,000.)

This annual increase of the younger man's salary—always three-fourths of the previous year's overage—continues until the year comes when his income equals that of the older doctor's.

From this time on, they are equal partners and the income of the partnership is split fifty-fifty.

All productive activity of both partners belongs to the partnership.

Sick leave and part-time work must be arranged equitably.   (cont.)

Having decided to go into solo practice, I was straightway confronted with many factors, problems, and decisions—as, of course, you will be.

I have already mentioned the advisability of taking your final years of training in the area and, if possible, in the community where you intend to practice; but before you actually open your office, you should reconnoiter carefully, making sure that you have selected the part of the country that suits you best. You are going to be living there for a long time, and you need to be comfortable and pleased with your surroundings; it is just plain short-sighted to start out in the snows of New England when you love the sun of Florida.

You must find out, too, whether the population of your chosen area can support the type of practice that you plan. You do this by finding out the number of doctors already in your kind of practice in the area that you intend to serve. Obviously, if you are a neurosurgeon you must settle in a city large enough to support your type of specialty. However, if you are in general practice, a "family doctor," you can settle almost anywhere—*unless* there are already too many general practitioners in that community. The best ratio of the various specialties to population, and information about the number of these men already practicing in the area, can be obtained from any state medical association.

Then, too, you should get information regarding per capita income and the population growth rates of a community. These can be secured from the chamber of commerce.

I can remember a costly mistake that my brother made in not considering these and other factors involved when starting a medical practice. As an ear, nose, and throat specialist, he selected a Northeastern city with the highest per capita income of the whole Eastern seaboard; he felt that nose and throat prob-

---

Provision for vacations, medical meeting attendance, dissolution of the partnership, and possible recall to military service must be incorporated in the agreement.

Settlement of accounts, management of office, and management of practice in the event of death of a partner must be determined in the partnership agreement.

lems would be plentiful in such an area. All of this was true, but he discovered after settling and establishing a practice that other doctors also had the same statistics and there were more ear, nose, and throat specialists, relative to population, in this community than anywhere else in the Northeast. Moreover, hospital facilities were already overcrowded and he found it virtually impossible to secure operating space for the few patients that came to him.

Once you have selected the locale of your practice, go visit there and don't cut your visit short. Stay for a while. Get the feel of the place. Interview the chamber of commerce, local bankers, local physicians, and make certain that there are hospital facilities available for the type of practice you wish to enter.

You note that I suggest talking with the bankers and with other physicians. From the former you may be able to borrow for setting up your practice and maintaining your living until you are self-supporting; from the latter you may be able to get leads on part-time jobs which may feed you until you are established.

How long will getting established take? This is another of those inevitable and entirely proper questions and it can never be answered exactly. The time will be in inverse proportion to how highly specialized you are and will also depend on how good you are at making contacts.

Obviously, the highly specialized neurosurgeon will be longer getting established than the internist. Also, the neurosurgeon will be completely dependent on his colleagues for referrals, plus, of course, the work he can secure from the big hospital emergency rooms, much of which will be charity. However, if he can prove himself at this level—and usually he must offer such proof—then he will begin to get more referrals.

I feel that the beginning physician should have available, through private funds or bank loans, enough cash to set up his office, to run it, and to provide for his family for a minimum of nine months. Most times the necessary loans can be secured from local businessmen or bankers, particularly in those communities where there are needs for physicians.

Now for the actual selection of the office. To begin with, it should be conveniently located. At the present time, the trend is away from the metropolitan congested areas to the suburbs where attractive single-story buildings with good parking facilities are available. Ease of getting to the doctor's office, and a place to park after you get there, have become matters of major importance.

In setting up an office, avoid making temporary arrangements. The furnishings should be good, the over-all effect one of stability and success. Get a decorator to help you; it is worth the small fee. Good equipment and furnishings still look good ten or fifteen years later, and, besides, by that time people will have become accustomed to them and to you.

Perhaps the most important asset to your office will be your secretary—and your secretary should not be your wife if there is any way possible to avoid it. This woman should not be a glamour queen, but preferably a stable, capable person who will really take an interest in the people coming to the office or talking to her on the telephone. Her genuine interest in trying to aid people, and in remembering them as individuals, will be of greatest help to the success of your practice.

Your secretary, who is likely to double as your official nurse— at least in the beginning—looks better in an immaculately fresh white uniform and she should be well groomed. Her telephone manner should be professionally correct and yet personally cordial at all times. She must remember that the people contacting her often are sick, and, as sick people, they can be most demanding and unreasonable. Dealing with people is her job and her manner, in a way, is an introduction to you, for she is your front to your patients and your buffer from much unnecessary trivia.

Once the patient passes her and comes into your office, then a sincere interest without any suggestion of intimacy is the ideal professional manner. This, in the beginning, can be a bit difficult for the young physician to manage. Coolness or aloofness can turn a patient away, but too much warmth may produce "situations" with lonely women or lead to awkward social invitations from other patients. A wise physician can recognize and anticipate the emotionally hungry female patient, and, if he is careful, he will always have his secretary within earshot and never examine any female without proper chaperonage.

More important than the selection of a secretary is the doctor's choice of a wife. She is the key to his success, for she must provide him with a calm and happy retreat from the demands of his practice. Her ability to handle his home telephone calls is essential because people expect her to have knowledge and interest, if only for the reason that she lives with the doctor. She must manifest this interest in the individual patient and always offer some constructive advice or reassurance until the doctor can be found. Often she can handle minor problems with reassurance which may be only common sense, but coming from the doctor's wife is looked on as medically wise.

Her activities in the community and church will be an asset to him. She can keep him informed of changes in the neighborhood, of civic projects which are in progress, and she can generally help him in all his nonprofessional relationships. One unwritten law which must be observed is that the doctor's wife shall never make any comment about his patients or their condition. Generally, it is better for the patients to feel that their cases are not even discussed by the doctor with his wife. This can avoid awkward situations, particularly when the doctor's patients are also family friends.

Most patients like to think of their doctors as exemplary in the art of family living. Certainly the man to whom they turn in trouble should be able to handle his own personal life. They expect their doctor to have a good standard of living, to wear good clothes, to drive a good car. As a result of this same thinking, any ostentation in clothes, in cars, or in spending habits can damage the individual physician's standing as well as that of the whole profession. When such evidences of poor taste are seen, it is probably a reaction to the long, lean training years when most of us had barely enough to eat.

A question in the mind of every intern, resident, or young doctor is this: After I have opened my office, how do I build a practice?

I was fortunate in my first year in that, through an older doctor, I secured a job as a school physician, and this kept my family. There may be such jobs to be found and they can tide a man over and help him get started.

Examining life-insurance applicants for the various companies is a common way for young doctors to make contacts and earn some income. It is not the best sort of relationship, because the doctor is in league with the agent in selling the patient a service, but I have examined applicants in restrooms, in garages, and once even in a chicken brooder house. How well I remember one cold February night when I met an agent and drove with him eight miles out into the countryside to an isolated farmhouse. Everything was pitch-black when we arrived; but, undaunted, the agent led the way around to the chicken house where he aroused our disgruntled client, who had been sleeping, fully clothed, on a pallet beside the brooder stove. By lantern light, and by probing through many layers of odoriferous clothes, I did the best I could to make a satisfactory examination. . . . Needless to say, as soon as the young physician is able to support himself otherwise, this is the first work that he abandons.

A physician must become known in his community. Indeed, one of his earliest problems is how to maintain his dignity as an individual, and his integrity as a doctor, and still let people see him, become acquainted with him, and be given a chance to judge him. How can this be done? Each man must find his own way, adapting himself to whatever openings there may be for him. I was fortunate to have had a prisoner-of-war experience, and since an account of it—an American doctor retreating with the German army—had been published in *Atlantic Monthly* magazine, I was invited to speak at various gatherings. Despite preferring a whipping to making a speech in public, I addressed the DAR, the women of the church, civic clubs, and even had a pretty successful night with the PTA on the horrors of war and a doctor's role in battle and in prison. This gave the people of my community a chance to evaluate me as an individual and to make up their minds as to whether they wanted to have me as their personal physician. (Be certain, any time you are going to speak in public on any *medical subject,* to mention it to your local medical society.)

Much of your early practice, after you have become somewhat known in your community, will be an overflow from the practice of the older doctors, either when they are not available or when they are so crowded that they ask you to assist them. You must be scrupulous about sending back to your colleagues any patient you may have seen in this way at their request. Once the doctors find that you have this integrity, as well as competence, they will send more of their patients to you when they are pressed.

However, you should understand that patients who come to you voluntarily, because they cannot secure the services of their own physician, become fair game and if they elect to stay with you, this is ethical. I remember that one of my earliest conquests was an elderly woman complaining of an abdominal pain. Her regular physician had been treating her for nine months with X rays and weekly shots for anemia. One of her neighbors had suggested that she try me. Swallowing my pride at thus being called in distinctly on trial, I grabbed the black bag and visited the lady.

Her family was assembled as a kind of jury, a large family of grown children, and with them looking on I discovered a mass in her right lower quadrant and informed them that this should be investigated in the hospital and the sooner the better. Subsequently, a cancer of the cecum was removed and the lady has visited me yearly for the last twelve years with no recurrence. During this time, she and her ten grown children have referred fifty-five patients to me.

One can never be sure how his practice will begin to put itself together and to grow. Even some of the most difficult and undesirable neurotics, those who come to a doctor because he is new in the community, because he is somebody they haven't yet had a chance to tell their story to, may leave him seemingly dissatisfied and disgruntled. But these very people, if he has been considerate and patient with them, may refer others to him for whom he can offer real help.

In your early days, your practice can be extremely trying. My office used to be across the hall from an established physician and it was difficult for me to sit there completely idle and yet trying to appear busy. A man can eat his heart out, sitting in an empty room and watching a continuous flow of patients turning in across the hall. It takes a certain amount of courage, I believe, not to become hostile to the other man and also to maintain faith in yourself.

Then, too, things happen in the early days which can terrify a young doctor. A friend of mine, who had been an intern when I was, began practice by sharing office space with an older man. His examining table had not yet arrived and he was using an old X-ray table with a pad over it. On a Wednesday afternoon, when his older friend was away, a rather difficult patient presented herself with abdominal cramps. She wasn't much pleased with the young substitute but allowed herself to be placed on the makeshift table. About the time the examination was beginning, the young doctor was called urgently to another room to check a hemorrhage. Suddenly, there was a creaking crash and a scream from the room he had just left. The terrified young physician rushed back to find the patient pinned under the table and screeching threats of a suit. She had pulled some long-unused lever and the table had tipped over on her.

My young friend extricated her, called for help, and rushed home to tell his wife that they had better start packing and getting ready to leave because he was ruined in that town. The older doctor returned the next morning and called in the patient and examined her. Treating her with special care, he managed to cajole her into considering the whole episode a joke. My friend is now a highly respected internist in that community; but he says he still remembers the way the blood froze in his veins when he rushed back into that room and saw his first patient pinned under the X-ray table.

From the day that you begin practice, establish your policies and do not be stampeded into changing them. Decide the type of practice you are willing to undertake and determine the limits you intend to put on it. I feel that you should also restrict the community area that you are willing to serve, for unless this is established early and adhered to, you will find yourself losing valuable time from patient care in driving back and forth to all kinds of remote areas.

In regard to time: it is right that you should give yourself as fully as you can to your patients, but don't forget your own family. Establish a schedule for being with them because, even though you may be pressed financially, regular time spent with your wife and children in your home, and occasionally off on trips with them, will make you live longer and your family will be more pleasure to you. It is foolish to build up a fine practice at the cost of losing a close relationship with your family. Careful planning should enable even a truly busy physician to participate in home meals, in church and school activities, and in planned and regular family affairs.

One thing more about the doctor and his manner. A successful doctor is one who inspires confidence. He should be intellectually honest with himself, with his colleagues, and his patients. At the same time, and without any trace of dishonesty, he can appear competent to manage the patient's problems, even though he admits that he cannot give an exact diagnosis or treatment at that moment. Most patients are confused and frightened; they need the reassurance and comfort that a trained person can give them. A rattled physician is no comfort in a crisis.

In summary to young men and young women who are beginning practice: Set your sights high and don't compromise with what you want, but at the same time be realistic in your aims and be prepared to wait. People don't trust their lives to an unknown young doctor, even though he may have been well trained and has several diplomas framed on his office wall. A young physician must become known as a level-headed professional man, a qualified member of the community, a doctor who merits the confidence of his fellow townsmen and the respect of his colleagues, both as to his professional ability and his personal integrity.

A genuine interest in people and their problems is a requisite for your success as a doctor. A man really interested in his patients can even make a mistake now and then and they will still praise him, but not even skill can always silence the criticism aimed at a cold and impersonal technician. Naturally the competent physician, genuinely and humanely interested in his patients, in their weaknesses and their strength, and with a sincere desire to help them, will have a rewarding practice. Often it will burden him with its many demands, but almost always it will leave him with the satisfaction of being valued and appreciated by the people who look to him to take care of them.

5 *You as a*

SPECIALIST IN

INTERNAL MEDICINE

—AN INTERNIST

BY DWIGHT L. WILBUR, M.D.
CLINICAL PROFESSOR OF MEDICINE
Stanford University School of Medicine

DR. DWIGHT L. WILBUR

Born: 1903, Harrow-on-the-Hill, England

Stanford University: A.B., 1923
University of Pennsylvania: M.D., 1926

Commander, United States Navy, 1942–46

Mayo Clinic:
  First Assistant, Section of Pathologic Anatomy, 1929–30
  Staff of Division of Medicine, 1931–33
  Associate in Division of Medicine, 1933–37
  Consulting Physician, 1931–37
  Instructor and Assistant Professor of Medicine, 1933–37
Stanford University School of Medicine:
  Assistant and Associate Clinical Professor of Medicine, 1937–39
  Clinical Professor of Medicine, 1949—

Chief of Medical Services, French Hospital, 1946—
Area Section Chief in Gastroenterology: Veterans Administration, 1949–53
Staff Presbyterian Medical Center, Childrens Hospital
Consultant Letterman General Hospital
Consultant United States Naval Hospital, Oakland
Consulting Physician Southern Pacific Hospital
Member of Civilian, Health and Medical Advisory Council: Department of Defense, 1953–1958
American Association for Advancement of Science
Association of American Physicians
American College of Physicians: President, 1955
Member, Council on Medical Education and Hospitals, American Medical Association
American Gastroenterological Association: President, 1955
American Council for Clinical Investigation
National Research Council
Trustee:
  Lux College, 1949–55
  Miranda Lux Foundation, 1955—

Editor:
  California Medicine, 1946—
Editorial Board:
  Modern Medicine
  Post Graduate Medicine
  Gastroenterology: Chairman of the Editorial Board, 1958—

OF ALL the specialties in medicine, internal medicine is the largest and the most important. The internist who practices it is a physician trained as a specialist in the diagnosis and medical treatment of internal diseases in the adult. He is the "physician" of "physician and surgeon." Most people know about surgeons, dermatologists, obstetricians, and other specialists, but the term *internist* they may confuse with *intern* and not recognize that the internist is a physician who is an expert with special knowledge of diseases of the heart, digestive tract, lungs, kidneys, blood, and other internal organs. By some he is thought of as the modern family doctor, by others as a consultant, while Will Rogers amusingly described this physician as "the traffic cop who directs patients from one doctor to another."

Internists have a special interest in a variety of different diseases, including *infectious diseases* such as tetanus, malaria, tuberculosis, typhoid fever, syphilis, pneumonia, and meningitis; but happily, what with modern methods of sanitation and public health, with chemotherapy and antibiotics, infectious diseases have come increasingly under control. Consequently, internists have been turning their attention more and more to what are called *degenerative diseases*, essentially diseases of aging—diseases which affect all organs but are particularly recognized as occurring in most forms of adult heart disease, of arthritis, high blood pressure, strokes, and arteriosclerosis. *Malignant tumors*, such as cancer and leukemia, are of primary concern to the internist, as are a group of diseases which might be called *chemical or metabolic diseases*, that is, disease of the endocrine glands— the thyroid, parathyroids, pituitary, adrenals, pancreas, and sex glands—all of which have profound effect on tissues throughout the body. Furthermore, he is concerned with conditions in which there is a lack of one or more essential substances within the body, or in which abnormal pigments or chemical substances are formed, producing a variety of diseases. Modern-day tensions, "ulcers," emotional disturbances, and what often are called disturbances or *disorders of functions*, also occupy much of the time of the modern internist. There is so much for him to know, to be able to identify, and to deal with.

Basically then, an internist behaves like a scientifically trained detective. He must find out what is wrong with the patient, why he has the symptoms he has, why he has pain or is short of breath, why he has a heart murmur, a headache, albumin in the urine, a low level of sugar in the blood, insomnia, fatigue, or "nerves." The process by which he does this is called making a diagnosis. It is always intriguing and challenging. At times very simple, at other times it is very difficult, calling on all the resources at the command of the physician and his associates. It may lead him through intricate paths of the patient's personality, his contacts with other people, his background of medical experiences in life, his relations with his family, his work, and his community. Even more, it leads the physician to a careful examination and then to a variety of laboratory tests which measure the physiological, chemical, and physical characteristics of the patient—blood pressure, pulse rate, urinalysis, blood sugar, cholesterol and blood fats—to electrocardiograms and a multitude of other tests which must be carefully selected to meet the diagnostic needs of each particular patient. Furthermore, the internist calls on the radiologist or expert in X rays to study the chest, the stomach, the colon, the kidneys and other parts of the body for diagnostic help. Usually by these methods the internist comes to the proper diagnosis and conclusions, but sometimes he sees the patient so early in the course of the disease, or the disease itself is so obscure, that the doctor must delay before the diagnosis can be made. For example, the rash of measles may not come out for several days after the previously diagnosed bronchitis or cold is first noted.

Many years ago my father, Dr. Ray Lyman Wilbur, a distinguished physician and internist, on alighting from a train at Palo Alto after a year of study in Europe, was met by Louie, an old patient and friend, a Chinese cook at a fraternity house on the Stanford campus. "You come see my wife—she sick," was Louie's request. Despite my father's plea that he had not even been home from the trip and his suggestion that another physician be called to see the sick woman, Louie insisted. His telling (and winning) argument was, "Other doctors come look—you come look, see." This expressed beautifully in a few words the role of the internist. As he goes about making a diagnosis and undertaking treatment, he must not only *look* at the patient with the cold knowledge of medical science but must *see*, with warmth and human understanding, the whole situation—the patient, the disease, the family, the environmental setting, and the relationships of them all.

Perhaps just as intriguing to the internist as diagnosis—if not more so—is the treatment of the patient. Once the diagnosis has been made, there comes the opportunity for the internist to use his skill, to apply what he knows of the art and science of medicine in treating a particular patient. He may know exactly what to do, but all too often the patient will not accept or follow his advice. Why? Is it a lack of confidence on the part of the patient or his family? Does it seem impossible economically? Is the advice not practical? Does the patient have a psychological block? Is the condition hopeless? The physician must use all his knowledge of the patient himself and all his understanding of practical applied psychology.

Sometimes his success as a physician depends on his skill in directing a patient to a better or more suitable job. Sometimes it depends on getting him to guard the lessening resources of a failing heart, to accept the need for dietary care in diabetes, or gradually to develop a more mature emotional outlook toward a problem which cannot otherwise be successfully met.

There may be satisfaction in life equal to but none greater than being able to help the sick, the despairing and suffering person as does the physician by artfully applying his scientific knowledge in the diagnosis and treatment of disease.

How does one go about becoming an internist? Does one need certain inherited or basic qualifications in addition to training? Obviously acquiring all the necessary skills takes much education, training, and time, and yet as I look at my colleagues

throughout the country—internists who are at the top of the profession—I note many different sorts of people. One does not have
to be a particular type to become a good internist. A certain
degree of intelligence is, of course, essential; but if one has been
at least a reasonably good student in a good university or college,
he probably has the intellectual capacity to be a physician.
Beyond this, certain qualities have great value for a prospective
internist.

He should have a *good memory* because he must remember
many important facts in medicine and about a patient or a disease. He should have *imagination* so that he can solve difficult
problems in diagnosis and treatment, and in a sense be able to
see through the eight ball behind which lies the correct diagnosis
and the proper treatment. He must have *curiosity* to motivate
him to look and think beyond the usual and what might ordinarily be expected in the patient and in the disease, seeing, too,
into the patient's environment and its significance. More, he must
take into account the potential relationships between all these
factors and examine the whole in the light of the most recent
knowledge he has acquired.

He will do much better if he has or develops *emotional maturity* because then he can more objectively attain the judgment
which is necessary in the management of the problems of sick
people. And, finally, the internist who wishes to practice medicine *should like people,* for he will be dealing with them constantly and in considerable part his success will be based on his
feeling of friendliness toward them, his understanding of them,
and his appreciation of their strengths and weaknesses. (For
the internist who wishes primarily to teach, the need to like people is less important; for the internist who wishes to engage in
research, emotional maturity and liking people are helpful but
not essential.)

A good example of how some of these factors may, in an individual, combine to produce a brilliant result is indicated in the
work and accomplishments of my friend and colleague, Dr.
Philip S. Hench of the Mayo Clinic. An internist of great intelligence, interested in rheumatology (bones and joints), he observed that patients with a disabling type of arthritis temporarily
showed marked improvement during the course of pregnancy

or when afflicted by liver disease with jaundice. This observation he added to other bits of information of the kind that gives exercise to an active mind. Now his imagination and curiosity came into play and he bethought himself of a strange item of resemblance between pregnancy and liver disease. In both, there might be an alteration in function of the adrenal glands. He pursued with vigor the idea that there might be a relationship between the products of these glands and the disabling arthritis.

His colleague, Dr. Edward C. Kendall, had years before produced compound E from the cortex or outer layer of the adrenal gland. Now, owing to the fortuitous turning of a questing mind, it was found that, when given to a disabled patient with rheumatoid arthritis, compound E (or, as we now know it, cortisone) produced outstanding results—a "temporary cessation" of symptoms and marked improvement in the disease. Even more important, cortisone and its related substances, including ACTH or corticotropin from the pituitary gland at the base of the brain, not only improved other serious diseases, but use of them led to methods of study and understanding of glandular and other chemistry of the body which in the past dozen years have revolutionized much of medicine. For this great discovery, born of intelligence, a good memory, imagination, and curiosity, Drs. Kendall and Hench won the Nobel Prize in physiology and medicine.

The medical education of the internist may be said to begin in the premedical years of college or university where basic education and training in biology, chemistry, and physics are acquired. Whether these occupy two, three, or four years is optional and depends on the needs and desires of the student for general education, including the humanities, and for maturing.

Medical school takes four years, and here, during his "free" time, the prospective internist will profit by getting all the information he can about biochemistry, physiology, biophysics, and the care of patients. Additional training in mathematics and statistics will be helpful.

Beyond medical school comes a year of internship and then three years of residency or fellowship in internal medicine or one of its subdivisions. During this period the future internist will do well to learn as much as he can about other fields of medicine such as surgery, neurology and psychiatry, obstetrics and gynecology, radiology, and pediatrics. As an internist he will have to make, for his patients, decisions which require familiarity with the general principles of these branches of medicine, albeit not with their details. Can this patient tolerate and survive a gall-bladder operation? Can this woman with heart disease successfully go through pregnancy and delivery? Is this patient really stable enough in his present environment successfully to handle his ulcer? How far can X-ray studies of this patient really help in diagnosis? These are some of the practical points illustrating a need for broad knowledge.

During his period of three-year residency or fellowship the embryo internist may follow one of many different pathways. He may spend it all with patients, advancing steadily in knowledge, judgment, and responsibility; he may spend part of it in clinical investigation, which is the study or investigation of new things about disease or conditions of patients; or he may occupy a year in research in the laboratory. Some will spend the last year in a special division of internal medicine such as cardiology, gastroenterology, or hematology, which are studies of conditions of the heart, digestive tract, and blood. He may choose to spend a fourth or a fifth year in one of these special divisions so that he will be recognized as a cardiologist, gastroenterologist, or hematologist.

On completion of his formal training, or perhaps even before it, the young internist may have his career interrupted by two years of military duty. Generally he will have a much more productive and interesting time in military service if he completes his training before going on active duty, so that he can have experience as an internist in military hospitals or institutions. Thereafter comes practice or teaching or research.

First, he passes the state board examinations so that he will be licensed to practice medicine in the state of his choice. Then, after at least three years of residency or training in internal medicine, and two years of practice, comes the examination by the American Board of Internal Medicine to test his qualifications for practice as an internist. When he "passes the Board," consisting of a written examination, and, one year later, a practical examination, he will be certified as a specialist in internal medicine and will be recognized as a specialist by his peers, by members of hospital staffs and by others.

For those internists who wish additional recognition beyond the American Board of Internal Medicine, there are further board examinations and certifications in the subspecialties of allergy, cardiovascular diseases, gastroenterology, and pulmonary diseases.

When all the previously mentioned steps have been taken, the internist has concluded his preparation to practice, to teach or to do research; and now, at thirty or thirty-two years of age, probably by this time with a wife and children, he is on his own. He has selected a place to practice as an individual or in a group, and, with confidence born of long years of preparation and experience, he starts his real career.

Most internists go into the practice of medicine and hang out the proverbial shingle. The practice of internal medicine varies very widely, depending on the desires and wishes of the individual physician, on the nature of medical practice in the community in which he chooses to live, and whether he practices alone or in a group. The solo practitioner will take care of his patients in the office, in the home, and in the hospital. He has the great advantage of running his own show and of independence; but if he is going to do a good job he will have to be available at all times, will have less freedom to get away, and will find it harder to keep up with recent medical developments than if he is in a group.

More and more internists practice in groups, consisting sometimes only of other internists and sometimes of physicians in various divisions of medicine, as in a clinic. This sort of practice has many advantages, including a doctor's close association with experts in his own field and others, greater ease of consultation, and of opportunity for advancement in knowledge and in practice. Since no one physician can be an expert in more than a limited field, the physician practicing in a group has a feeling of satisfaction that his patients are receiving better medical care than the average that can be provided by a single physician. However, practicing in a group requires giving up some independence and a willingness to recognize the group as of more importance than the individual.

The internist practicing in a group or even in solo practice is often, in the previously cited words of Will Rogers, "the traffic cop who directs patients from one doctor to another." He seeks the advice and opinion of other specialists concerning a patient and synthesizes what he learns from them and from his own observations in making a diagnosis and determining treatment. He is the keystone, the essential cog of the group. The surgeon, the obstetrician, the dermatologist, the specialist in eyes, ears, nose and throat, turn to the internist when they are in trouble. He is the one who understands the basic factors in disease, the underlying chemical and physiological disturbances, the psychological quirks of people, and he is the expert in diagnosis and treatment.

More and more the practice of medicine is centered about the medical center and the hospital. The reasons are simple. The old-time beloved physician, carrying his black satchel, relieving and comforting the sick, dispensing hope and courage along with his medicines, is passing or has passed from the scene. The "black satchel" has been expanded into the tremendously complex facilities and services of the modern medical center and the general and special hospital. Modern medicine simply cannot be practiced without laboratory tests and X rays which require complicated and expensive apparatus and equipment. Equally important is the need for an innumerable variety of trained persons in what are called the allied health professions and services— nurses, laboratory, X-ray, and other technicians; physical, occupational and other therapists; medical secretaries and record librarians, dietitians, psychologists and the like. These persons and the physician constitute the health team.

Whether the internist practices in his office, in the patient's home or in the hospital, the great joy of his work will be in establishing a professional relationship with his patients. This is called the physician-patient relationship. Francis W. Peabody, one of the great young teachers and internists in America in the 1930's, expressed it this way: "The practice of medicine in its broadest sense includes the whole relationship of the physician with his patient. It is an art based to an increasing extent on the medical sciences but comprising much that still remains outside the realm of any science." This relationship may lead the physician by use of his scientific knowledge rapidly to cure the patient with pneumonia by giving penicillin or the patient with meningitis by administering sulfadiazine. Much more often absolute cure cannot be brought about, and in order to attain maximum improvement he must, with great skill and art, apply what scientific knowledge he has to improve and relieve the patient's symptoms even though the cause of the disease cannot be significantly approached. And all too often, when there is hopeless illness such as cancer or heart disease, all the physician can expect to do is to relieve and comfort the patient and his family.

The internist in the hospital will have duties beyond the care of his patients. He is certain to be on a hospital staff committee, there to take an active part in considering the innumerable problems that arise in the running of any complicated organization. Even more important, he will probably do some teaching. This may consist of teaching nurses, technicians, dietitians or other ancillary personnel, and perhaps "house staff"—interns, residents, fellows, and possibly medical students. There is no more important function that he can perform. Teaching requires clarification of one's own ideas on a subject; it requires concentration to keep ahead of the students, and it greatly satisfies the urge to help other people. The internist should seize every opportunity he can to teach. It will broaden his view and also tend to keep him from going to sleep in medicine—awaking at last as did Rip Van Winkle, unknown and out of touch and out of sympathy with the times.

Finally, many internists will engage in full-time or part-time research in medical schools, hospitals, government services, and industry. More and more young men in medical school and in residency training are exposed to research, engage in it, and are fascinated by it. The eternal search for the truth, the great desire to understand the unknown, the nature of disease and the physiological, chemical, and physical changes that accompany it, draw internists into the laboratory, the research institute and the medical school. Because of his basic training and knowledge of disease and of patients, the internist is peculiarly well adapted to medical research and to participate in it as an important member of the research team.

In his relationship with other physicians, the internist is commonly an associate or partner; but often he is a consultant too, because of his special knowledge in diagnosis and treatment. Specialists in other fields of medicine—surgeons, obstetricians, and so forth—will ask him to see and care for puzzling, difficult, and unresponsive patients. Frequently the physician in general practice turns to the internist for help. Why does the patient have a persisting fever or pain? What can be done to stop this patient's heart irregularity? Why, after operation or delivery, doesn't the patient recover strength and health more rapidly?

A fascinating example is that of an apparently healthy, stable, married truck driver of forty with a splendid record of no accidents for fifteen years who suddenly began to get tickets for traffic violations. He would run his truck through red lights, he would head the wrong way into one-way streets, he would be found far off his route. Thorough study and examination revealed no abnormality. He did not have evidence of a brain tumor, although his changed behavior turned suspicion in that direction. Obviously the man had to be relieved of his duties even though he seemed quite well. At this point he was seen by an internist. Upon careful study it was noted that his infractions all occurred late in the morning or afternoon and never on weekends. This was the important diagnostic clue. Perhaps it was related to eating and to a low level of blood sugar. Tests showed that indeed it was and the blood sugar was much too low several hours after a meal. When food was withheld, the patient fainted, then could be promptly restored to normal by taking orange juice. These studies led to an operation and the removal of an insulin-producing tumor of the pancreas, followed by restoration to complete health and his job. Simple? Yes, but the internist as a diagnostician had to sit down with the patient and figure it out.

It is as a consultant that the internist gets involved in the most fascinating variety of problems, calling for all his scientific and diagnostic skills. Moreover, besides problems in the art of medicine itself, he may at this time be facing other challenges, being called on to satisfy the needs of a patient, the patient's family, and the requirements of the patient's physician or physicians. These times in consultation call for all his knowledge, experience, and wisdom, and it is probable that consulting with other physicians represents the high point in the career of an internist.

Before World War II, many physicians beyond medical school made little formal effort to keep abreast of developments in medicine. State laws did not require it, board certification was in its early stages, and the great developments of our day in medical science, such as antibiotics, steroids, radioisotopes, and medical genetics, were largely in the future. In the past twenty years this situation has radically changed. Now, for the practicing internist, it is "once a student, always a student." The developments in medicine are coming so rapidly that if the internist wants to stay in the forefront, he must keep up with what is going on. He can do this in many ways, but he must have the will and the drive to do so. When he sees a patient with a complicated problem or is called in consultation, he must have knowledge of recent developments in internal medicine. Is the antibiotic that is being used the most suitable one for the patient? Could this patient's ulcer and intestinal bleeding be the result of cortisone that is being given for treatment of arthritis? If so, how should the ulcer and the arthritis be managed? Should anticoagulants, which slow the clotting of the blood, be used in this patient with a stroke? What are the chances that this patient's blood pressure will be lowered or cured by operation on the artery running to one of his kidneys? These questions can be answered only by the internist who is up to date.

As an example, in 1938, a patient came into the San Francisco General Hospital with diarrhea so severe her general condition was critical. She was weak, irrational, dried up, and wasted. Her response to treatment was poor—in fact, there was no response. A week or so later she was seen by a bright young internist who recognized the mental symptoms, the changes of the skin, and the diarrhea to be due to pellagra. It was just before this time that the vitamin *nicotinic acid*—Vitamin B—was discovered to be helpful in pellagra. (Later it was found to prevent and cure it.) The young internist had read about it in a recent medical journal and had learned more about it at a medical meeting. The substance had just become available in pure form, and, when given to this patient, it promptly stopped the diarrhea, cleared the mental symptoms, and gradually restored her to health.

Keeping up to date requires participation in what is called "continuing medical education." This is education beyond the residency or fellowship, and, as yet, it is in its early stages of development. Generally, the internist secures it by membership in special societies of internists such as the American College of Physicians; by reading regularly ten or twelve of the leading medical journals in his field; by attending postgraduate courses, seminars, or panel discussions; and by visits to university medical centers. The American College of Physicians now comprises the leading 12,000 internists in the United States and Canada. It sets high standards for membership. Its annual sessions are three- or four-ring circuses of panel discussions, lectures, television sessions, and clinics to bring its members up to date on the latest developments in internal medicine. Regional meetings in various states and postgraduate courses sponsored by the College help to do the same thing.

Special societies such as the American Heart Association, the American Gastroenterological Association, the American Rheumatism Association, and others also do this sort of thing for internists with interests in these and other special fields. For those who are interested particularly in teaching and research, organizations such as the Association of American Physicians, the American Society for Clinical Investigation, and the Central Society for Clinical Research serve these special purposes. The informal discussions and friendships, which develop outside the formal programs of these meetings, are among the most satisfying and rewarding that the internist will experience.

University medical-school centers generally are the leading centers of medical advancement in this country, and association with them, or visits to them, or other contacts with them, will help keep the internist up to date.

By tradition, because they are educated men and have the qualities of leadership, physicians have played a vital role in community life. Furthermore, their specific knowledge of sanitation and public-health matters made it essential to community living that they assume responsibility and leadership in the control and prevention of infectious diseases. This objective has largely been accomplished, except for a few diseases, and the internist in particular now volunteers, or is asked to participate, as a citizen in the community. His obligations in this respect can be met through participation in voluntary health agencies; through Community Chests and United Funds; through development and active support of clinics and hospitals for the underprivileged; through active participation in PTA's, Chambers of Commerce, service clubs; through working in, and co-operation with, agencies of his community's government, such as projects dealing with mental health, chronic alcoholism, venereal disease, and air pollution. In a sense he becomes a physician to the community.

This responsibility has been beautifully expressed by one of the greatest physicians of all time, Dr. William J. Mayo, who spoke on behalf of his brother and himself when he wrote: "our father recognized certain definite social obligations. He believed that any man who had better opportunity than others, greater strength of mind, body or character, owed something to those who had not been so provided; that is, that the important thing in life is not to accomplish for one's self alone, but for each to carry his share of collective responsibility."

Some internists with more than usual energy and ability will carry their talents beyond community activities to those at state or national levels; to national voluntary health associations, such as the American Cancer Society and the American Heart Association; and to the government, in advancing medical knowledge in the armed forces, the Public Health Service, the National Academy of Sciences, the National Science Foundation, and similar organizations. The possibilities are without limit.

As a member of the medical community, the internist will join and actively participate with his colleagues in local and county medical societies. In these organizations and in the state and American Medical Associations, he can be an effective force in keeping high ethical standards, in furthering standards of good medical and hospital practice, in helping to meet the medical needs of his community, state, and nation. He can play his part in fostering high standards of medical education, and in furthering the great programs of voluntary health insurance which, with their rapid growth since the late 1930's, have almost completely revolutionized the economics of medical care.

Further, he will participate in the care of patients in city or county hospitals, and in free or part-pay clinics, reaping the rewards of helping his community's health institutions and of learn-ing much about the practice of medicine.

As a physician, the internist deals with a large variety of condi-tions. Many of his patients will have high blood pressure, heart disease, diabetes and arthritis, and some will have obscure and rare conditions. His abilities in diagnosing and treating these conditions often will be taxed as he applies what he knows about the science of medicine. Specialists in other fields commonly deal with a single organ or group of organs such as the eyes, the ears, nose and throat, the urinary tract, the reproductive system, the skin, or the nervous system. One of the most stimulating features of internal medicine is that it deals with all of them and par-ticularly with their interrelationship. In this interrelationship, the internist must increasingly consider the patient as a whole. He must see beyond the individual organs and consider not just the units but the whole person—and this is one of the great fasci-nations of internal medicine.

As he practices this specialty, the internist more and more realizes that from one-third to two-thirds of the patients he sees have symptoms due to disturbance in function, generally based on mild to moderately severe emotional disturbances: the patient with headaches from too much tension; the young housewife and mother with fatigue and irritability; the business executive with frustration, indigestion, and insomnia; the older person with all sorts of symptoms and a sense of futility and depression. These patients commonly tax the skill of the internist in the art of medicine, for he must be sure of the diagnosis, which is often obscure and intriguing; then he must deal with the whole patient and consider him as an individual with a unique personality, a family, a job, a conscience, a need for human dignity and for help.

In meeting these responsibilities, the internist needs to develop certain qualities which may lie latent within him. First, he must have an *understanding of human beings*. In many walks of life an understanding of people is an important part of a job or pro-fession; in medicine it is essential. The handling of normal peo-ple can be difficult enough—that of abnormal or sick people, more difficult still. The proper use of applied psychology, of some of the principles of psychiatry, and of just plain savvy is often the difference between the ordinary and the exceptional physician and internist. As a part of this understanding, the internist must also have a *recognition of human frailties and weaknesses*. If he does, he will not expect perfection in his patients, or unquestioning acceptance of all the diagnostic and therapeutic advice he gives; nor will he be too disturbed when the patient recurrently gets into difficulty because he is just the sort of person he is. Thus, *patience and tolerance* are among the greatest qualities of the internist. Commonly he must wait it out, so to speak, until the diagnosis can be made and the effects of the treatment become apparent; or until the patient struggles with himself, and his environment, to a more mature outlook on his problems, or perhaps on his disease. The internist must know when to wait and when to act; but above all, he must know what he is doing and why he is doing it.

The internist must have *perseverance*. He must stick with the problem until the diagnosis is made and treatment initiated. It may take him much time and effort to discover finally the early cancer that has produced vague but persisting symptoms, or to find out that the chest pains and shortness of breath in a middle-aged business executive are traceable not to organic disease in the patient himself but to unconscious identification with the heart disease of a relative or a friend. He must constantly ask himself how and why any of this happened.

One of the greatest qualities for the internist is *hope*—the one thing that all of us want and need when we are in trouble—and the sick person is in trouble. Hope is basically related to human survival, and the preservation of it in a patient is the goal of the physician; he knows that maintaining hope is one of the most important means he has of helping all persons in his care. Even when a situation seems to be hopeless, some semblance of hope should be maintained because the most seriously ill patient may reverse the trend of his illness and survive. The capacities of the human constitution for recovery, for overcoming disease, and withstanding apparently overwhelming emotional and environmental difficulties, are magnificent. Human history is filled with stories of the frail, the sick, the weak, the despairing who have risen to conquer themselves and fate.

The internist must have *charity*. In his understanding of people and their weaknesses he must always call on charity, a quality properly recognized in Corinthians: "And now abideth faith, hope, charity, these three; but the greatest of these is charity."

Finally, the internist should develop the qualities of *imperturbability* and *equanimity* so well expressed by Sir William Osler, the "father" of internal medicine: "Imperturbability means coolness and presence of mind under all circumstances, calmness amid storm, clearness of judgment in moments of grave peril, immobility, impassiveness. . . . It is the quality which is most appreciated by the laity though often misunderstood by them; and the physician who has the misfortune to be without it, who betrays in indecision and worry, and who shows that he is flustered and flurried in ordinary emergencies, loses rapidly the confidence of his patients. . . . A calm equanimity is the desirable attitude."

The need for all these qualities in the physician and especially the internist was beautifully expressed by Lord Lytton when he wrote: "To the true physician, there is an inexpressible sanctity in the sick chamber. At its threshold the more human passions quit their hold on his heart. Love then would be profanation. Even the grief permitted to others he must put aside. He must enter that room—a calm intelligence. He is disabled for his mission if he suffers aught to obscure the quiet glance of his science. Age or youth, beauty or deformity, innocence or guilt, merge their distinctions in one common attribute—human suffering appealing to human skill."

The young physician going into internal medicine will find the future of this specialty bright and stimulating. Its rapid growth of the last twenty-five years will continue. More internists will pursue a branch of internal medicine such as cardiology or gastroenterology and confine their activities to the heart or the digestive tract or other phases of internal medicine.

The growth of internal medicine will cause an increasing number of internists to practice in clinics or in groups of eight or ten or twelve, each one trained to a knowledge in the whole field, but having even more particular knowledge of a division of internal medicine such as hematology (the blood), rheumatology (bones, muscles, and joints), pulmonary diseases (chest and lungs), and so forth. This trend will continue and be increasingly useful for physicians and patients alike.

Many internists will become the family physician and health counselor, others important consultants. Basically, however, the internist will remain the pivot man of the health team, directing the patient from one physician to another, while himself making the final decisions. In the future he will do more teaching than in the past; and more and more internists will give all or part of their time to it. Likewise he will observe, participate in, or engage full time in medical research, which is becoming increasingly essential in the effective practice of internal medicine.

Already some of the important tools that will greatly advance internal medicine are being well used. These include the electron microscope which magnifies cellular structure over 100,000 times and which has opened new doors to knowledge of the structure of the cell, and its components and of the function of them. Another tool is the radioisotope, which permits tagging of atoms with radioactive materials that can be traced as they are introduced into the body, become a part of it, actively participate in the function of it, and then gradually are destroyed or eliminated. Studies by this method give us a much clearer understanding of the chemistry of the body. Biochemical studies of all sorts of body constituents, fluids, and tissues provide important means of learning about disease and in understanding the nature of life, of growth, of heredity, and of degeneration.

The study of countless enzymes which are the catalysts that speed up and determine chemical reactions, of nucleoproteins and nucleic acids which are the basic stuff of life, and of hormones which regulate much of the chemical activity of cells and tissues—these are the studies that will fascinate and aid the internist of the future. Along with the important studies of genetics, which will play an increasingly useful role in understanding of disease, these studies of biochemistry will lead to establishment of what is called molecular medicine or molecular disease. As our understanding of life and disease has advanced, we have passed from consideration of the person to consideration of the tissue, then to that of the cell, and now to that of the molecule.

The use of investigative tools by medical and other scientists will greatly advance the diagnostic and therapeutic skill of physicians. These tools will vastly enlarge the field of chemotherapy of disease—the use of chemical substances to inhibit or kill disease-producing organisms or viruses and to modify degenerative processes. They will increase our knowledge of immunology and its related fields, to the practical end that tissues can be successfully transplanted from one individual to another. And they should make it possible for us to make more healthy and useful the lives of countless persons, prolonging lives for twenty to thirty years by the conquest of infectious diseases. Many of these people now languish in unhappy retirement or huddle in small apartments, hotels, or rooming houses, too often alone, unhappy, unwanted, "outside society and the community," waiting and hoping for the end. Others with failing minds and bodies are in nursing homes, in hospitals, or in state institutions beyond rehabilitation with our present medical knowledge and skill.

The internist of the future must be equal to the task of understanding the medical science he must use in the practice of his profession. For this he will have to depend to an ever-increasing extent on physicians who are specialists in other fields, or on basic medical scientists, or on the laboratory and personnel of medical centers and hospitals. Most of all, even in so complex a setting in so complex a society, he himself must remain an individualist, and always remember that he is not taking care of people in general but of persons as individuals. There is much in the care of an individual that is nonscientific, and that care is, indeed, an art. Our specific knowledge of human relationships, and particularly of the physician-patient relationship, is in a primitive stage and will be for a long time. So will be our understanding of the symptom-provoking tensions and the trying circumstances of life that have been recognized for thousands of years, but which modern urban living in an atomic age seems to have swollen to great proportions.

The internist of the future, therefore, in the care of his patient, will "look" with the science of medicine, and "see" with the art of medicine, as with compassion and understanding he practices his profession—"human suffering appealing to human skill."

6 _You as an_

OBSTETRICIAN

BY NICHOLSON J. EASTMAN, M.D.

PROFESSOR EMERITUS OF OBSTETRICS
Johns Hopkins University School of Medicine

DR. NICHOLSON J. EASTMAN

Born: 1895, Crawfordsville, Indiana

Yale: A.B., 1916
Indiana University School of Medicine: M.D., 1921
University of Chicago: D.Sc., 1958

Indiana University School of Medicine: Instructor in Obstetrics, 1922–24
Peking Union Medical College, Peking, China: Associate in Obstetrics, 1924–28
Johns Hopkins University: Instructor and Associate in Obstetrics, 1928–33
Peking Union Medical College: Professor Obstetrics and Gynecology, 1933–35
Johns Hopkins University: Professor of Obstetrics, 1935–61
Johns Hopkins Hospital: Obstetrician-in-Chief, 1935–61
Retired from Johns Hopkins University and Johns Hopkins Hospital, 1961

President American Association of Obstetricians and Gynecologists
Chairman of the Section on Obstetrics and Gynecology of the American Medical Association
President of the American Academy for Cerebral Palsy
Chairman Expert Committee on Maternity Care of the World Health Organization
Chairman of the Expert Committee on Midwifery Training of the World Health Organization
Director of the Passano Foundation

Books: *Expectant Motherhood*
Textbook of Obstetrics
Handbook of Obstetrics for Nurses (with L. Zabriskie)
Editor-in-Chief: *The Obstetrical and Gynecological Survey*

OBSTETRICS is that branch of medicine which has to do with childbirth, its antecedents and sequels. It is the happiest of the medical specialties since it deals, for the most part, with a normal, physiological function—a richly rewarding function—rather than with disease. This function is the crowning achievement of a young woman's life to which she has probably looked forward with mingled feelings of joy, curiosity and, it must be added, more or less apprehension. As an obstetrician, you are her guardian throughout this Great Adventure, the creation of a new life.

The transcendent objective of obstetrics is that every pregnancy culminate in a healthy mother and healthy baby. It strives to reduce to a very minimum the number of women and infants who die as a result of the reproductive process or who are left injured therefrom. It aims further to minimize the discomforts of pregnancy, childbirth, and the subsequent "lying-in" period; and, at the same time, so to safeguard and ease the whole course that both mother and child will conclude the experience in a healthy state, both physically and mentally.

The magnitude of obstetrics as a branch of medical practice is shown by the number of registered births each year. At the present writing this figure for the United States exceeds four million; and competent authorities estimate that by 1970 the number of registered births will approach six million. Another index of the magnitude of this specialty is the proportion of hospital admissions occasioned by childbirth. As reported by the Health Information Foundation, admissions for childbirth or conditions directly related thereto accounted in 1957–58 for 24.1

per cent of all admissions to general hospitals in the United States. Admissions in this category easily rank first in frequency; indeed, the next two causes for admission—allergic and respiratory diseases (15.8 per cent) and accidental injuries (8.2 per cent)—do not quite equal, when combined, the percentage of obstetrical admissions.

Only a few decades ago the number of women who died in the course of childbearing was approximately one in a hundred. This was a grievous social and economic loss, since almost all these deaths occurred in young women who were in the bloom of health and who often left motherless children behind them.

Today, the number of women who die from causes directly associated with the reproductive process is about four per 10,000 births, or less than one-twentieth of the former figure. To what do we owe this dramatic and salutary change? As we shall see, many factors have been responsible; but, first and foremost, we owe this achievement to a type of maternity care vastly superior to that which existed earlier in the century. This is synonymous with saying that we owe it to a vastly superior type of medical personnel and medical training concerned with maternity care. The modern obstetrician, as the result of extensive tutelage and training, has at his finger tips a larger number of skills and drugs which were unknown before 1930. But even more important than these is what we call "obstetrical judgment"—the seasoned knowledge, gained from precept and example, of what to do and what not to do under any given circumstance. All this, as I say, must be at the obstetrician's "finger tips." This is all-important because complications in obstetrics often develop suddenly and call for lightninglike decision and action, if the mother and baby are to be saved. As an obstetrician, it will be your responsibility to possess and exercise these skills and this fine judgment.

In fact, if you are to call yourself a specialist in obstetrics, it is mandatory that you acquire these qualifications, and two important and powerful organizations will make certain that you do. One of these is the American Board of Obstetrics and Gynecology and the other, the American College of Obstetricians and Gynecologists. Although without legal authority, the American Board of Obstetrics and Gynecology is the generally endorsed body which certifies specialists in this field.

The standards it has set are high. A candidate, after graduation from a Class-A medical school and after an internship, must have had three years of special house-staff training in an acceptable hospital; he must have practiced his specialty for several years thereafter and must submit detailed reports of the more important cases he has managed personally; and finally, he must pass rigorous written and oral examinations. If the candidate meets successfully these several requirements and tests of his competence, he becomes a "Diplomate" of the Board. Of these, there are now more than 6,000.

To become a Fellow of the American College of Obstetricians and Gynecologists, the candidate must first be a Diplomate of the Board. In addition to this requirement, the College, in the election of its Fellows, lays a great stress on the esteem in which they are held in their own communities, especially as stated by their colleagues in the specialty. But the objectives of the American College of Obstetricians and Gynecologists are much broader than endorsement of professional competence and standing, for they encompass all matters that bear on the welfare of womanhood insofar as the reproductive organs are concerned.

One of these objectives is the intensive educational programs it sponsors. For example, at its annual and district meetings, from seven-thirty in the morning until late each night, the days are filled with teaching conferences on every phase of obstetrics and gynecology, in addition to systematic postgraduate courses and formal presentations of original scientific papers. As an obstetrician, you will derive much inspiration and general benefit from belonging to both these organizations.

In the foregoing paragraphs, it may have been noticed that the names of the two organizations discussed couple "obstetrics" with "gynecology" and "obstetricians" with "gynecologists." It may have been noted also that the interests of the American College of Obstetricians and Gynecologists extend to "all matters that bear on the welfare of womanhood insofar as her reproductive organs are concerned." This brings us to the important fact that obstetrics and gynecology are actually one specialty, gynecology dealing with the female reproductive tract in the non-pregnant state, and obstetrics in the pregnant state. But there are many overlapping areas.

Almost all medical schools in the United States, the British Commonwealth, and other countries combine the two disciplines in a single department and teach the subject matter as a single canon of medical knowledge. Moreover, most practitioners of obstetrics practice gynecology as well, and vice versa. These circumstances have a most important bearing on you as an obstetrician since, if you are to be an obstetrician, you must also be a competent gynecologist and obtain thorough training in both fields; indeed, to become a Diplomate of the American Board of Obstetrics and Gynecology, you must pass examinations in gynecology as well as obstetrics. The subject of gynecology is admirably discussed in another chapter of this book, and we shall limit our consideration here to the reasons why obstetrics and gynecology are regarded as one specialty.

From the viewpoint of underlying science, obstetrics and gynecology deal with the same set of organs, the female reproductive tract. Hence, the anatomy concerned, both gross and microscopic, is the same. Likewise, the physiology involved is common to both fields. For example, a certain change in the interrelationships between two hormones of the ovary causes both the onset of menstruation and the onset of labor. Similarly, aberrations in the female endocrine glands are responsible for some of the most frequent disorders met in both areas. For instance, inadequate function of the ovaries is responsible for irregular, abnormal bleeding from the nonpregnant uterus, one of the most-often-encountered conditions in gynecology; while in the pregnant state it is responsible for most miscarriages, one of the most common complications in obstetrics. Tumors of the uterus and ovary are also shared by both fields, according to whether the patient is pregnant or not.

In actual everyday practice, moreover, there is a large common area. Thus, when a woman complains of inability to become pregnant or of having repeated miscarriages, a sound knowledge of female endocrinology both in the pregnant and nonpregnant state is essential for intelligent management. In addition, many of the operations performed are the same whether the patient is pregnant, or not, such as hysterectomy (removal of the uterus) and oophorectomy (removal of an ovary). Finally, in cases of mistaken diagnosis (which, regrettably, are not infrequent), obstetricians sometimes have to deal at the operating table with gynecological abnormalities in nonpregnant patients, while gynecologists are occasionally faced at the operating table with an early pregnancy with or without associated gynecological abnormalities.

In present-day obstetrics about 5 per cent of all deliveries in the United States are accomplished by Caesarean section and a considerably larger propotion by forceps. These are surgical procedures and, as an obstetrician, you must be adept at these and other surgical techniques. Moreover, in certain uncommon but very grave complications of pregnancy, extremely difficult abdominal surgery may be entailed; and with this too you must be familiar. Your training in gynecological surgery will be most helpful here.

The *sine qua non* of any successful undertaking is well-trained, knowledgeable personnel. We have hence discussed at the outset the background of tutelage, training and experience that you, as an obstetrician, must possess.* Let us now consider the several ways in which you will be applying this knowledge to promote the welfare of your mothers and their babies.

The Chinese count a person's age not from the day of birth but from the time of conception, a good way of reminding your expectant mothers, as well as you yourself, that all this time a living, human creature is being nourished, who will soon be "nine months old." During this vital, formative period the child is in greater need of proper nourishment and suitable environment than at any other time in his life. His well-being in this period depends, naturally, upon the health of the mother; moreover, his well-being in the years to come, as well as the well-being of the mother, are based in substantial degree on her condition during the prenatal months. Accordingly, you can confer no greater boon on these unborn children, and on the future welfare of their mothers, than by rendering the most meticulous care throughout

* For details of requisite house-staff training in this specialty, see Dr. Te-Linde's chapter on "You As a Gynecologist."

this period. You will have many helpful suggestions to make about the kinds of food which should be eaten to ensure the growth of a robust baby and about the sort of routine that is most conducive to normal development. By judicious and timely advice regarding details of personal hygiene, you can do much to obviate minor discomforts and to prevent them from developing into menacing complications.

Prior to the rise of present-day obstetrics, the physician usually had only one interview with his patient before he saw her in labor and often at this interview he merely sought to compute the expected date of confinement. When he next saw her, she might be in the throes of an eclamptic convulsion (one of the gravest complications of pregnancy) or striving vainly to overcome the resistance offered by a contracted pelvis. It is in the prevention of such calamities as these that care and supervision of the pregnant mother, in the course of frequent office visits, have been found to be of such value. Indeed, prenatal care is an absolute necessity if a substantial number of women are to avoid disaster; and it is helpful to all.

From a biologic point of view, pregnancy and labor represent the highest function of the female reproductive system. As has been mentioned previously, this should be considered a normal process. But the numerous physiologic changes which occur in the mother's body during pregnancy demonstrate that the border line between health and illness is less distinctly marked during pregnancy than during the nonpregnant state. A slight variation in bodily function, which might be of but little significance if the woman were not pregnant, may be a warning signal of potential abnormality in pregnancy which could seriously threaten the health of the mother or the child or both. Examples of such symptoms might be a weight gain of several pounds during one week or a persistent headache. Health supervision and teaching begun early in pregnancy are often the means of avoiding complications of pregnancy; and in the event that symptoms do occur, their early detection and prompt treatment may avert serious problems.

Since expectant mothers are subject to the same diseases that affect nonpregnant women, the obstetrician must frequently care for gravid women who have heart disease, diabetes, anemia, tuberculosis, pneumonia, inflammation of the urinary tract and countless other diseases. Of these, heart disease imposes the greatest risk on the mother and diabetes on the baby. But they all may raise serious problems in regard to treatment and/or management at the time of labor. You, as an obstetrician, must therefore have a considerable acquaintance with medical diseases if you are to handle these cases with intelligence. In fact, these so-called coincidental conditions loom so large in the everyday practice of obstetrics that an internship in internal medicine is an excellent preparation for definitive training in obstetrics and gynecology.

The climax of this long period of expectant motherhood is, of course, the onset of labor with the final arrival of the much-coveted baby. Provided the prenatal course has been entirely normal, one of your main concerns in the course of labor will be to keep your patient comfortable. The pains of childbirth have been the stock and store of intimate conversation among women since time immemorial, and many young women approach childbirth in dread of the ordeal. It is no easy task to dispel this age-old fear, but from the first prenatal visit the obstetrician must make a conscious effort to give his patient a wholesome point of view. He must instill in her not only confidence, but also the feeling that he is her friend, a medically wise friend, who is sincerely desirous of sparing her all the pain possible provided that this is compatible with her safety and that of the child. The very presence of such a friendly doctor and the realization that he is competent to handle any emergency is in itself a potent basic analgesic. But all this involves qualities which cannot be put into a code of instructions. The attitude I have in mind comes only as the result of long nights in the labor room and then only to those of understanding heart. It is the very stuff of which good doctors are made and is at once the safest and most welcome of obstetric anodynes.

The crusade against pain in childbirth, concerning which we read so much in women's magazines today, is not new but represents the culmination of a campaign which is more than a century old. It may be said to have started late on the evening of November 4, 1847, in the dining room of a house at 52 Queen Street, Edinburgh, Scotland. Three men sat huddled over as many glass tumblers on the dining-room table. One of the group—a big-headed, shaggy-haired man whose black eyes sparkled with enthusiasm—was busy with a series of evil-smelling bottles. As if to sample the contents of each bottle, he would pour a small quantity from each, one by one, into the tumblers. From all outward appearances, this might well have been a wine-sampling party, or a search after the elixir of youth. But all the men did was to bend over the glasses, as each was newly changed, and inhale deeply. For many evenings this same curious performance had been going on, but inhale what they might, nothing happened. It was not until this particular evening, when a rather sweet-smelling substance was placed before them, that their quest was finally satisfied. With the first whiff of this chemical, an unwonted gaiety seized the group; with the second, an overwhelming sleepiness befell them; and scarcely had they taken the third inhalation when the three lay sprawled on the floor, not to awaken for two or three minutes. It was in this quaint fashion, over his dining-room table in Edinburgh, that Sir James Y. Simpson, together with two friends, discovered the anesthetic value of chloroform. And to this day, every mother is the debtor of this great Scotch doctor, for his chief purpose in thus seeking a new anesthetic was to relieve pain in childbirth.

But Simpson faced a stubborn, uphill fight, for no sooner had he announced that the pains of childbirth could be relieved by chloroform than a storm of invective befell him, from the clergy and the public, as well as from many members of the medical profession. "It is unnatural thus to interfere with the pains of childbirth which are a *natural* function," they cried.

"But is not walking also a natural function?" replied Simpson. "And who would think of never setting aside or superseding this natural function? If you were traveling from Glasgow to Edinburgh, would you insist on walking the distance on foot simply because walking is man's natural method of locomotion?"

Exclaimed an Irish lady to him one day, "How unnatural it is for you doctors in Edinburgh to take away the pains of your patients when in labor." "How unnatural," he replied, "it is for you to have swum over from Ireland to Scotland against wind and tide in a steamboat."

To the clergy's objection that such anesthesia was contrary to the Bible, and the birth-pang curse of *Paradise Lost*, he cited the "first surgical operation" and the "first anesthesia": "And the Lord God caused a deep sleep to fall upon Adam, and he slept: and he took one of his ribs, and closed up the flesh instead thereof."

Countless other objections were hurled at him, but to each he had an answer; he pointed out, moreover, that all things new are likely to arouse censure, particularly censure of a religious nature. Thus, he recalled, when vaccination against smallpox was introduced, various clergymen attacked the practice as irreligious, referring to it as a tempting of God's providence and therefore a heinous crime. He cited further the introduction of table forks. At first this innovation was regarded as a very sad and uncalled-for intrusion upon the old and established natural function of the human fingers and a number of preachers denounced it "as an insult to Providence not to touch our meat with our fingers."

To anyone acquainted with the women's magazines of today, these old disputes sound very modern, for the debate over pain relief in childbirth still continues. But, be this as it may, you will be expected, as an obstetrician, to keep your patients reasonably comfortable in labor; and with modern drugs and various anesthetic techniques, you will be able to do so in the great majority of instances. This requires, however, a rather extensive acquaintance with the pharmacology of pain-relieving drugs, especially with their effects on the child.

Much might be said—and large volumes have indeed been written—about the many other problems which childbearing women present to the obstetrician. But let us recall at this juncture that the obstetrician, unlike other specialists, has two patients under his care, the mother and the baby; and it is high time that we consider the responsibilities that you, as an obstetrician, will assume in relation to the baby. In regard to the mother, as we have seen, her outlook has improved immeasurably during the past few decades so that the number of women dying in childbirth in the United States today is quite small *provided* they receive good care throughout pregnancy and the birth process. But, alas, for the unborn child (or fetus, as we call it), the story is quite a different one. His hold on life from the moment of conception to delivery is a hundred times more precarious than that of the mother.

The total number of babies born dead in the United States during 1958 was approximately 93,000, while the number of infant deaths during the first month of life was approximately 82,000. By adding these two figures, the total infant loss which occurred in close proximity to the birth process was about 175,000. Of these, the vast majority were the direct result of factors associated with pregnancy and the birth process.

Expressed in a different way, the number of infants lost in close association with the reproductive mechanism constitutes more than 10 per cent of all deaths in the United States at all ages and from all causes. The same circumstance is observed year after year and indicates the relative magnitude of the infant loss which is associated with pregnancy, labor, and the early weeks of life.

About half of these deaths occurred in the first day of life. Indeed, the deaths occurring during the first twenty-four hours exceed in number those occurring during the second, third, fourth, fifth, and sixth months of life combined. The causes responsible for this huge wastage during the neonatal period are many. However, the most common by far is premature birth. Thus, of the 82,000 neonatal deaths occurring in 1958, over one-half took place in premature infants, that is, in infants who weighed less than five and a half pounds at birth and who, for the most part, were born a month or more early. The factors which are responsible for these premature births, although evident in some cases, are completely unknown in 60 per cent of the total number of cases.

It is true that the number of deaths just cited for infants lost in close association with the reproductive process is less than the figure for deaths in the United States each year from diseases of the heart, blood vessels, and kidneys (900,000) and from cancer

(250,000). There are few people who have not lost a father, or a mother, or some other relative from one of these diseases and anyone acquainted with them knows full well the suffering and anguish they cause. Certainly we would not want to minimize in the slightest the gravity and tragedy of these diseases. Nevertheless, in fairness to all concerned, let us consider for a moment the following figures.

The average age of persons suffering from cancer at the time of the initial diagnosis is fifty-eight years. What is the average life expectancy of United States citizens who are fifty-eight years old? As shown by the most authoritative actuarial statistics, it is sixteen years.

By comparison, what is the life expectancy in the United States of a newborn baby? Basing our data on the same actuarial data, it is sixty-nine years—sixty-nine years, moreover, which span the prime of life, the decades of greatest vigor, initiative and achievement. The conclusions you draw from these data will depend in large part on how you assess life's values. They will depend in goodly measure on the relative values you put on the life of a one-minute-old baby and that of a fifty-eight-year-old man or woman. In this connection you will perhaps recall the question that a skeptic once asked of Benjamin Franklin about his discovery of electricity. The question was: "Of what value is electricity?" The same question might be asked about a newborn baby.

But far exceeding the infant loss we have just discussed is the fetal wastage caused by miscarriage. Since about 10 per cent of all pregnancies terminate spontaneously in miscarriage, it may be estimated that the number of these accidents which occur annually in the United States is of the order of 400,000. A large proportion of them are due to faulty germ plasm (defective egg or defective spermatozoa); many are the result of unsatisfactory environmental conditions in the uterus, while still others are of unknown etiology. But if we are to know the total number of potential human lives obliterated each year in this country by miscarriage, it is necessary to add to these spontaneous miscarriages a huge but quite unknown number of criminal interruptions of pregnancy. The sum total is approximately one million.

There is, perhaps, an even greater tragedy than the actual death of a newborn baby. That is the birth of a baby whose brain never develops, who continues, like a vegetable, to grow and develop physically, but who lacks the cerebral centers which govern speech, muscular co-ordination and reason. The frequency of this condition, cerebral palsy, is much higher than most people would probably suspect. In a study conducted in 1948 in Schenectady County, New York, an incidence was encountered of 5.9 cases per 1,000 live-born infants who survived one month. This means that if you, as an obstetrician, should serve on some obstetrical service—such as some large hospital service—with 3,000 births annually, about 18 of the babies born there each year will develop cerebral palsy.

The very first observation published on cerebral palsy stressed the causative importance of pregnancy and the birth process. Thus, the two early papers by an English surgeon, Dr. William J. Little, one published in 1853, and the other in 1863, emphasized the birth process as the main causative factor, the title of his second paper being: "On the Influence of Abnormal Parturitions, Difficult Labors, Premature Births and Asphyxia Neonatorum on the Physical and Mental Condition of the Child, Especially in Relation to Deformities." Ever since the publication of Dr. Little's observations, there has been widespread debate concerning the causative factors concerned, but the preponderance of opinion has leaned toward Dr. Little's original view that pregnancy and the birth process are the most important causative factors.

Every year in the United States, among some four million births, about 1½ per cent of the babies born, or more than 60,000, will continue to be medical and social problems, demanding special care and rehabilitation for years to come. Many of these 60,-000 will be afflicted with cerebral palsy; still more will be mentally retarded; some will have epilepsy, and others will be blind or deaf. All will be sources of daily heartache to more than a hundred thousand parents throughout our land—a grievous social as well as economic loss.

Why will this huge number of children, born in the enlightened year of 1962, be so tragically afflicted? This is the transcendent question—because, even if only a partial answer could be forthcoming, it would provide hope that steps might be taken to prevent some at least of these dire afflictions.

Why, then, does the brain-damaged child happen? One fact is certain. In the majority of cases, at least two-thirds, *something* unfavorable to the fetus takes place *sometime* between the moment of conception and the moment of birth, that is, during fetal life. The question then becomes what is this "something" and when is the "sometime" at which it occurs.

Before attempting to answer this question, let us underscore the fact that more than 80 per cent of cases of cerebral palsy *are* clearly the result of unfavorably intra-uterine environment. This is the figure calculated by the Research Committee of the American Academy for Cerebral Palsy after an extensive study of every conceivable causative factor; and all students of the subject agree that this figure is approximately correct and may even be an underestimate.

Cerebral palsy is certainly not a hereditary condition as shown by the comparatively few instances in which multiple cases occur in the same family. As for cases which owe their genesis to circumstances which develop after birth, such as infectious diseases in infancy and childhood or traumatic head injuries in the first years of life, these are occasionally seen, it is true; but they constitute a small minority only. Moreover, as we have shown in our own clinic at the Johns Hopkins Hospital, if the obstetric records of the mother throughout pregnancy and labor are sufficiently detailed, a retrospective study of such records in cases in which the infant later develops cerebral palsy usually disclosed evidence of some type of intra-uterine injury which the infant had sustained as a fetus, using the word injury to include injury from oxygen lack, injury from virus infection, injury from blood incompatibilities as well as traumatic injury from difficult delivery.

In the present state of our knowledge, the most important cause of the brain-damaged child is premature birth, that is, birth a month, two months, or perhaps three months before the normally expected date of delivery. In the United States at large, 7 per cent of all pregnancies terminate in premature birth. This figure of 7 per cent, the usual incidence of premature birth, will serve as a standard or control against which we may evaluate the following figures: In cases of cerebral palsy, a history of premature birth is recorded in 30 to 35 per cent of cases; in epilepsy, in 13.7 per cent; in mental retardation, in 17 per cent; in blindness, in 90 per cent; and in deafness, in 25 to 30 per cent.

It is true, of course, that some of history's pre-eminent figures, such as Julius Caesar, Isaac Newton, John Keats and Winston Churchill, were premature babies; and it is true also that the majority of surviving premature infants develop into normal children and normal adults. Nevertheless, by and large, premature birth is an unfavorable event from the viewpoint of infant well-being, and, as the figures just cited show, premature birth—especially premature birth two or three months before term—contributes a large proportion of our cases of cerebral palsy and of other neuropsychiatric disorders. Indeed, if premature birth could be eliminated, the number of new cases of brain-damaged children would *ipso facto* be reduced by one-third.

The question then becomes: What causes premature birth and what can be done to prevent it? In all obstetrics there is no more important problem and obstetricians the world over are trying assiduously to solve it.

This brings us to the subject of research in obstetrics. Obstetrics is not a static field, but a dynamic branch of medicine which is moving ahead every day with new discoveries. You, yourself, may not be inclined to enter this research area in any active way; but whether you do or not, it is imperative that you keep abreast of new developments so that you may apply them in your practice. If, however, the many unsolved problems in obstetrics so intrigue you that you desire to carry on serious investigative work, you will find in obstetrics, particularly in fetal physiology and its vicissitudes, a fairyland for research. But he who would storm its ramparts must not come to the attack empty-handed, because any modicum of success in this field demands a sound background in physical and enzyme chemistry, as well as in the general physiology of respiration. Hence, if you anticipate an academic career in this specialty, training in certain of the basic sciences, such as chemistry or endocrinology, is essential even though it may be necessary to take a year or two of laboratory work to obtain it. Liberal fellowships are now available for such purposes.

Obstetrics is a many-sided subject and its relations to the other branches of medicine are numerous and close. We have already noted the overlap with gynecology. The newborn baby, of course, brings obstetrics into close contact with pediatrics, while the many coincidental diseases from which pregnant women may suffer brings internal medicine into its scope. Psychiatric problems interject themselves more frequently into maternity work than even the obstetrician may be aware. As an example, the so-called "morning nausea" of pregnancy has, in most cases, an important neurotic element which must be treated accordingly.

In the international field of public health the World Health Organization has manifested its interest in the broader aspects of obstetrics by sponsoring the activities of two committees; namely, its Expert Committee on Maternity Care and its Expert Committee on Midwifery Training. The objectives of maternity care, as set forth by these committees, reflect the wide horizons they envisage:

The object of maternity care is to ensure that every expectant and nursing mother maintains good health, learns the art of child care, has a normal delivery, and bears healthy children. Maternity care in the narrower sense consists of the care of the pregnant woman, her safe delivery, her postnatal examination, the care of her newly-born infant, and the maintenance of lactation. In the wider sense it begins much earlier in measures aimed to promote the health and well-being of the young people who are potential parents, and to help them to develop the right approach to family life and to the place of the family in the community.

Obstetrics is also related to certain fields which are not strictly medical. Thus, it owes much to the science of nutrition and in time will probably owe more, since many disturbances of pregnancy are suspected of being dietary in origin. In cases of fetal malformation, the science of genetics frequently comes to the fore because only with its help can any intelligent prognosis for future offspring be established. Since the mother-child relationship constitutes the basis of the family unit, the obstetrician is continually meeting social problems. Not the least of these is the 100,000 illegitimate births which occur in the United States each year. In addition, obstetrics has important legal aspects. This is especially true in cases of criminal abortion, in cases of alleged traumatic abortion (taxicab accidents, for example), and in instances of questionable legitimacy of the child.

But you, as an obstetrician, will be practicing in the future— and what of the future? Although the recent decline in maternal mortality has been phenomenal, let no one suppose that the millennium is here or even near at hand. Over 50 per cent of maternal deaths are still preventable, as attested by maternal mortality reports throughout the land. This means that each year some 1,000 women die unnecessarily in the United States as the result of childbearing. Many of these deaths are due to sheer lack of adequate facilities; lack of properly distributed prenatal clinics, lack of suitable hospital arrangements, and lack of quickly available blood.

Others are due to gross errors of management on the part of the obstetric attendant. Some of these are errors of omission; such as failure to provide prenatal care, failure to follow the patient carefully throughout labor and for one full hour thereafter, and failure to call consultation.

Some are due to errors of commission; among these, unnecessary operative interference looms largest. Today's obstetrics is quite different from that of thirty years ago. Otherwise, we should not have witnessed such a decline in maternal deaths. It stresses conservatism in obstetric surgery and, above all, the avoidance of trauma. Accordingly, the attendant who operates unnecessarily (and, by the same token, often traumatically) practices the obstetrics of a quarter of a century ago and will meet a corresponding mortality.

These several deficiencies in maternity care are obviously the first to be corrected if maternal mortality is to be brought to an irreducible minimum. This mortality can and doubtless will be lowered—until it at least approaches the minimum—by the same methods which have proved so efficacious in the past; more and more personnel, more and superior facilities, all more equitably distributed.

We have a right to anticipate a more successful care of mothers; but with our knowledge in its present state, the outlook for reducing the 175,000 infant deaths associated with birth each year and the 400,000 spontaneous abortions—all of them potential American lives—is less promising. Here new knowledge must be forthcoming if any substantial inroads are to be made. This forecast is based on two considerations. In the first place, over the past twenty years the same caliber of obstetric and pediatric care has been directed toward saving the newborn as has been directed toward saving mothers. But the success of all efforts to reduce stillbirths and neonatal mortality, while appreciable, has been only a small fraction of the success of saving mothers and reducing maternal mortality. In regard to the newborn, it is true that expansion of existing facilities may be expected to lessen significantly the infant loss associated with birth; but if we may judge from past performance, this program of itself promises nothing to satisfy us without new discoveries and the introduction of new knowledge.

The second consideration concerning infant death has to do with obscure causes responsible for stillbirths, neonatal deaths and miscarriages. We are powerless to combat some of these causes in any effectual way because we do not know the underlying mechanism of the complications. An example is toxemia of pregnancy (high blood pressure for the mother, swelling of extremities and face) which is responsible for many stillbirths and neonatal losses. Premature onset of labor is responsible for an even larger number of fetal losses. What initiates labor prematurely? In most instances, we do not know. In fact, we are even ignorant of what initiates labor in full term.

The causes of most spontaneous abortions are also obscure. The same is true of many diseases which lead to fetal exitus. To unearth the etiology factors responsible for the many premature labors, the many spontaneous abortions, and the many other complications which threaten the infant as well as the mother, is a Herculean charge, but one which must be met if any great reduction in our fetal losses is to be anticipated. Only with the advent of such knowledge can any true millennium be promised for maternity.

If we look to the future from another viewpoint, it seems likely that pronounced changes will take place in the manner in which obstetrics will be practiced. Attention has already been called to the fact that the number of births predicted for the decade of the 1970's is six million a year or more, a 50 per cent increase over the figure for 1960. As for the number of physicians who will be available to handle this sharp increase, it is forecast that the number of practicing physicians per unit of population will be less in 1970 than it is today. This poses one of the most serious problems that faces obstetrics, namely: Who is going to take care of this huge number of births?

One way in which the question may well be answered is through what we call "group practice" by three, four or five obstetricians working as a team. For example, on a given day, while obstetricians A and B are seeing expectant mothers in the office and handling all day telephone calls, obstetrician C is spending a full twenty-four hours in the delivery suite, managing labors and answering all night calls, while obstetrician D is completely off duty for twenty-four hours. From the viewpoint of a well-ordered life, there would be no night calls whatsoever except for the man on twenty-four-hour duty in the delivery suite; and every fourth day each man would be entirely free. From the standpoint of good maternity care, the patients would be assured of the services of a wide-awake and alert obstetrician who, when on delivery duty, would be able to give his undivided time to the needs of the parturients. From the viewpoint of the threatened paucity of personnel, four obstetricians in such group practice can handle perhaps eight times the number of cases which any one obstetrician could manage in solo practice. This means a doubling of work output for the group. Finally, there is good reason to believe that programs of this type would make obstetrics a more appealing specialty. Group practice of the type described is not new but has worked successfully and to the complete satisfaction of patients in many localities.

In sum, obstetrics is a specialty of many facets. Since most pregnancies terminate normally, its largest area provides one of the happiest relationships that the physician can experience with patients and their families. On the other hand, from time to time, the obstetrician is faced with heart-rending disappointment and tragedy in the form of miscarriages and infant deaths, which call for the utmost in sympathetic understanding. Obstetrics, accordingly, provides a field that is at once broad, stimulating and rewarding.

7 *You as a*

GYNECOLOGIST

BY RICHARD W. TELINDE, M.D.

FORMER CHIEF GYNECOLOGIST
The Johns Hopkins Hospital

DR. RICHARD W. TELINDE

Born: 1894, Waupun, Wisconsin

Waupun High School
Hope College, 1913–1915
University of Wisconsin: A.B., 1917
Johns Hopkins University, School of Medicine: M.D., 1920

Intern Medicine, Intern Surgery, Assistant Resident and Resident in
   Gynecology: Johns Hopkins Hospital, 1922–25
Private practice of gynecology, Baltimore, 1925—
Appointed Professor in Gynecology: Johns Hopkins University, 1939
   Emeritus Professor, 1960
Appointed Gynecologist-in-Chief, Johns Hopkins Hospital, 1939
   Emeritus, 1960
Returned to private practice, 1960

Visiting Gynecologist:
   Union Memorial Hospital
   Hospital for Women of Maryland
   The Church Home and Hospital
American Gynecological Society:
   Secretary, 1937–41
   Vice-president, 1952
   President, 1953–54
American Gynecological Club: President, 1949
Society of Pelvic Surgeons
Southern Society of Cancer Cytology
American Academy of Obstetrics and Gynecology
Honorary Membership in Obstetrical and Gynecological Societies in
   Peru, Brazil, Bolivia, Argentine, El Salvador, Costa Rica
Société Francais de Gynecologie
International College of Surgeons

Author: *Operative Gynecology*
   Many articles on gynecology, female urology and gynecological pathology

NEXT TO selecting a wife, perhaps the most important single decision that a young man makes is that of deciding upon his life's work. The proper decision results in happiness for all his working years. An erroneous decision may result in a frustrated individual who never gets real satisfaction from his job. Men occasionally realize the error of their choice in middle life and change in midstream; but this is difficult in medicine for medical schools today rarely accept older candidates, and, indeed, it is extremely difficult for an older person to assimilate the vast amount of learning required by the modern medical school. Even if one already has his medical-school education, and his training in one specialty, then later finds that he is not happy in his choice, it is impossible for him to get adequate training in another specialty in middle life. This is particularly true in a surgical specialty where the nimble fingers and quick mind of youth are essential to the training. Hence, time spent in long and serious thought, when deciding on a career, medical or otherwise, or developing an interest in some specialty within that career, is time well spent.

Before considering any medical specialty whatever, the student should be certain in his own mind that he has the proper motivations to become a doctor. If he is beset with doubts, he had better not tackle the long and arduous road that lies before the medical student, the intern, and the resident; but if he believes that medicine is his best future, then he should know that there is more than one route he can follow.

The young man contemplating medicine as a career may have a yen to be a bedside physician, or a brilliant surgeon, but his motivation does not necessarily have to be in this direction only. Medicine also needs pure scientists. These individuals may have little interest in directly healing the sick. In fact, it is doubtful if both qualities, the devotion of the bedside physician and the ardor of the pure scientist, are ever combined to a degree of excellence in one individual.

The healer may possess some scientific curiosity, and if this impels him to do research, it is apt to be of a practical nature, for he is generally looking for some ultimate benefit to the patient in his hoped-for solution to the problem he is investigating. The pure scientist, on the other hand, may scarcely be conscious of the needs of patients; though the knowledge produced by him often finds its way into the practical field of diagnosis and treatment and becomes very useful. It is a common mistake to urge such a scientist to waste his time in clinical activities. I have never seen one who could successfully practice the healing art.

These two avenues, then, lie before the prospective medical student. If he does not possess an intense motivation in either direction, he had better not start a medical career. But even though a young man has this desire, and is certain of it, I believe it is a mistake for him, or even for the young medical student, to try to define his exact interests too early. In the course of the medical curriculum, he will come in contact with various sciences of which he knows nothing at the onset, and, given this time of study and development, he will be able to make a more useful and enduring decision as to the direction in which he wishes to go.

Regardless, though, of his interests, and regardless of what his early leanings may be, he should attempt to learn during his medical school years as much as possible of all the branches of practical medicine, and of all the allied sciences; for this will be the one opportunity in his lifetime to view the whole field. As he makes this broad study, he must bear in mind constantly that he should first be a doctor, and later consider specialization.

The time will come, though, and it comes at varying periods for different men, when more specific interests will begin to show themselves and will be recognized. The recognition may not be sudden, and may not even be clear at first; but he will come to know the area in which he particularly wants to work.

If his interest proves to be in gynecology, then this chapter is especially addressed to him.

But before considering the specialization itself, its pros and cons, we might do well to define the term. "Gynecology" is derived from the Greek word "gynaike," meaning woman, and "ology" meaning the study of. The word is pronounced differently in different parts of the English-speaking world. Webster's Unabridged Dictionary gives the preferred pronunciation as jĭn-e-kŏl-o-jĭ whereas the British mostly prefer the pronunciation as gī-ne-kŏl-o-jĭ.

In writing a chapter such as this, the author, who is in the twilight of his active career, cannot refrain from looking back at his own choice and wondering whether he would have had a more satisfying life if he had chosen another specialty. I doubt that I could have chosen a specialty that would have given me more personal satisfaction. Personal satisfaction with one's job is essential to one's best efforts and to success, and it is not selfish for a young man, when deciding on a career, to take into account what satisfaction there will be in it for him.

I came into gynecology through the door of general surgery, rotating through the specialty as part of a general surgical internship. Pelvic surgery has remained my greatest interest, though this is not to indicate that it comprises the whole specialty; one of the attractive sides of gynecology is the fact that it is a multifaceted specialty, consisting of pelvic surgery, irradiation therapy, female urology, a basic knowledge of obstetrics, endocrinology, pathology, and psychiatry.

Good pelvic surgery is based upon an adequate knowledge of gynecological pathology. Without this knowledge, and the application of it at the operating table, surgery becomes a mechanical job. With this knowledge, every surgical case becomes a biological, as well as a technical, exercise. There is in the United States today much unnecessary pelvic surgery done. Much of this is due to a lack of knowledge of pathology on the part of the surgeon.

The generative organs and the organs of the urinary tract in women are closely allied anatomically and functionally. Therefore, the training of a modern gynecologist should include training in the diagnosis and treatment of urological conditions in the female. The ability to view the interior of the bladder through a cystoscope is, to my mind, essential to the proper treatment of cervical cancer. The cervix (the neck of the womb) and bladder lie in close apposition and frequently the spread of malignancy of the cervix is to the bladder. Knowledge of this is essential to correct treatment. Childbirth injuries may result in damage to the urinary tract, causing a vesico-vaginal fistula (an opening between the bladder and vagina) or even more commonly, because of injury to the sphincter mechanism, bringing about urinary incontinence. These are but a few examples of the close association of the urological and genital systems.

Training in gynecology should also include some fundamental training in obstetrics. After all, the primary purpose of the reproductive organs is to bear children. In most universities the departments of obstetrics and gynecology are combined under one administrative head. The result of this has been the training of men to an ordinary skill in both specialties; or to a real skill in one, and only a mediocre skill in the other. It is true that a satisfactory routine practice of both can be done successfully, but it is equally true that real excellence in both fields has never been attained in a single individual. The obstetrician with some training in gynecology may do the routine hysterectomy or vaginal plastic operation reasonably well, but progress in technically difficult pelvic surgery has only been made by those men who are primarily gynecologists. The same is true of obstetrics. Williams of Hopkins, Irving of Harvard, and DeLee of Chicago were pure obstetricians and their interest was not divided. They are the immortals in their field and it is the teachings of these men that have had a lasting influence upon their successors.

For real progress in both obstetrics and gynecology, there should be, in all American medical schools, men whose primary interest is either obstetrics or gynecology. These men should be at the policy-making level so that their influence may be felt by the students. Unfortunately this is not the case in most American universities today and, as a result, one or the other specialty suffers. Most university departments progress in the direction of the interest of the director. The usual pattern is for the director of the department to center his major interest in gynecology or obstetrics, and the other specialty goes by default. Therefore, it behooves the medical student or intern who is interested in obstetrics, or in gynecology, to investigate thoroughly the primary interest of the various departments, making certain that the department which he chooses for his residency training coincides in its interests with his own.

In the field of investigation, these two branches of medicine have much in common and much that is not in common. The purpose of the generative organs is the reproduction of the human race. Both specialties are interested in reproductive physiology and a combined laboratory for its study is desirable. Much remains to be learned in this important field and investigations in embryology, biology, and biochemistry are essential. From the point of view of practice, obstetricians are interested in the pathological conditions which occur during and immediately after pregnancy. These conditions are often acute and serious, and require prompt action of an emergency nature. The gynecologist, on the other hand, is concerned more with the late effects of child-bearing, such as injuries to the vagina and urinary tract.

A large part of gynecology has to do with neoplasms (tumors) of the generative tract. Fortunately many of these are benign such as myomata (fibroids) of the uterus which are the commonest of tumors occurring in women. These tumors, being benign, only require removal by surgery or treatment by irradiation when they give rise to definite symptoms. There are many more fibroid tumors which need never be removed, than there are those which require surgery.

Next to cancer of the breast, cancer of the cervix is the commonest malignancy occurring in women. It is most often a disease of middle life, the average age incidence being forty-eight years. Many women in this age group still have small children to raise and all too frequently death from this disease robs these children of their mother. The disease is one of the more malignant of the cancerous tumors and two decades ago only about 25 per cent of women with this condition survived for five years. Now the survival rate has reached approximately 50 per cent in the better clinics. I mention this disease, particularly because the recent progress in its treatment demonstrates the importance of a knowledge of pathology on the part of the gynecologist and a definite scientific and clinical accomplishment in this field.

How has this come about? It is the result of screening women by means of the cytological cervical smear (Papanicolaou smear), and of microscopic recognition of cervical cancer while it is still on the surface and has not invaded the subjacent tissues. Our knowledge of the Papanicolaou smear is the result of the work of George Papanicolaou, an anatomist, and Herbert Traut, a gynecologist. The cervix and vagina are simply wiped with a spatula and the cellular debris smeared on a glass slide. After staining, the properly trained microscopist can detect cancer cells which have been shed off of the tumor, often too small to be seen by inspection of the cervix with the naked eye.

When such cells are detected there is a strong suspicion that cancer exists and it is up to the gynecologist to find such a tumor by biopsying the cervix (removing a small piece of tissue for microscopic examination). Often this tumor will be found in the very early pre-invasive stage (that is, when it is still confined to the surface). The microscopic picture of pre-invasive cancer has been observed for many years, but there were serious doubts as to whether it was really a forerunner of true invasive cancer. The important unsolved link in the evidence was the proof that these early lesions eventually became true cancer.

It has now been shown that true invasive cancer, which is often a lethal disease, is preceded, in the great majority of times (possibly always), by the pre-invasive lesion. The pre-invasive lesion may exist many years before it becomes invasive cancer and it is probable that many women die of other causes before the pre-invasive lesion develops into the real cancer, capable of killing the patient. The disease in its pre-invasive stage is curable in nearly 100 per cent. It is probable that it is curable in 100 per cent provided accurate studies, undertaken before the operation, demonstrate that it is still truly pre-invasive, and provided proper surgery is done for its eradication.

This accomplishment in early detection of this disease is the result of a co-operative effort between the laboratory workers and the clinician. I venture to say that in one more decade advanced cervical cancer will become so rare that it will be difficult to find a case to demonstrate the disease to medical students.

By virtue of this work on the early detection of cervical cancer, gynecology has invaded the field of preventive medicine and a large part of every gynecologist's practice is the routine annual check-up of women's pelvic organs. Next to the detection of early cervical cancer, the greatest reason for the routine check-up is the detection of ovarian tumors. These tumors, both benign and malignant, are usually silent growers and give no symptoms until they are well advanced.

The situation with ovarian growths is quite different from that of benign fibroid tumors of the uterus. A fairly high percentage of ovarian growths are malignant. Therefore, it is necessary to remove them because it is often impossible to distinguish the benign from the malignant until they have been removed. In some instances, the microscope will be required to make the decision. Hence, the best hope of detecting ovarian growths while still curable is by the routine check-up of the apparently healthy woman. The old adage about an ounce of prevention being worth a pound of cure has surely been true in gynecology, and in the future the specialty is destined to play a major role in the field of preventive medicine.

In the course of many years I have seen many lives saved as a result of annual check-ups of the pelvis. One instance comes to my mind as an example of a cure of an almost incurable disease. A woman who came regularly for an annual examination was found to have a small mass, the size of a golf ball beside her uterus. It had not been present on her previous examinations and I concluded that her pelvis should be explored surgically. At operation, a small cancer of the left Fallopian tube was found and a suitable operation done. This woman is still well and without evidence of disease ten years later, and she is the only patient with this rare condition that I have ever cured. This type of cancer is a silent grower and practically never gives rise to symptoms until it is hopelessly inoperable. Her faithfulness with an annual check-up saved her life.

Let us leave the field of pelvic surgery and consider the urinary tract. The bladder and ureters are intimately associated with the generative tract anatomically. The ureters pass into the pelvis in close apposition to the tubes, ovaries, uterus, and vagina. The bladder is separated from the vagina by only a very thin layer of tissue. Diseases of the ureters and bladder may cause discomfort simulating that caused by diseased generative organs and vice versa. Therefore, it is essential that the well-trained gynecologist be equipped with the knowledge and skill to use the cystoscope and be familiar with urological diagnostic methods. Those of us who have practiced gynecology for many years can recall numerous instances in which women have been treated for symptoms thought to be arising in the generative tract when the real lesion lay in the urinary system.

Injury to the urinary tract in the course of pelvic surgery is not uncommon, especially by the surgeon who is not sufficiently familiar with the anatomy of the parts. I have very recently seen an example of this which very nearly ruined the life of a sixteen-year-old girl. She had been born without a vagina, a rare condition but not too difficult to correct surgically. In attempting to form an artificial vagina, the entire urethra (the tube leading from the bladder) was destroyed and the patient was left without control of her urine. She then fell into our hands and we were able to construct a new urethra by plastic surgery and restore her urinary control. This case is cited only to demonstrate the necessity of pelvic surgeons being thoroughly familiar with the proximal female urinary tract.

Let us consider further pathology as applied to gynecology. We have spoken of the necessity of the gynecologist being an expert in the early detection of microscopic cancer of the cervix which often means the difference between life and death of the patient. The endometrium (the mucous membrane lining the interior of the uterus) is also subjected to many benign and malignant changes. In the menstruating woman, it is undergoing constant change, day by day, as the menstrual cycle progresses. The changes, under the influence of the ovary, are reflected in the microscopic picture of the endometrium. Samples of the endometrium may be obtained by curettage (scraping) of the interior of the uterus, and, when intelligently studied, give valuable information concerning the function of the ovaries. This may be of great value in studying the problem of infertility. This same tissue may, in later life, become malignant and the detection of the earliest changes indicating malignancy is the work of an expert in gynecological pathology. Again, this early detection may mean saving the life of the patient.

Finally, the ovary is one of the most remarkable organs of the human body. It, too, undergoes changes throughout each month of the menstruating woman's life. At birth, the female baby's ovary contains hundreds of thousands of small structures (primordial follicles) capable of growth and the production of a mature egg with the potentialities of forming a human being. Only relatively few of these structures do mature and produce an egg capable of fertilization (one or, very rarely, more per month during the woman's menstrual life). But each one of these eggs has the capacity, when fertilized, of reproducing a complete human being. Even when not fertilized these ova may, under certain poorly understood conditions, have the potentiality of developing into bizarre tumors.

In addition, the ovary contains many other types of cells capable of development into benign and malignant tumors. Some of these tumors are active from the standpoint of secreting hormones capable of producing excessive feminizing characteristics in the woman. Others may produce masculinizing changes in the woman. These hormonally active tumors are rare; but malignant ovarian tumors and malignant change in otherwise benign ovarian tumors are not rare, and their detection at the operating table is essential. This is only possible by the pelvic surgeon who is well grounded in gynecological pathology. The recognition of the impetus responsible for the spark which touches off the development of these many diverse tumors is a field ripe for investigation, which is today practically unexplored.

Endocrinology as applied to gynecology is also a facet of this specialty which welcomes the investigator. There is much more for you, the coming generation, to fathom than is known now. Endocrinology is very imperfectly understood and better understanding would give us new and valuable knowledge which would be of great practical as well as scientific value. The average normal woman begins to menstruate at the age of approximately thirteen. But in the years immediately preceding this, she

begins to develop sexually and her secondary sexual characteristics, such as breasts and pubic hair, begin to grow. These secondary sexual characteristics are dependent upon the production of a hormone called estrogen which is developed in the
ovary.

When menstruation begins in the child at puberty, there develops another hormone within the ovary after each ovulation,
which normally occurs at about halfway between menstrual periods. Following ovulation, the hormone progesterone, is formed,
and continues to be poured into the blood until just before menstruation. These hormones have an effect upon the lining of the
uterus (endometrium) in anticipation of the reception of the fertilized egg. In case pregnancy occurs, the production of these
hormones continues. If pregnancy does not take place, the formation of estrogen and progesterone ceases temporarily and
their withdrawal from the blood has its effect upon the endometrium which is shed off. This causes bleeding which is the outward evidence of menstruation. This is a bare outline, and over-
simplification, of the phenomen of the menstrual cycle. It is
actually much more complex and much is still to be learned
about it. For example, just what triggers ovulation at the mid-
cycle is still a mystery.

In addition to its role in the menstrual cycle, estrogen has an
effect upon the woman during her entire menstrual life. Its effect can best be noted by observing the effect of its withdrawal
at the menopause which normally occurs in the late forties or
early fifties. Then the ovaries, uterus, vagina and vulva become
atrophied. These changes in the vagina may be slight or excessive, and, when they are marked, may interfere with the woman's marital function. In addition to the withdrawal effects on the
pelvic organs there are changes elsewhere in the body. The skin
becomes wrinkled and loses the flush of youth. There is a
change in body conformation, the breasts becoming smaller and
flabby, and fat is apt to be deposited on the abdomen. In other
words the woman is "over the hill" as far as her youthful appearance is concerned. Many women welcome the menopause, being
glad to be free of the nuisance of monthly bleeding. To other

vain women it is a terrific blow to pride. I will go into this further when we consider the psychic side of gynecology.

It is in endocrinology as applied to gynecology that great unexplored fields of research lie. For example, painful menstruation (dysmenorrhea), is one of the commonest conditions encountered in the practice of gynecology and one of the least
understood. What the common cold is to the internist, dysmenorrhea is to the gynecologist. We have not been able to hide our
ignorance by blaming a "virus," a common habit of medical men
in speaking of a "cold" and other minor illnesses. Much also remains to be done for a complete understanding of infertility.
There are mechanical causes that are readily understood, but
these are not the factors in the majority of infertile women. The
cause undoubtedly often lies in the realm of endocrinology. To
illustrate this, it is not uncommon in this age of frequent divorces
to have a sterile couple divorced; both parties to remarry, and
both to have children promptly and repeatedly. This clearly indicates that there is a factor which is as yet completely unsolved.

Also many women cease menstruating temporarily or perma-
nently in early life. In some instances the cause can be determined, but in most instances the endocrinological disturbance
responsible is not discernible with our present knowledge.

Still another common occurrence in married women is repeated abortion—the inability to carry children to term. Occasionally a mechanical factor can be found to explain this, such
as a cervix which is incompetent of holding the fetus in the
uterus, or a malformed uterus. More often the cause lies in the
field of endocrinology. Some of the factors are understood, but
much remains to be learned.

Finally, psychiatry is an ever-increasing part of gynecology.
Women come to their gynecologist with many problems which
do not involve organic disease. Often they are of the opinion that
some organic disturbance is responsible for their trouble, and the
first duty of the gynecologist is to find the organic trouble or rule
it out. Many times their problems involve their marital life.
These delicate disturbances assume great importance in their
minds and often they hesitate to discuss them even with their

husbands. Some of these difficulties may be prevented by pre-
marital examinations which are being done with increasing frequency today among educated women. Such examinations may
disclose slight physical defects which can easily be remedied before marriage, permitting the marriage to get off to a good start
rather than having difficulties which eventually may be magni-
fied and lead to marital failure. In addition to searching for
physical defects, the gynecologist should give the prospective
bride an opportunity to ask any questions she wishes about marital life.

One of the most frequent problems in every gynecologist's office is the woman who presents herself with various aches and
pains in the pelvic region and wishes to know if there is a physical cause for her discomfort. Sometimes an obvious cause can be
found, but more often than not the pelvic organs are normal and
the complaints are on a psychosomatic basis. The completely
normal woman will be satisfied and grateful when told that her
pelvic organs are normal, and, whatever the cause for her discomfort, she can be assured that it is of no consequence. The neurotic woman will not be satisfied with this explanation; it then
becomes necessary to delve deeper into her problem to determine the reason for her complaints. This is often difficult but the
busy gynecologist should take the time and effort to do so.

One of the occasions for the use of psychotherapy is presented
by the menopausal woman who is excessively disturbed nerv-
ously. Much can be accomplished by the proper administration
of a hormone (estrogen) in allaying her nervousness and especially her hot flushes. But this is not the whole story. Some
women regard the menopause as a great tragedy in their lives.
They are aware that the prime of life is over and that the signs
of old age which inevitably follow do not add to their attractive-
ness as women. They are worried about losing the affection of
their husbands and look forward to their declining years with
dread. The administration of estrogens will not cure this state of
mind, but a sympathetic understanding and advice by the gynecologist can be most helpful.

An example of the relation of psychiatry to gynecology comes
to my mind and I believe it is worth recording here. A woman in

her late thirties complained of incapacitating menstrual pain. She had been unsuccessfully treated for this by her family doctor and gynecologists. The family doctor had on several occasions given her injections of morphine. Finally, at the age of forty-two, her uterus was removed with the hope of saving her from morphine addiction. She continued to complain of incapacitating pain for several days each month. X rays were then used to stop her ovarian function. She continued to complain of severe pain and bled vaginally every month; her family doctor continued giving her morphine. We were at our wits' end, but the patient made one mistake of which we took advantage. She insisted that the periods were perfectly regular. I asked her when her next period was due and she named the date. I sent her into the hospital the day before the expected period and the next morning she began to bleed and writhe in "pain." We took her to the operating room and anesthetized her for examination. About halfway up into the vagina was a cut in the vaginal wall from which she was bleeding. She apparently had been cutting herself each month to demonstrate menstruation as a means of getting the morphine.

What should be the training of a student who wishes to prepare himself for the broad specialty of gynecology? The American Board of Obstetrics and Gynecology requires three years of training in the dual specialties after one year's internship. Following this training, and a certain period in practice, the candidate is entitled to take the examinations for certification as a specialist in the field. There is no doubt that the requirements in training for the examinations have done much to elevate the general standard of practice of obstetrics and gynecology. In my opinion this has been accomplished by insistence on minimal requirements of training, rather than by the preparation of the candidates for the actual examination.

I seriously doubt whether it is possible fairly to evaluate a candidate's capabilities by any verbal or written examination. I have known many men who practice poor gynecology yet, nevertheless, successfully passed the board examination. On the other hand, I have known a few well-trained men who failed in their first attempt to pass the examinations and yet became leaders in their specialty and even professors in good medical schools. The trainee should constantly bear in mind, while in his training period, that his primary objective is to get the best possible training and not merely sufficient training to meet the board requirements. These requirements are minimal and the trainee who aspires for excellence should aim higher.

Let us set up an ideal training program. It will give us something to aim at, although it is obviously impossible for everyone to be fortunate enough to get this training. First of all, there is the financial barrier which prohibits some from participation in a long-term program. However, this barrier is only relative and can be overcome in most instances if the motivation for first-class training is strong enough. There are people of means who are glad to finance young men showing real promise. The unmarried man has a great advantage here, for his living costs can be cut to a fraction of those of the married man, especially one with children. The suggestion of Osler that the young man interested in the best training in medicine put his affections temporarily on ice is good practical advice, but is seldom accepted today. When the trainee without financial resources marries, he should bear in mind that his added responsibilities may make it more difficult for him to get the best training.

In my ideal training program, I would prefer that the trainee first take a year's internship in internal medicine. In making this statement I am speaking from personal experience. I was fortunate enough to obtain such an internship and I am confident that I learned more that year than any year of my life. The graduate of even the best medical schools knows very little about medicine the day he receives his diploma. I know of no better way to supplement the superficial knowledge of medicine to which he has been exposed in medical school than by a year in general medicine. An internship in general surgery is valuable to the prospective gynecologist, but exposure to general surgery at a higher level of training is of more value. A rotating internship may be substituted for the year in general medicine; but, in my opinion, it is not as good, for the intern gets only a smattering of the various subjects as he passes through the different departments.

However, it is a more practical smattering than he had in medical school and hence is of value.

Having completed his internship, the candidate for specialized training in gynecology should seriously consider his objective. If he has a family and financial pressure, or if he is going to be satisfied with the routine practice of obstetrics and gynecology, he can accept the usual training program of the average hospital which is more or less equally divided between obstetrics and gynecology for a three-year period. He will thus qualify for his board examinations and will be able to perform the usual duties of the private practitioner of obstetrics and gynecology. Mention of such minimal training is not made in a deprecating manner. The country needs such men to do the vast amount of routine work in this field, but we also need men with better training to excel in their specialty.

If the candidate has his sights set at a somewhat higher goal—such as teaching, investigation, or practicing the specialty of gynecology at a higher level—he should look for a different type of training. By practicing at a higher level I mean this: In each community of considerable size, there are outstanding men in all specialties to whom other specialists refer their difficult problems for solution. If the candidate believes that he possesses the qualifications to rise above the average, he should seek another type of training than that required by the boards. In doing this, let me repeat that he should investigate the philosophy of the department head before accepting an appointment.

The program which I am about to outline is designed to train men of the above-mentioned type and I shall describe it in some detail. An abundance of clinical material is a prime requisite for such training, and the candidate should assure himself that this material is available before attaching himself to the service. Such services are found mostly in the East and South and in a few of the larger cities of the Midwest. A city with a large medically indigent population is a requisite for this type of service. In addition, the gynecologist in charge of the service must have a true conception of a long-term residency training. Unfortunately a comprehension of this is not possessed by all department chiefs.

The first year of specialty training is divided equally between clinical obstetrics and gynecology. In obstetrics, the trainee does a great many normal deliveries and many of the less serious operative procedures. In gynecology, he works in the operating room as second assistant and in an active outpatient department where he examines innumerable patients, his examinations being checked by a senior resident or visiting man. During part of his six months he is on call in the accident room where his diagnostic acumen and clinical judgment is put to a real test. He is privileged to call a senior resident to confirm his opinion whenever he is in doubt.

During the second year, the trainee spends his full time in general pathology, doing autopsies on all types of cases but especially on those from the obstetrical and gynecological services. During this year he acts as instructor to the medical students in general pathology. He is also given the privilege of doing a piece of research work in pathology which generally is oriented toward gynecology. I say "given the privilege of doing research," for today there is a great tendency to induce trainees to do research, which in my opinion is an error; its acceptance has become a means of currying favor with the department head with the hope of promotion. Such research is seldom of value and such trainees seldom continue in research later in life.

After this year of grounding in general pathology, the trainee spends the third year in the gynecological pathology laboratory. He is responsible for the "signing out" of the official diagnoses of the specimens which come from the operating rooms. He has the privilege of consulting with a senior on all questionable cases, but it is important that the responsibility of the diagnosis lie with him. Speaking of responsibility, it constitutes the heart and soul of real residency training. Simply putting in time, year after year, with no increased responsibility is to a great degree a waste of time. During this third year the trainee spends half of his time in clinical work, and gets a great deal of first assisting in the operating room, doing many major operations which are selected as not being too complicated.

At the beginning of the fourth year the trainee returns to obstetrics, where he is entrusted with the more complicated obstetrical procedures. After six months of this, he returns to gynecology. He is then given more complicated surgery to do in preparation for his fifth year as chief resident in gynecology.

During his fifth—final—year he is cock of the roost and has full responsibility for the ward service, subject to consultation with the chief and other members of the attending staff. Again it is important that he have full responsibility and that a superior not be watching his every move. Whenever the problem is beyond his knowledge or experience, the chief is available for consultation and help. This principle of calling for consultation is an important one for every doctor to learn and to practice. No matter how expert a man may eventually become, he will at times encounter problems beyond his knowledge and experience. To barge ahead alone in such cases is unfair to the patient and may result in disaster. The chief resident is entrusted with deciding which cases he is capable of caring for surgically, and on which to ask for help. He also has the responsibility of handing down to his assistants the less complicated cases.

During various parts of his time on gynecology he is assigned to the urological clinic, the radium clinic, the endocrine clinic, and at all stages of his clinical training he is required to spend some of his time in the outpatient department.

Thus equipped with five years of intensive training in his chosen specialty, he must then decide which of two ways he will go in that specialty, choosing between academic medicine and practice—or a combination of both of these on a part-time basis.

Each of them, academic medicine and practice, has its own rewards, but they are different. Scientific attainment in academic medicine gives a source of satisfaction which cannot be bought with dollars. Nor is there any way to measure the satisfaction attained by caring for private patients; it is a heart-warming experience.

One factor which used to play a part in the decisions of some men, generally tending them away from academic medicine and toward general practice, no longer is a significant influence. Financially, the great divergence between full-time academic medicine and practice has lessened. Greater university salaries, the retirement income provided by universities, and the leveling influence of taxes, have narrowed the gap. And, besides, the dollar never has been a proper basis for a medical decision. It is in medicine itself, and, for some, in gynecology in particular—and these I consider especially fortunate—where the doctor will ultimately find his true reward and a satisfaction beyond any counting.

8 *You as a*

PEDIATRICIAN

BY SYDNEY S. GELLIS, M.D.

PROFESSOR AND CHAIRMAN OF PEDIATRICS
Boston University School of Medicine and
DIRECTOR OF PEDIATRICS
Boston City Hospital

DR. SYDNEY S. GELLIS

Born: 1914, Claremont, New Hampshire

Harvard College: A.B., 1934
Harvard Medical School: M.D., 1938

Captain, Army Medical Corps, attached to various commissions for investigation of epidemic diseases

Intern in Pediatrics, New Haven Hospital, 1938–39
Assistant Resident in Pediatrics, Children's Hospital, Cincinnati, 1939–40
Research Fellow in Pediatrics, Children's Hospital Research Foundation, 1940–41
Chief Resident in Pediatrics, Johns Hopkins Hospital, 1941–42
Instructor in Pediatrics, Johns Hopkins School of Medicine, 1942–46

Member: Army Epidemiological Board, 1943–46
Consultant to Secretary of War in Infectious Diseases, 1943–46

Harvard Medical School:
  Instructor in Pediatrics, 1946–47
  Assistant in Pediatrics, 1947–48
Children's Hospital: Boston
  Assistant Physician, 1947–48
  Physician, 1948—
  Chief, Medical Outpatient Department, 1948–50
  Assistant Physician-in-Chief, 1948–51
Harvard Medical School:
  Associate in Pediatrics, 1948–51
  Assistant Professor of Pediatrics, 1951–56
  Lecturer in Pediatrics, 1956—
Pediatrician-in-Chief, Beth Israel Hospital, Boston: 1951–56
Boston University School of Medicine: Professor of Pediatrics and Chairman of the Department, 1956—
Boston City Hospital: Director of Pediatrics, 1956—

Society for Pediatric Research:
  Secretary, 1951–58
  President, 1959–60
The American Pediatric Society
New England Pediatric Society

Editor: *Yearbook of Pediatrics*, 1952—
Associate Editor: *American Journal of Diseases of Children*, 1957—

THE PURPOSE of this book is to present to students who are interested in a career in medicine the numerous and varied roles which the physician may play. It will be inappropriate for any of us writing here to extoll in glamorous terms the virtues of a medical life; we should not attempt the "soft sell" of Madison Avenue fame. Rather should we endeavor to offer an honest picture of the physician's roles with proper weighting of the good and bad features of the specialty we present.

My assignment is a description of the responsibilities, interests, characteristics, and training of the physician known as a pediatrician. This term is derived not from the Latin "pes, pedis" meaning foot, but from the Greek "Pais, Paidos" meaning child. The first book on pediatrics written in the English language was published in 1545 by Thomas Phaire and was entitled *The Boke of Chyldren*. In his preface Phaire says: "But my purpose is here to doo theym good that have moste nede, that is to saye, children."

The pediatrician takes as his responsibility the health of the individual from birth through adolescence to adult life. Inasmuch as individuals vary in the age at which adult life is reached, the pediatrician considers that adult life is attained between eighteen and twenty-one. In recent years the pediatrician has found that he must be interested in his patients before they are born because the nutrition, the infections, the blood groups, the family history and the drugs administered to the pregnant woman have a distinct bearing on the state of health of her offspring. For example, Gregg, in Australia, noted that although pregnant women who developed German measles early in pregnancy had a relatively mild disease, a high percentage of their offspring had cataracts, deafness, and maldevelopment of the brain and heart.

The pediatrician may even be called upon to give advice before a child is conceived, for he has considerable knowledge of genetics, the mode of inheritance of various defects, and his advice may be sought as to the advisability of child-bearing. Abnormalities may be inherited in many different ways; hence a thorough understanding of the history of disease within a family may be of great importance to its future members.

Thus we must redefine the pediatrician as a physician interested and trained in the problems of health and disease of the human from conception to adult life. The reader will note that health has been placed before disease; more than any other physician, the pediatrician has been interested in preventive medicine—that is the maintenance of the health of the individual and the promotion of those procedures which will prevent disease and disability. One of his most important functions has been the development and use of immunization procedures to safeguard the health of his patients.

The pediatrician must be a careful observer and an excellent diagnostician, for he receives no help from his patient who, until he learns to speak, is able to offer little assistance by voicing his complaints. Thus the pediatrician is completely dependent on his eyes, ears, nose, and fingers to determine if the infant is in good health and free from congenital disorders. To the new parents the pediatrician is more than a doctor; he is a friend and adviser and is expected to warn of problems which lie ahead.

As the infant grows older, the pediatrician must be able by his skill to evaluate the child's growth and development and recognize the danger signs which warn of a mental defect or of a metabolic disease which may impair normal intellectual achievement. This requires considerable skill and experience. It is obvious that the evaluation of the intellectual capacity of an individual, who is as yet unable to communicate with the observer, is no simple task. At the same time the pediatrician must advise the parents as to the methods of obtaining optimum nutrition for their child and must immunize the infant against a number of diseases. As the child continues to grow, the pediatrician must be constantly alert to detect signs of emotional illness in his patient. During the child's adolescence, the doctor is called upon to interpret to the parents the many emotional and physical problems of this period of life; in turn he helps the adolescent understand himself and the problems of his parents. The pediatrician thus, over a relatively short time, may watch a newborn infant grow from a completely helpless and dependent creature to one who is thinking about a career in medicine.

From this brief review of the pediatrician's responsibilities it is relatively simple to summarize the characteristics and qualifications necessary to his success. First, he must like children and must be sympathetic to their needs. It is not difficult to acquire this feeling, for it is inherent in most of us to be fond of the young of all species. The kitten and puppy are far more charming and captivating than the cat or the dog. Next, he must have utmost patience, as well as understanding, and these he must have in a measure beyond that required by physicians in other fields. Although the pediatrician along with his patients continues to age, he retains a sympathy and outlook which are young, for the problems with which he always deals are those of the young in heart and spirit. Even in his later years, he continues to see through the eyes of the child the fears and agonies of childhood, the first day at school, the first separation from parents, the first reprimand from the teacher, the first date. This love for children, this sympathy for the weak and helpless are probably the prime movers in attracting the young physician into pediatrics in order to "doo theym good that have moste nede, that is to saye, children."

The training of a pediatrician after his graduation from medical school consists of at least three years of postgraduate work. One year of internship may be taken as a medical, rotating, or pediatric internship. The two subsequent years are devoted entirely to pediatrics. During these years the house officer learns to take careful and complete histories of pediatric patients and to do thorough physical examinations. He works in emergency sections with acutely ill patients, with contagious diseases, in newborn and premature nurseries, in delivery rooms, and on wards for older infants and children. He devotes a good part of his time to outpatient clinics, seeing chronic and less acute problems, and attends specialty clinics in which children with various disorders are followed over long periods of time—cardiac, kidney, allergy, psychiatry, metabolic, endocrine, hematology, etc.

During his last year of training he carries more responsibility, determining which patients require admission to the hospital, the treatment for those who are admitted, and deciding about those who are to return to their homes. He accepts responsibility in the training of junior physicians and medical students assigned to his wards. After the three years of training required to fulfill minimum requirements, the pediatrician may elect to enter practice, take additional training in certain specialties within pediatrics, or teach and do research.

If he enters practice, he may work alone, although today there is an increasing tendency to practice with one or more pediatricians. The advantages of such an arrangement are obvious; the newcomer has ready access to a contemporary with whom he can discuss his difficult problems. In addition he has someone to share with him the coverage of a practice at night and on weekends. He gains free time to attend meetings, indulge in hobbies and travel.

In the past, many a pediatrician has complained of the arduous life. It is not an easy one, for the questions and problems which come his way are more numerous than those in the field of adult medicine. An adult who does not feel well may wait another day or two before seeking medical help. When an infant or young child appears ill, there is no delay on the part of anxious parents in consulting the physician. As a result of their worries, the pediatrician is consulted more frequently than physicians in other fields.

Other pediatricians may take further training in a particular field and then assume responsibility for their subspecialty within a hospital setting or they may practice in this field. Others may become full-time teachers in a medical school, helping to train medical students and pediatric house officers. In addition, these men and women do clinical or laboratory research in problems relating to children. Pediatricians who practice near medical centers usually devote time to teaching medical students and to making hospital rounds with the house staff.

Some pediatricians take additional training in public health and have careers as public-health officers serving an entire community or state.

Although I have referred repeatedly to the pediatrician as "he," numerous women enter this field because of their inherent interest in children. Although the young woman in pediatrics may be temporarily diverted from work in her field by marriage and the birth of her own children, she usually finds some time to spend in special clinics or research until her children are grown, at which time she may return to full-time work.

Perhaps the description of a typical day in the life of the practicing pediatrician may be of interest to the reader. The pediatrician usually begins his day early. He has set aside a period during which the parents of sick children may call him and he will offer advice as to treatment or will suggest that he will see the patient in the office or at the home. Because of increasing ease of transportation, fewer home visits are being made by physicians and there is now an increasing tendency for sick children to be brought to the office where the help of the nurse and the availability of laboratory aids make diagnosis and management more skillful and exact.

Next the pediatrician makes his hospital rounds, attending to the problems of children he has hospitalized for treatment or study. He examines newly-born infants and discusses their problems and his findings with their mothers. Perhaps, too, an infant is to be delivered by Caesarean section or the obstetrician anticipates trouble; in which case the pediatrician may be asked to be present at the birth and take over responsibility for the infant as soon as it is born.

If the pediatrician has medical-school or hospital teaching assignments, he will do these usually late in the morning, checking on the clinical work of medical students or advising pediatric house officers in the handling of difficult problems. If he is associated with a hospital which has no students or house officers, he is responsible for ward patients as well as his own private patients.

During the afternoon, he holds office hours by appointment and will examine a varying number of children. The modern pediatrician arranges appointments so that at certain times he will see adolescents only, to spare them the annoyance of a waiting room occupied by infants and young children. At the end of his office hours he may have sick children to be seen in their homes. During the evening, if he is free of patient problems, and is excused from social responsibilities by his wife and from tutoring help for his own children, he will read medical journals, for there are numerous monthly publications from the United States and abroad devoted solely to the problems of childhood.

In this field, as in all other areas of medicine, the physician must until the day he dies continue his education and training, for new advances and discoveries are constantly being made. The pediatrician considers this no chore, for his delight in making an astute diagnosis, because of something he may have recently encountered in his reading, is beyond description. He must frequently turn to his own medical library or that of a hospital or medical school for assistance, since it is humanly impossible to hold in his memory all of the minute details which have bearing on the ills and defects of the human being. Although the majority of the problems he encounters are straightforward, he usually has several patients who present difficult challenges. He must be constantly on guard, for what may appear simple on the surface may be complex and dangerous. The infant with apparently mild croup, an illness consisting of hoarseness and a barking type of cough, may have a foreign body in his trachea or larynx, or he may have early diphtheria.

The pediatrician must be constantly alert and inquiring; he functions as a detective in the ills of childhood, piecing together the bits of information proffered by the parents, his own knowledge of the child's past history and family history, the physical findings, and his familiarity with the infections which are current in the community. From all these he makes his diagnosis, and frets if an illness does not fall into the proper scheme of things. If he is unable to arrive at a solution which is satisfactory, he may call upon X-ray and blood and urine examinations to assist him. If still at an impasse, he may hospitalize the child for more extensive studies. One of the great joys of his day-to-day experience is the fact that he deals with the young who cure quickly, and with recovery have a long fruitful life ahead. This to the pediatrician is a constantly refreshing experience in contrast to those physicians who care for the aged.

As in so many other areas of medicine, the face of pediatrics is constantly changing. Only a relatively few years ago the pediatrician gave almost all of his time and attention to acute and chronic infectious disease. He coped with mastoiditis, pneumonia, meningitis, dysenteries, the communicable diseases such as scarlet fever, diphtheria, whooping cough. With the advent of antibiotics, the problems shifted and the modern pediatrician rarely hospitalized his patients for many of these illnesses, for they are either treated before they can give rise to serious illness or he has prevented them by means of appropriate vaccines.

Today the pediatrician devotes more time to a search for congenital abnormalities, that is defects with which the child is born, many of which could not be treated fifteen to twenty years ago, but are readily correctible by modern surgery. The writer was a pediatric intern during the days when all infants with heart murmurs were diagnosed as having congenital heart disease. There was no point in trying to distinguish the various heart defects with which an infant might be born, since there was at that time nothing which could be done to help. Similarly, infants born with atresia of the esophagus, or absence of a part of the esophageal tube, died untreated, with the physician watching helplessly. An intern in that era, once he had made a diagnosis of tuberculous meningitis, wrote out the death certificate in advance because no one had ever saved a child with this disease. With modern therapy there is no excuse for losing such patients.

Similarly the pediatrician formerly paid little attention to mental defectiveness. If it was sufficiently severe, he merely signed commitment papers enabling the family to put the child into a state institution, there to spend its remaining days. Now he has learned to view each of his young patients with an eye to metabolic defects which can produce brain damage, for a number of these can now be diagnosed promptly by the astute clinician and can be treated to prevent brain damage. A good example of such a condition is known as phenylketonuria; if this is not diagnosed in the early months of life, irreversible brain damage ensues. A special urine examination permits early diagnosis; a special diet prevents injury to the brain. This urine test is rapidly becoming universal for infants at the age of six to eight weeks. The discovery of methods permitting early diagnosis and preventive treatment of such conditions has spurred tremendous interest on the part of pediatricians in all aspects of research into brain damage, a most important and previously most discouraging field.

Finally, as antimicrobial agents have altered greatly the impact of infections on the life of the child, the pediatrician has developed increasing interest in the emotional problems presented by both patient and parent. Through his knowledge of the family, he is in an unequaled position to predict and often prevent the more common psychological difficulties which confront the growing infant, child and adolescent. He must be friend, adviser, comforter, and interpreter, as well as the physician caring for the emotional and physical needs of the child. In all these roles his understanding of the emotional trials and tribulations involved in moving from infancy to childhood, from childhood to adolescence, and from adolescence to adulthood gives him a rare opportunity to help mold the character of the child, a role which he shares with parent, minister, and teacher.

The practice of pediatrics is a difficult one, mentally as well as physically. It is not as rewarding financially as many other fields and demands much more time and patience. It is not a life's work for those who demand regularity and orderliness in their existence. However, the pediatrician by his daily contact with children—the only humans who live in cheer, hope, and the certainty that all will be well with man and his world—gains more rewards from his work than does any other physician.

_9_ *You as a*

PRACTICING SURGEON

BY WARFIELD M. FIROR, M.D.

PROFESSOR OF SURGERY

Johns Hopkins University School of Medicine

DR. WARFIELD M. FIROR

Born: 1896, Baltimore, Maryland

Baltimore Public Schools
Johns Hopkins University: A.B., 1917
                              M.D., 1921
Western Maryland College: D.Sc. (Hon.) 1957

Johns Hopkins Hospital:
   Intern, Resident in Neurosurgery, Resident in General Surgery, 1921–27
   Acting Chief Surgeon, 1938–41

Johns Hopkins University School of Medicine:
   Full-time status, Department of Surgery, Instructor, Associate Professor,
   1923–38
   Part-time status, Department of Surgery, Associate Professor, Professor
   of Surgery, 1938—

Hospital Appointments: Visiting Surgeon
   Johns Hopkins Hospital
   Church Home & Hospital
   Union Memorial Hospital
   Hospital for Women of Maryland
   Maryland General Hospital (Chief of Staff, 1949–58)

American Board of Surgery: Member, 1945–51
                               Chairman, 1949–51

Conference Committee on Graduate Training in Surgery, 1951–57

American Surgical Association: Member, 1937—
                             Secretary, 1943–49

Society of Clinical Surgery
Southern Surgical Association
American College of Surgeons
Society of University Surgeons
American Physiological Society
Society for Experimental Biology & Medicine
American Medical Association

Presbyterian Mission Board:
   Miraj, India, 1930–31
China Medical Board, Consultant:
   Yonsei University, Seoul, Korea, 1957, 58, 61

Author: Numerous articles for medical literature.

THE LIFE of a general surgeon is an exceedingly strenuous one. It requires a long period of preparation, and makes great demands on one's physical, mental, and emotional stamina. It is, however, an immensely satisfying vocation. This is so because the practice of general surgery provides variety, hard work, responsibility, independence, and rich rewards. The latter are not primarily monetary, but rather the satisfaction of achievement. The results of a successful operation are realized within days or weeks. Surgeons get results. They do something for the patient, and at times this "doing something" is tremendously dramatic. For instance, connecting the large blood vessels of the body to an apparatus that takes over the work of the heart and lungs, so that the surgeon can stop the heart beating for an hour or so while he opens it and sews in a plastic valve to replace an incompetent one. After sewing up the heart and chest he starts the heart beating and the lungs breathing before disconnecting the heart-lung machine. The greater part of a surgeon's life, however, is less dramatic. It is not taken up with operations on the heart, but consists of meeting a steadily changing succession of people needing his help and understanding. This can be a source of interest to an enquiring mind, and give a sense of deep gratification. Surgery is not just operating, but an ever-expanding art which gives opportunity for the exercise of many different faculties.

For the sake of clarity, let us consider the training period separate from the actual practice of surgery. There was a time in the United States when anyone with a high-school education could study medicine either in a school or from a group of doctors. If he passed the state board examination, he was licensed to treat every conceivable illness. He brought children into the world; he attended the aged on their deathbeds; in between he prescribed for all medical diseases, and operated when he thought necessary. Ordinarily this family doctor acquired his operative skill by helping older doctors operate, and, as soon as he dared, would undertake surgical procedures on his own.

One of the greatest turning points in American medicine came in 1893 when a college degree was required for matriculation by the Johns Hopkins Medical School. An equally great event was the institution of the system of postgraduate training called "a residency." This form of training was modeled after the German system, and provided several years of intensive training in a specialty. Post-doctoral institutional training not only turns out men who are skilled clinicians, but incites them to become teachers and investigators. Finally, in 1910, the whole structure of medical education in the United States was radically altered by the Flexner report, which brought about the elimination of all proprietary schools, and laid the foundation for the present standards of medical education. Widespread acceptance of the residency training system came very slowly, and it was not until the advent of the specialty boards in the 1930's that this form of training became popular. There are now more than twenty specialty boards, each of which is autonomous and sets its own prerequisites for examination. Each board requires a period of residency training, and each gives examinations to determine the proficiency of the candidate in its particular branch of medicine.

The American Board of Surgery was organized in 1937. At present it requires that a candidate shall have completed a residency in general surgery which has been approved by the Conference Committee on Graduate Training in Surgery. This committee sets the minimal standards for training programs, and is constantly reviewing previously approved programs to be certain that the trainee gets what he is supposed to get in the way of supervision, instruction, and experience. Despite the efforts of the Conference Committee to regulate the composition and quality of residencies in general surgery, these vary widely in different hospitals. The most desirable residency is usually in a hospital connected with a medical school, and training in such a place is essential if one plans to teach or do research rather than to enter private practice. As has been pointed out elsewhere, there are about 5,000 more internships available each year than there are graduates from medical schools in the United States. This disparity does not exist when it comes to residencies in general surgery, for the number of men willing and able to go through this post-internship training just about equals the positions available. In 1961, there were 704 approved programs in general surgery in this country.

A residency in general surgery acceptable to the Conference Committee requires at least four years of work in a hospital after the internship. Some require more. During this period the resident gets a certain number of operations to do entirely on his own, but the number is not as important as the variety and the magnitude. Another essential element in an approved residency is that increasing responsibility for the entire care of surgical patients is delegated to the trainee. Many training programs provide time for research; others include experience in some of the subspecialties such as orthopedics, neurosurgery, or urology. There are naturally many variations in the composition of residencies in general surgery because this term is interpreted differently in different institutions. In smaller hospitals, general surgery includes all of the subspecialties, whereas in some teaching institutions the term has come to mean "residual surgery"; that is, the part which remains after all the subspecialties have been organized as independent services.

During the years of hospital training, the young doctor gets paid very little. The monthly stipend varies from $100 to $300. The larger amount may or may not include room and board. Unfortunately there are no foundations which subsidize men during this period, but bankers are usually willing to make loans if necessary. There are few, if any, recreational facilities because there is little or no time for recreation. Up until World War II most residents in surgery were not married, but celibacy is now the exception. Actually a substantial number of medical students, interns and residents are supported by the earnings of their wives. There is an occasional hospital which permits the trainee to supplement his income by outside work when off duty. By and large this is a poor arrangement since it tends to undermine a man's health, and puts a false emphasis on the monetary aspects of practice.

The years of residency training are hard, but often there is an esprit de corps among the staff which makes them some of the most wonderful in life. There are days when the resident works from 16 to 18 hours; there are nights without sleep; but there are adequate compensations. There is always something new to see and to learn. There is the great satisfaction of being part of a team both in and out of the operating room. Surgeons get things accomplished, and it is thrilling to be on a team that works harmoniously in restoring a critically ill patient to vigorous health. Above all, there is the incessant challenge of our ignorance of disease processes. This often comes into sharp focus at the operating table, for there one gets a chance to examine directly the internal organs in the living. Moreover, there is the satisfaction that comes from constantly learning new techniques, and in trying out new ideas. Frequently opportunity is provided for teaching medical students and pupil nurses. Some of the finest friendships in life come about from these long years when men work side by side in the hospital.

Assuming that you have finished a satisfactory residency in general surgery, and have passed the written and oral examinations of the American Board of Surgery, what can you expect to do? Are there vacancies in teaching institutions waiting to be filled? Are there jobs with large industrial corporations, or with the Government? Is it easy to get started in practice, and how does one begin? These are the practical questions which face a resident in his senior year. First, let it be pointed out that even if one fails to pass the specialty board examinations one can still practice. The diploma of the board is not an absolute necessity, but it is an asset, since there is a growing tendency for hospitals to require board certification before granting staff privileges, and it is recognized everywhere as an evidence of competence in one's specialty.

Now to answer the above questions. Openings for full-time

teaching appointments are few in number, and are nearly always given to young men who have shown special aptitude for investigation. The resident who has found time to carry on research, or who has acquired proficiency in a special technique, is the one most likely to be kept as an instructor in a medical school. As for employment with large industrial corporations, one can say that few, if any, require a full-time surgeon, but many do offer employment on a part-time basis. Men just starting in practice often find this a source of much-needed income.

The positions with the Federal Government, either with the armed forces or Veterans Administration, are nearly all on a full-time basis. Most of the VA hospitals are affiliated with medical schools, and the faculty has considerable control over the appointments. The same is true of some of the largest and finest municipal hospitals. Many private hospitals are following the lead of the teaching institutions by putting some of their staff on a full-time basis; this means that members of the staff are paid a salary, given an office in the hospital, and in return the institution receives all fees for professional services. A modification of this "economic full time" is "geographic full time," in which the doctor has an office in the hospital where he concentrates all of his clinical work, teaching and research, but keeps part or all of his professional fees in lieu of salary.

The majority of surgical residents go into private practice as soon as they complete their training. Where they go is a matter of individual choice. Many join up with contemporaries in other specialties and form a group; others find openings in clinics or groups already established. Still others pick out the city in which they wish to live, secure hospital privileges, and open up their office. In this case it is helpful to be known by the general practitioners in the community. This brings up one of the most difficult of all ethical problems facing a surgeon, namely fee-splitting—refunding to the referring doctor a percentage of the surgeon's fee. This is obviously demoralizing since it tempts the family doctor to refer his unsuspecting patient to the surgeon from whom he can collect the largest percentage, and who is apt to be the least competent. Such pernicious practice tempts the surgeon to increase his fee accordingly.

Pressure is sometimes put upon young surgeons to perform operations which in their judgment are not necessary. Even at the risk of offending the referring doctor, it is unwise to yield to such pressure. The American College of Surgeons wages an unremitting campaign against fee-splitting and unnecessary operations, but the former is done so secretively that it seems almost impossible to eradicate it. In the final analysis, one cannot legislate honesty into a person; this is a matter of integrity and self-respect.

It is a matter of regret that so much of the foregoing has had to do with the difficulties that may arise in getting started in practice. Is it all worth while? The answer to this is a firm and resolute "yes." What counts in life, costs; but remember, what costs, counts. The rewards that come to a surgeon are great, and in the remainder of this chapter an effort will be made to give you a glimpse of some of the experiences you may expect to have if you go into surgery.

First, let us look at some of the more general assets of being a surgeon. You have the immense satisfaction of hard work, the kind of hard work which brings quick and obvious results. You have endless variety, for there is nothing monotonous in general surgery, since no two patients are identical. You are in the center of a rapidly expanding science, and it is stimulating to learn and to use new techniques. You have the deep satisfaction of carrying great responsibility. At every operation you have the opportunity to teach and to train younger men. This means you are exchanging ideas and associating with young minds. You acquire an ever-increasing number of grateful patients, many of whom owe their lives to you. There is real gratification in restoring a useful citizen to perfect health. You have the opportunity for constant self-education and the stimulus for investigation. Finally, in common with all reputable doctors, you have a position of respect in your community.

Before describing some typical surgical cases, it might be wise to take a look at some of the reactions of a surgeon during a major operation.

Frequently in the scrub-up room the operator discusses with his assistant the anticipated procedure. Once the operative field has been prepared, and the patient covered with sterile drapes, the surgical team tends to be primarily occupied with the execution of the operation. There is no trace of nervousness, for this has been removed by years of experience, and only when there is some change in the patient's condition is the surgical team's attention diverted.

The actual incision through the skin and deeper tissues, the clamping of blood vessels, and the placing of retractors (the instruments to hold apart the edges of a wound during an operation) are routine. When the surgeon comes upon an anatomical anomaly or a diseased condition which he does not recognize, he must make a decision which could alter or end the patient's life. Bodily structures are sometimes displaced or deformed so that identification is difficult. Usually this problem can be resolved by further dissection. I recall coming down upon a tumor which arose within a large nerve leading into the thigh; the fibers of the nerve were separated and spread out over the surface of the tumor as tiny filaments. The tumor was encapsulated so that it was impossible to identify it as malignant or not without a biopsy. To have cut through the encasing capsule to establish the diagnosis might have disseminated cells, probably causing a fatal recurrence. The alternative was to cut the nerve above and below the tumor and remove it intact. This would result in partial paralysis, which seemed the lesser of two evils, and this decision was made. This was a serious decision, affecting the patient's whole future way of living, but such decisions confront a surgeon and he must make them.

At times every surgeon is faced suddenly with situations in which the patient's death seems imminent. The first of these occurs in the anesthesia room. Soon after induction the patient may stop breathing and become blue and, if artificial respiration is ineffective, an emergency tracheotomy (making an opening into the trachea) has to be done. Later, during the course of the operation the operator may be confronted with another critical situation: a sudden and tremendous welling up of blood, the source of which must be determined rapidly and controlled effectively. If this is impossible, the area is packed tightly with gauze, a temporary procedure to give the surgeon time to start a transfusion and to re-evaluate the situation. As the gauze is re-moved, the torn vessels are hastily clamped, subsequently tied. Many years ago, before we had a blood bank, I removed a large spleen and found the splenic vessels so brittle that the ligatures cut through them, causing profuse hemorrhage. The only way to deal with this emergency was to clamp the veins, leaving the clamps in place for several days, by which time the vessels had become sealed with scar tissue.

A recurring cause for anxiety during an operation is the necessity of deciding how much to do. This uncertainty may be brought on by the precarious condition of the patient, or the extent of the disease. I recall operating on a man bleeding from a duodenal ulcer. He received twelve pints of blood in six hours, but this was insufficient to keep abreast of the hemorrhage. When the operation began, he was in poor condition; his pulse rate was 140; blood pressure 80/50. The abdomen was opened rapidly; the duodenum exposed and opened, and the bleeding vessel transfixed. The question then arose, should I resect the ulcer, or leave it in with the risk of another hemorrhage. The decision to resect was determined by these factors: the patient's blood pressure was rising steadily, and we had plenty of compatible blood on hand for transfusion.

The extent of the disease process often raises the question: Is this lesion operable or must one be content with a palliative procedure? The question is not uncommon, and, at times, it must be answered in the operating room. Only experience and the knowledge of one's own ability can determine the decision. Furthermore, the answer from different surgeons is not always the same. Recently I saw a patient whose right colon I had resected with a part of the abdominal wall; this was seven years ago and he is still doing well. Yet three months before I operated on him, he had been operated on elsewhere and had been told that the tumor could not be removed. This is no suggestion for second operations, for often they are not at all desirable; this case is mentioned solely to indicate that the decisions of surgeons vary, and the variance can affect the health, and even the lives, of patients.

Nothing is more exhausting to the surgeon than an inexperienced anesthetist and an awkward team, and nothing is more harrowing than the death of a patient on the table.

Now for some of the actual experiences of the general surgeon. First, an illness needing prompt action. The patient is an eighteen-year-old college freshman who has had excellent health since childhood. Yesterday forenoon he was aware of pain in the upper abdomen but carried on with his classes; by evening his cramps became worse, and he had no desire for food. He figured that he had eaten something amiss, and took a cathartic. This was the wrong thing to do and made him worse. By midnight he decided to go to bed and sleep it off, but became nauseated and vomited. His roommate urged him to go to the infirmary, but he objected to this. By morning he gave in, and went. It did not take the nurse long to suspect that he had acute appendicitis. He had fever, rapid pulse, and tenderness on the right side of the abdomen. The surgeon was called and confirmed the diagnosis. There was no time to lose because the symptoms had already been present for twenty-four hours. An emergency operation was arranged. At operation an inflamed appendix, which was greatly distended but not ruptured, was removed through an incision which separated the muscles without cutting them. This permitted quick healing. Two days later the patient was out of bed, and returned to his classes one week from the onset of his illness.

A situation in which surgery is elective: The patient is a man aged thirty-five, the father of three children. He is a salesman under constant pressure to make his quota in the face of severe competition. He is worried because his oldest child is having difficulty in school. To add to his concern, his aged mother has come to live with his family. For several months he has been troubled with a burning sensation in his stomach, which was at first relieved by food or soda. Recently the burning has become actual pain which wakes him every night. Reluctantly he reports all this to his company doctor who suspects an ulcer in the stomach. This diagnosis is confirmed by X-ray studies. The man's father died of cancer of the stomach, so he is panicky over the possibility that his ulcer might be malignant. A surgical consultation is held. Should this patient be given a medical regimen consisting of diet, medicines, and rest for a period of three or four months in order to let the ulcer heal; or should he be hospitalized and have the ulcer removed? Here one has to decide which form of treatment will get this wage earner well and back to full employment more quickly. Usually surgical removal of the ulcer is preferable since recovery is quicker, and the chance of recurrence of the ulcer is less.

A true emergency: The surgeon is at a meeting and is called to the phone. A boy aged ten is in the accident room of the hospital in severe shock. He was riding his bike and was struck by a car. He was able to get up, but complained of severe pain in his right side. Bystanders realized he was seriously injured and hurried him to the hospital. The intern urges the surgeon to come at once because the patient is obviously in critical condition. Within ten minutes the surgeon is at the hospital where he finds a frightfully pale lad whose pulse is exceedingly rapid and so feeble that it can scarcely be counted. The boy is anxious and restless, asking constantly for water. His breathing is rapid. There is clear evidence of fracture of the lower six ribs on the right side. Further examinations make it apparent that he is bleeding internally, probably from a torn liver. The intern has already drawn blood for matching in order to give the patient transfusions. The boy's condition is deteriorating so rapidly that the foot of the bed is elevated, the lower limbs are wrapped in tight bandages, and intravenous fluids are started. Drugs are added to these fluids to maintain the blood pressure, while preparations are made for immediate operation.

Time is of the essence, and blood is the all-important factor. Several transfusions are required before the operation can be started, and during the operation blood is forced in under positive pressure. On opening the abdominal cavity, the surgeon finds it filled with blood and estimates the amount at three litres. This free blood is quickly removed and the rent in the liver temporarily packed with gauze, while the surgeon makes certain that no other organ is injured. Following this, the bleeding wound in the liver is sutured; drains are inserted in the wound so that any bile which may leak from the liver will come to the outside and not cause chemical peritonitis. The abdominal incision is closed in the most expeditious manner so as to shorten the period of anesthesia

and get the patient to the recovery room where oxygen and sup-
portive measures are instituted. The patient's condition is considered critical until all evidences of shock have disappeared.
During the convalescence this patient is carefully watched for
the occurrence of secondary hemorrhage. Since no complications
develop, he is ready for discharge in three weeks.

The reluctant patient: Mrs. A. has been referred to a surgeon
because her physician found a lump in her breast. She is fifty-
four years of age, and has had no serious illness since childhood.
The lump is painless; in fact she had a hard time finding it. The
surgeon's examination of the patient confirms the fact that she
seems to be a healthy obese individual. The only abnormality
is a hard lump, about 1 cm. in diameter, in the right breast. When
the patient raises her right arm over her head there is a telltale
dimpling of the skin over the lump. The surgeon knows that this
lump is probably an early cancer, and that a very extensive
operation, removing the breast and the underlying muscles, is
the only possible way to eradicate the disease. After his examination he makes clear to the patient the necessity for prompt action
to establish the diagnosis. This can be done only by removing the
lump for microscopic examination. It is good judgment to explain
that this operation should be done under general anesthesia, and
that the diagnosis can be made in a few minutes. Should the
lump turn out to be malignant, the extensive operation can be
completed while the patient is still asleep. The patient cannot
believe that such a small and seemingly insignificant lump might
require such radical surgery. She wishes to watch it in the hope
that it might go away. In this situation the surgeon needs firm-
ness, coupled with practical psychology. He has to size up this
patient's emotional and intellectual status, and then decide the
most effective way to win her consent. When the reluctant
patient refuses necessary surgery it is advisable to inform the
patient's nearest relative of the situation.

The exasperating patient: One of the most trying situations
facing the surgeon, or any doctor for that matter, is having to
deal with a Schlemiehl—with one of those individuals who seems
always to attract misfortune. He is the chap who secures a good
position after months of unemployment, and during the first

week slips on a wet floor and breaks his hip. He confronts the surgeon with an injury for which hospitalization is imperative, but the patient has allowed his insurance to lapse. With the aid of the Social Service Department, arrangements are made for hospital admission, and the fracture is treated. After some months the patient returns to work, and is not heard from until the night before the surgeon is to leave on his vacation, at which time the man calls again—now with acute abdominal pain. After completing his questions, the surgeon believes that the patient may have intestinal obstruction. It is not fair to pass this impecunious chap over to a confrere, so the surgeon gets up and goes to see the patient, only to find out that he has had the pain for weeks and has waited until midnight on this particular night to call a doctor. Actually, the whole matter is a false alarm. There is no acute condition, only severe constipation. The next contact is in the midst of a truly hectic day, one in which the surgeon is being harassed by innumerable problems, when the man comes in after having cut a large artery in his wrist while trying to open a jammed window. And on and on! Many a surgeon has just such a patient as this—perhaps more than one—who has the knack of getting himself into trouble and always turning up at the most inconvenient time, often with complaints that are exaggerated but occasionally with serious need for the surgeon's care.

The patient with cancer: A common group of patients are those with malignant disease. Such patients are becoming increasingly frequent as the life span of our population lengthens. Cancer is not an entity, but a large body of disease processes that have one thing in common, namely the unrestrained growth of abnormal cells. Any tissue in the body may for some unknown reasons begin to produce cells which take on the power of invading the surrounding normal tissue or of jumping to other parts of the body, where they take root and grow. Since tissues vary greatly in their chemistry, and since the body has defense mechanisms which can sometimes destroy or restrain the abnormal cells, the manifestations of cancer differ greatly. Some malignancies are fatal in six weeks, others run a course extending over thirty years. In our present state of ignorance, the surest way to rid a patient of cancer is for a surgeon to remove it completely. Unfortunately one can never be absolutely certain that this has been done. To most patients the realization of having malignancy fills them with fear and dread. For this reason it is just as important to help the patient psychologically as it is to do thorough surgery.

So much has been written in the lay press in recent years about the danger signals of cancer, and the increasing number of people dying from it, that the average person goes into a state of panic at the least suspicion of this trouble. Surgeons frequently have to deal with people who become alarmed over a completely harmless condition. It is necessary to make a thorough examination in order to convince these people that their fears are groundless.

One of the common sites of cancer is in the large intestine, and the evidences of this disease may vary from the appearance of small amounts of blood in the stool to complete stoppage of the bowel. When the former is the case, the doctor carries out certain examinations to establish the diagnosis. This is an instance when it often takes firm but tactful persuasion to gain the patient's consent for an abdominal operation. When it is pointed out that complete removal of an early cancer of the large bowel frequently results in permanent cure, whereas waiting for pain or obstruction to occur usually means it is too late to effect a cure, the patient consents. This operation is not very painful to the patient, and does not require a long convalescence.

When cancer of the intestine has progressed to the point of complete stoppage of bowel movements, the patient offers little or no objection to surgical relief. Such operations are imperative and often have to be done in stages, that is, a temporary opening of the bowel must be made on the abdominal wall to relieve an otherwise fatal obstruction. Subsequently the growth is removed and the continuity of the intestinal tube restored.

At times the growth is so placed that the opening on the abdominal wall (called colostomy) must be permanent. At first this seems like an intolerable situation to the patient, but the surgeon must take time to explain that such is not the case. The colostomy can be irrigated, and the bowel movements regulated, so that the patient may carry on with the normal activities of life. It is wise to point out specific cases in which this has been found to be true. It is important for the surgeon to take the necessary time to advise the patient with a colostomy about diet, medication, and exercise, until perfect regulation is attained.

The third possibility facing the surgeon when he operates on a patient with cancer of the bowel is that the disease has already spread to other organs, and curability is beyond surgery. Of course much can be done to relieve the patient of his acute symptoms, but the surgeon is confronted with two difficult problems; first, what to tell the patient and family; and second, the continued care of the patient. Let us take up the first problem. Ordinarily it is good judgment not to be brutal and not to be too dogmatic. On the other hand, there is nothing gained by lying. The handling of these situations must of necessity differ with each individual. In general, it is wise to tell the patient that you are going to explain what was found at the time of the operation and what was done. You never destroy all hope, because no one can predict what a particular growth will do; nor does anyone know what new discovery will be reported in the medical journals tomorrow. Most patients fear being abandoned by the surgeon who finds an inoperable condition. They also fear pain, the inability to work, dependence on others, and death. All these fears can be dealt with if the surgeon is interested in the patient as a person and not just as a case for operating.

Patients often ask point blank "Have I got cancer?" This calls for a direct and nonevasive answer, but can be handled tactfully by explaining some of the facts about malignant disease. Emphasis should be placed on the relative benign course of many malignancies; the various types of tumor; and the adjuvant forms of therapy which we now have available. When one can truthfully say to the patient that he had a slow-growing type of tumor which was completely removed, one is justified in being optimistic. On the other hand, when the facts are otherwise, one tries to encourage the patient by pointing out that, although complete extirpation of the tumor was impossible at operation, there is still much to be done. In these instances one uses X-ray treatments and some of the newer drugs to retard the growth or to destroy the remaining tumor.

One is never justified in giving an entirely bleak outlook or death sentence. There are cases on record in which apparently hopeless malignancies were spontaneously arrested, or even disappeared. As an example, one can point to the veteran who was operated on for cancer of the rectum. The growth had extended so far that removal was impossible. The tumor had also spread to the liver. One of the secondary growths in the liver was removed to prove the diagnosis. All that could be done was to give the patient a colostomy. It seemed probable that he would live only a few weeks, but he regained his strength and returned to work. He has been followed for five years in the outpatient department of the hospital; there has been no detectable spread of the cancer. For some reason the growth has remained absolutely stationary, and may continue to do so for an indefinite period. However, this is an isolated case, and often the time comes when the surgeon must treat the patient rather than the disease. Here is one of the great opportunities to face up to a difficult task.

As stated before, patients with incurable cancer fear abandonment, and the assurance that the surgeon will walk along with the patient and the family is a source of immense comfort. Then, too, it is important to help the patient to take each day as it comes, rather than to let him project himself into an unknown future and to burden himself with imaginary problems.

Many patients with malignant disease in its terminal phase do not suffer physical pain but, when they do, the alleviation of it is imperative. This can be accomplished easily if one is not determined to withhold narcotics for fear of addiction. It is just as much the duty of a surgeon to help his patient to die comfortably, when death is inevitable, as it is to lengthen life while there is hope of recovery. Specifically, this means it is not enough simply to alleviate the patient's suffering; the surgeon should not prolong the patient's existence with useless transfusions and forced feedings.

Finally, it might be in order to say something concerning the basic attitudes which activate surgeons. There are three incentives which can motivate a surgeon. The first is the urge for monetary gain. The second, the quest for knowledge. The third, the desire to help his fellow men. All three have their place, but which is foremost? Should one look upon the practice of surgery primarily as a business; a scientific discipline; or a ministry of healing?

When the first is dominant, the surgeon approaches each patient as a customer, and his aim is to see how large a fee he can exact. Such a surgeon is likely to sacrifice all self-respect, and to stoop to fee-splitting in order to secure patients. He is also not above doing unnecessary operations. He may succeed in his ambition for wealth, but is poverty-stricken, by all other standards.

When surgery is considered primarily as a scientific discipline, every patient tends to be looked upon as an object for experimentation. This attitude is utterly impersonal and objective. It causes the surgeon to concentrate his attention on the disease alone, and to ignore the patient. People deeply resent this treatment which puts them in the category of guinea pigs. With this approach, the most the surgeon can hope to gain is a contribution to scientific knowledge, and academic honors.

When surgery is approached primarily as a branch of the healing art, the most durable satisfaction results. This attitude does not preclude either proper compensation for one's efforts or an investigative mind. If a doctor is genuinely interested in his patients, he will keep up with the constant advances in his specialty so as to be able to give them the best possible care. The greatest reward that comes to a surgeon is not the opportunity to perform a spectacular operation, or to make scientific contributions; nor is it the honors he receives, but simply the realization that he has been able to help people back to health, and in the process has been a counselor and a friend.

10 *You as a*

PSYCHIATRIST

BY KARL MENNINGER, M.D.
The Menninger Foundation

DR. KARL MENNINGER

Born: 1893, Topeka, Kansas

Washburn College: 1910–12
University of Wisconsin: A.B., 1914; M.S., 1915
Harvard Medical School: M.D., 1917
Park College: L.H.D., 1955
Jefferson Medical College: LL.D., 1956
Parsons College: LL.D., 1960
Washburn University: D.Sc., 1949
Kansas State University: LL.D., 1962

Menninger Foundation
    Chairman of the Board of Trustees and
    Dean of the Menninger School of Psychiatry

Author: *The Human Mind*
        Man Against Himself
        Love Against Hate
        Manual of Psychiatric Case Study
        Guide to Psychiatric Books
        The Theory of Psychoanalytic Technique
        A Psychiatrist's World

(This chapter is Dr. Karl Menninger, in his office in Topeka, Kansas, talking about psychiatry. He tells what it
is and what it accomplishes. He discusses psychiatry as
a career and tells how to study and prepare for it. His
talking—all of which was specifically for this book—was
recorded on tape and is transcribed here without much
editing, just about as he said it.)

WELL, now let's see. "What is psychiatry?" Classically, psychiatry is a branch of medicine, actually a part of medicine. Of
course medicine itself has undergone many changes in its forms
and constituencies since the days of Hippocrates, who had a
little medical school on a Greek island off the coast of Asia Minor.
Let me think about that question a minute.

That's really the hardest kind of question—"What is psychiatry?" Psychiatry has been so many things. While it has always
been a branch of medicine, psychiatry also used to be the polic-
ing of people who annoyed other people. Psychiatrists used to be
like sheriffs, or maybe just deputy sheriffs, who were supposed to
run disturbing people out of town. Of course they weren't doctors
then.

You must remember that for a long time the mentally ill were
not considered to be people, exactly. They were considered in-
capable of feeling either heat or cold, hunger or pain; consequently they were starved and beaten and left to stay outdoors
and freeze. They were supposed not to have the feelings even of
animals. But this was really kind treatment compared to what
they got a little later when they were regarded as being afflicted
with witches. The Bible said: "Thou shalt not suffer a witch to
live," so they decided that they should not suffer anybody who
had a witch to live. By a kind of illogical inconsistency, instead
of killing the witch, they killed the person that the witch
afflicted.

Then people got a little more merciful and instead of killing
these poor wretches, they just tortured them, the assumption

being, I guess, that if you made people suffer enough, the witch would go and find a healthier subject. The cruelties perpetrated by our ancestors on people they didn't understand—not only the mentally ill but people who spoke a different language from theirs, who had a different color, a different religion—I hate to think about what happened!

At any rate, there were all these phases of handling people whom other people didn't understand and were afraid of. We went through the sheriff phase, and we went through the public-executioner phase, which was supervised by priests and other churchmen of various kinds, and then taken up with great gusto by the lawyers and even by the doctors.

But a couple of Swiss doctors put a stop to that. They said: "Look, these aren't witches. They are diseases." And they said that these diseases are something that science can attack, can do something about. It isn't a question of morals and it isn't a question of superstitions or of witches; it is really a disease. These manifestations, these strange behaviors in people that you have been misunderstanding, are caused by mental disease and these people are suffering.

So the idea of disease, rather than witches, caught on. The doctors talked about the diseases and the people listened, but they didn't know what the doctors were talking about. They didn't understand mental diseases any more than they understood witches, so they just transferred their superstitions from one to the other. Actually, the doctors didn't know much more than the people, but they did know that disease was capable of chemical assault and so they gave pills to the mentally ill. No matter how obscure or complex the mental difficulty of a patient, he was given a pill and the disease was supposed to disappear.

The doctors then decided that they had to name all these diseases. They believed that there were a lot of mental diseases, all different, and that each could be isolated, and identified, and labeled—just as you label scarlet fever, or mumps, or any of the other physical diseases. It was about this time that the scientists of the world were being introduced, through the influence of a Swedish botanist—Carolus Linnaeus—to classification as a method of scientific study. As a result of this, everything in the world began to be classified according to families, orders, genus and species. Mental diseases didn't escape this; they all got classified, too, although it was very imperfectly established at the time that there were any such diseases as the names represented.

All this was somewhere around the middle of the eighteenth century, say around 1750, and—without getting too historical about it—the idea began to prevail that all diseases, mental and physical, not only could be identified and labeled, but could be ascribed to certain organs in the body. This disease came from the heart. This one came from the liver, or from the bowels, or from the brain. So the psychiatrists of the day—and they had psychiatrists, of a kind, back then—became the doctors who knew about the diseases that originated in the brain.

Gradually, though, after so long a time, doctors began to realize that most of the identifiable diseases of the brain—injuries, tumors, hemorrhages, and other lesions—caused not mental symptoms but neurological symptoms: paralyses, twitchings, convulsions, anesthesias, and so forth. The profession of neurology developed in a scientific way far ahead of psychiatry. One reason for this development was that neurology was helped along tremendously by the wars of 1870 in Europe and 1861 in America, when the caliber of the ammunition was such that there were many nerve injuries from which clinical neurologists learned to identify external areas of sensitivity and of function with specific areas of the brain. From this, the great medical specialty of neurology developed, *the* most systematically scientific branch of clinical medicine—scientific in the sense that it lends itself to demonstration of the relationship between structure and function so definitely. A man is blind in his right eye: ergo, the affection is in a certain part of the brain on the left side. Whether it was high or low in the brain, whether it was a little to the left or to the right was important, and this becomes most complicated down in the brain stem. All these things were traced largely as the result of the terrific number of casualties in which some of these nerves had been cut or these areas injured.

So it became clear that an injury to the brain could cause certain identifiable external changes. Some of these were "mental" or "behavioral." That was simple and easy to understand. But what about those people whose peculiar behavior wasn't connected with some injury to the nerves? It wasn't so easy to understand them and they began to be looked on as unfortunate exceptions to neurological science. Many doctors felt that such patients did not really belong in medicine at all. They were regarded as frauds, imposters, or at best something inexplicable. They were just *mad;* either mad, or fools, or frauds.

Since neurologists were called "nerve specialists," and since this had *something* to do with the brain, they were supposed to be able to do something about these strange and puzzling individuals who went to them or were taken to them by distressed parents or friends. The neurologists would listen to them and deal with them as sensibly as they knew how; but for the most part these people were not considered interesting cases, only nuisances. They were the pests of neurological practice, which the neurologists felt they had to put up with. What else could be done with them? They certainly did not belong anywhere else in medicine and perhaps their symptoms did have some relation to the central nervous system.

For the most part, the central nervous system control in these people was believed to have been disturbed in some way by bad education, or impaired motivation, or what was called during World War I "defective moral fiber." In other words, the blame for behavior that was later called "neurotic behavior" was sometimes ascribed to parents, sometimes to teachers, sometimes to heredity, and sometimes to the patient's own willfulness, laziness or desire for attention. These explanations added up to the fact that the doctor didn't like him. This dislike was often shared by others. But some of these cases were so very pitiable that some people, including some doctors, became very concerned and distressed about the inability of medical science to find a rational way to deal with this peculiar kind of illness.

By this time the old custom of mistreating people officially in institutions had been modified somewhat. It was no longer a question of mistreating them; the custom became one of just putting them away and keeping them there. The doctors and custodians had given up trying "to knock some sense into them," as they used to do. Poor King George III of England was knocked down many times by his doctors, or by the doctors' assistants who had charge of him; not because they were natively sadistic—though they may well have been—but because they considered this helpful. If you were rough enough with these people, they would "come to their senses." So the roughness, it was thought, was justified. As a matter fact, it was just outright cruelty of many kinds—whippings, freezing, frightening, and all that sort of thing.

But this finally died down after Doctor Pinel demonstrated (in France) that oftentimes the meaner you treated these people, the meaner and more resentful they got. He said, "Instead of antagonizing and irritating these patients, let us be kind to them, just ordinarily merciful and humane. Let us give them something fit to eat, something comfortable to sleep on, and take off these terrible and painful restraints." He didn't say much about being scientific, although he was more scientific than he generally gets credit for. Mostly he is credited for his humanitarianism.

"All right," the custodians said, "we'll be humane. We'll give them enough to eat and we'll keep them warm. We'll give them pretty good treatment, too, but we'll keep them penned up in the asylum until they die. And it is up to you to see that they stay there and not get out and hurt innocent people. If they hurt you, that's your problem. If they hurt us, that will be your problem too."

When I was a young psychiatrist, back around 1919, one of my teachers taught me—at least tried to teach me; I wouldn't accept it—but he used to say, "Look, the relatives should realize that once their son, or their father, or their mother comes in here, he or she is as good as dead. They should go home and forget him because he is out of their lives. If they keep on hoping, it is just going to break their hearts. Tell them quick. Tell them it's over. Tell them to forget this man." And they generally did forget him, him and all the rest of the people in these places. They were forgotten outside and they were almost forgotten inside. They were allowed to sit around in rocking chairs, day after day, week after week, year after year, rocking their lives away. Getting worse most of the time. They received no treatment. A few of them got well, but not many.

We know now how fearfully those people were *mis*-treated. Not with cruelty but with a kind of scientific neglect. We know that better than 80 per cent, perhaps as high as 90 per cent, of those patients could have been cured and sent home. But instead of that, something like 20 or 25 per cent ultimately went home. In some institutions it was 5 per cent. A good many died; a few escaped and disappeared, but the great bulk of the patients just stayed on the ward, rocking back and forth in their rocking chairs with an occasional walk on the grounds. Once in a long while there would be a dance in the auditorium, or a band concert. For the most part, no treatment, no program, no contacts with the world.

The tragic part of it is that right now, *today*, this is still the program (or rather lack of program) in 80 per cent of our state hospitals, according to the report, "Action for Mental Health," of the Joint Commission on Mental Illness and Health. Think of it! In only 20 per cent of the mental hospitals in this country are patients getting treatment, even though we know that with proper treatment most of these patients would be out and gone home in three or four months!

People are startled at this latter statement. They can't quite believe it. Of course it astonishes them. The possibility of cure for the mentally ill is one of the most startling facts in the whole history of medical care. The improved care of the mentally ill that has occurred in some places in this country in the past fifteen years is exciting in the same way that penicillin was, or the Salk vaccine, or other recent miracles of medical science. And what has been accomplished in these few places serves to call sharper attention to the lack of progress in so many others.

My brother, Dr. Will Menninger, has gone around the country to maybe twenty-five of the legislatures of the United States, at the invitation of the governors, to talk to the House and the Senate, and he has said, "Do you people *really* want to do something about the mentally ill in your state? You can, if you want to." In state after state the members of the legislature have risen in a body to give him a standing ovation. But he doesn't want

that; he wants them to *do something* about the mentally ill in
their own state. Some of them do. But in some places they don't
seem to hear him very well.

Kansas was forty-seventh among the states in the quality and
efficiency of its state hospital program fifteen years ago. Our
facilities were shabby and drab and miserable. Our "nurses" were
abusing and neglecting patients, and in more than one instance
they were accused of killing them, *accidentally* of course! Doctors were few and far between; a treatment program was non-
existent. Patients were packed in to the extent of nearly 25 per
cent overcrowding; they were sleeping on the floors and in corridors. They were being neglected medically. They were being
neglected surgically. They were being neglected in a great many
ways. Relatives had been told to stay away. Psychiatrists from
the outside were not welcome. Patients were fed in a routine
sort of way; they were provided with fly swatters instead of
screens and expected to keep themselves relatively comfortable.
Wards were fitted with low-candle-power carbon filament lights
burning dimly high up in the lofty ceiling. Going through the
place was like going through a medieval dungeon or some prison.

The situation in Kansas finally got so bad that we had to do
something to avert a very considerable scandal. So it came about
that we turned over a new leaf in this state under the leadership
of Governor Carlson.

The governor appointed a small committee, including the Dean
of the Medical School (Dr. Franklin Murphy, now Chancellor of
the University of California at Los Angeles), another physician,
and myself. It had been planned that, in order to take care of
the terrific overcrowding, the state would appropriate twenty million or more dollars for some hospital buildings; but the committee told the governor frankly that building new buildings
was not going to solve his problems—it was just going to
increase his capital investment. What was needed was a greater
appropriation for program, not buildings. The program should
include up-to-date scientific medical treatment. It should be accompanied by a training program. Young doctors want to study
psychiatry under teachers who want to teach them, and the state
hospital affords a wonderful opportunity for them to learn, for

them to treat patients under the supervision of more experienced men.

The governor and the legislature took our advice. They goggled a little at the increased cost of operations, but we told them that the new twenty-million-dollar hospital they were planning would not be necessary. So they put some of this money into an improved program. We got young men into those hospitals as superintendents, and, right away, they put groups of patients, as well as outside workmen, to cleaning the buildings, putting in new lights, new curtains, new chairs, new beds. Above all, we brought in new doctors, nurses, psychologists, recreational people, music teachers, craft workers, schoolteachers, and chaplains. We got fine psychiatric social workers and they invited the relatives of the patients to come and visit them, and to sit down with the social workers and discuss what was best for the patients and their future. Some of the young psychiatrists in the Menninger School of Psychiatry were assigned to work and study in the hospital.

Then we got together with the County Medical Society and arranged for a lot of sound medical consultation and instruction. Regular visits were set up for surgeons, for ophthalmologists, for dentists, for orthopedists, for gynecologists. All these people went to work together, studying and trying to help these patients.

First of all, they had to find out something about each of them. Medical doctors gave them physical examinations and tests and took X rays. The dentists looked at their teeth. The psychiatrists and the psychologists, and the rest of the staff, set about finding out what the situation was in their homes before they came here, finding out about their neighborhoods, their communities. They started carefully learning about these people themselves. What were their worries? What were the burdens they were carrying psychologically? Why were they frightened? Why were they angry? What was frustrating them? *Where was the big misunderstanding?*

In the case of every patient, we tried to answer this question: What can be done about the situation of this man or this woman? What can be done for his condition?

Patients who hadn't been able to read, and hadn't read anything for years—no book, no magazine, no newspaper, nothing—were given glasses. They had their teeth fixed. The men got haircuts that didn't come out from under a china bowl, and the women saw a beauty parlor and went into it, after having gone around dirty and unkempt and slatternly for years. They started sewing and weaving and building and listening to music. Some of them began to hum. Some began to sing. Some of them got up and danced. They took over responsibilities for themselves and for the wards. They began to know again what aspiration was, and hope. And they began to get well. On one chronic, "incurable" ward, where nearly every patient had been bedfast for years, three-fourths of them were up and around after only about two months of the new regime. They wanted to see television or hear music or talk with visitors. It wasn't very long until more than half of these long-time incurables had gone home. One of them had been there for over forty years!

All this created quite a stir. The word got around and the people of Kansas were proud of it. They voted to make a regular appropriation for new buildings annually. And the whole business got out of politics because no politician would think of opposing it. From spending almost the least of any state in the Union, we got up to the front ranks and spent more per patient, per day, than any other state. But please get this straight and let it sink in: While the cost for each patient for each day was the highest, *the cost for the total stay of each patient in the hospital was the lowest in the country.* Don't think the people didn't discover that little accounting gimmick. No politician could scare them with the "high costs," and so on. Good care *appears* to cost more, but actually it costs less. Our patients don't stay in the hospital for years and years any more and run up a big bill, so to speak. They come in and stay for a few months and get well and go out.

When we started this program in 1948 there were over 1,800 patients in the state hospital, stuffed into a building that had been built twenty-five years before to hold 1,500 patients. It was full of people, full of cockroaches, full of despair. Today in this hospital where there used to be 1,800 patients, there are now 900 patients. Today, *seven times* as many patients come *to* the hospital as used to come, yet we have only half as many *in* the hospital as we used to have. There are about 600 empty beds. There has not been a new state hospital in Kansas in over thirty years. I doubt if we will ever need one.

But you may raise a question: What about patients who come in and go out? Don't some of them have to come back in again?

Of course. Certainly. Maybe a fifth of them come back, maybe a fourth. They stay for a while, possibly for a few months, get some more treatment, and go out again. Don't physical patients have to go back to a hospital now and then to get treatment?

But that doesn't satisfy you and you bring up something else: What about those patients who are dangerous? Well, it may be hard to get you to understand the truth about these patients, after all you've heard about the dangerous ones. People tell stories about them and repeat all kinds of rumors about them. What the "crazy man" who lived across the street did. What they heard somebody say about the woman who lived somewhere in the next block. But the fact is, the simple truth is, that there are very few patients who are violent, *very* few. There are some, of course, and these we look for and keep in the hospital.

Don't we make any mistakes? Yes, occasionally, we do. Out of several thousand patients who have gone through treatment in the past few years, I remember a few about whom we were mistaken. In these instances, serious trouble followed. However, you must remember this; the doctor can't always control the situation. I remember one murder that occurred in a case in which we had pleaded with the parents not to remove the son, for we felt that he was dangerous. The father pointed out to us that the son was entirely rational, which was true; that he had recovered from his early confusion and disorientation, which was true; that he, the father, was a strong man and ought to be able to control his own family, which was true; and that we had no legal right to detain a man who was "sane" and whose parents wished to assume custody of him, which was true. But it was also true that the boy hated his father, and a few months later this protecting father was dead.

Of course patients can fool us, and sometimes they do; but in this same period how many prisoners have been released from state prison and gone out and killed people and committed various other crimes? Not two or three, but hundreds of prisoners have committed crimes, many of them serious. But the public, for some reason, has come to accept this, so far as prisoners are concerned. For some strange reason they retain their suspicions of psychiatric patients who, for the most part, are good citizens and very rarely are serious offenders.

Violence in psychiatric people, like violence perhaps in normal people, relates mostly to extreme fear. Patients attack because of fear, usually the fear that they themselves are being attacked, or are going to be attacked. That is one reason they come into the hospital. In the hospital they get a little sedation, a little kindness, a little respect, and they begin to lose their fear. When they do lose this fear of being attacked, then there is not much danger of their being violent and maybe, after a while, after a long while, or after a short while, they get better. This isn't always true and sometimes a violent patient may be in an institution for a very, very long time. But we never give up our hope, and we try never to let him lose his.

By now you may be wondering what this is that we have been talking about. Is this psychiatry? We started out to answer: What is psychiatry? And I haven't done it. At least not in any exact way, certainly not in the way that two and two make four. But suppose I put it this way: what we have been talking about is the subject matter of psychiatry. I haven't been trying to tell you what psychiatry *is*—that is almost too broad. But I have been trying to tell you some of the things that psychiatry *does*.

Maybe, though, you still want to know, "What is psychiatry?" The dictionary has a definition for it: "The medical specialty dealing with mental disorders." That is all right, I suppose. But that is not the way I think of it. I think of psychiatry in its total subject matter and in its action, rather than in any definition. I see it as a science, an art, and a skill, engaged in by many people, and by many kinds of people, all participating in many kinds of activities. Their *purpose* is to keep men, women, and children mentally well; but when somebody becomes mentally ill, their *practice* is to study these people, diagnose their mental difficulties, treat them and get them well. There is a lot more to psychiatry than that, but at least that is a kind of outlook.

Psychiatry, when you try to define it, is like medicine. Try to define medicine. It is hard to *define,* but it is easy to know what medicine *does.* It is all these doctors and nurses and technicians and everybody else in the medical world trying to keep people well, and when they get sick, to find out what is wrong with them and cure them.

In comprehending the practice and accomplishments of psychiatry, you must take into account its changes and the rapidity of its advance, especially within this century. Even when I was a young man, starting my medical studies, our teachers were interested in the "crazy" behavior of people, their antics and the grotesque things they did. We were kept busy watching the extraordinary behavior that some of them exhibited, walking over rooftops, hiding in the cellar for thirty days without food, enduring many delusions and queer hallucinations, and doing all sorts of bizarre and strange things. There are such patients now, but we don't let them suffer like that very long. Even more important, we don't let them get in that condition. We try to head off the illness before things get that bad.

When I was a medical student, I was led through the wards in the state hospitals of Massachusetts and I was shown these queer people, some of them pointing at the sun all day, some standing on their heads, some standing like marble statues, some taking off their clothes and walking around naked. They were shown to us as if they were museum specimens. The doctor would point at one and say, "Now this is an interesting syndrome." And he would point at another and say, "This is an unusual case." Each was looked at as if he had a separate disease, with separate symptoms, and each disease and symptom had to be sorted out and labeled. I had to learn them. Those diseases and those labels! Now I *abhor* all that! That isn't psychiatry, going around looking at people, hanging a tag on them and going on. That doesn't *help* people.

Suppose a medical doctor treated his patients that way. Suppose a doctor showed you somebody who had a *physical* illness that could have been relieved years ago and the doctor had let it get worse and worse and then showed it off: "Isn't this an interesting specimen?" The doctor should have relieved that condition long ago.

Missionaries who go to some outlying places find natives with these enormous tumors that could have been relieved years ago if somebody had cut them out then. That is the way it is with people who have mental diseases. They should never be allowed to get into such states of deterioration that they point at the sun all day, or hide in the cellar, or take their clothes off in public. These patients could have been helped. But sometimes, after they have been left without help for a long time, their condition can get worse and worse, and it can get to the place where there really isn't much you can do—except never to stop trying and never to let them, if you can possibly help it, stop trying either.

It is a peculiar thing how, even now, with all the advances that psychiatry has made—the treatment, the cures—you still hear the question: Can these mentally ill people be helped? Is there anything that really can be done for them? What do you *do* for them? What do you give them?

Of course they can be helped and I could talk about it for hours. But without telling the whole story of how they can be helped, without describing the details of their physical examinations, their case histories, reports on their families, reports on their communities, their social backgrounds—without going into all the diagnosis and treatment, I will tell you that our goal is to reorder, redirect, reconstruct their whole way of living. We use a psychological approach, a medical approach, a surgical approach, a social approach. We use all these and more, finding out all that we can, and then we treat these people. We try to give them a new way to go. We teach them. . . . We push them. . . . We pull them. . . . But first of all we try to understand them—each of them.

I should explain to you that a psychiatric hospital is very different from the ordinary hospital that one goes into. In the general hospital the patient is in bed. At most psychiatric hospitals the patient is up and around. In the general hospital, you want your patient to stay quiet and the doctor comes to him. In a psychiatric hospital, such as a state mental hospital, you want your patient *not* to say quiet; you want him to be up and doing something, painting a picture, weaving cloth, listening to music. You want him to go find the doctor, not the other way round. The whole program is different.

The staff of a mental hospital is different, too. There are the medical doctors, of course, because the physical ills and ailments of these mental patients must be diagnosed and treated. There are the psychologists who have studied the mind intensively and they are needed in the mental diagnosis. There are the therapists —activity therapists, occupational therapists, recreational therapists, all kinds of therapists. Then there are the social workers getting information about the family and so forth. And there are the psychiatrists who are in charge of the entire group. It is the reponsibility of the psychiatrist to go over all the findings, consider the suggestions and recommendations, and decide on the treatment.

This is the kind of work that is done in a psychiatric hospital and the way that patients are taken care of there. But the interesting and important fact is that, nowadays, the majority of our patients don't get into hospitals. This is something that all people don't know about. We treat them before there is any need for them to go inside a hospital. We head them off. Hundreds of patients here in Topeka are treated as outpatients. They don't get "inside" any more; they don't have to. They can be treated and go right on with their work. Maybe they need a little sedative, a little counsel once or twice a week, once or twice a month, once or twice a year, but they carry on.

They cease to think of themselves as having to come in and surrender, to run and hide in a hospital as if they were some kind of hopeless case. Their families and their relatives stop thinking about having to commit them and lock them up. I don't mean that we have made these diseases disappear; but we have found that there are stages of mental illness that people used to think were hopeless, and they just aren't hopeless. We can help these people, keep them going and living a good life. Cure most of them. It is no longer a matter of putting them away; it is restoring them to a full life, reimplanting some hope in them, some aspiration, helping them to some self-improvement, watching them leave and head out on their own.

Perhaps by now you are wondering about psychoanalysis. We have come all this way and haven't mentioned psychoanalysis. Everybody has heard about it and *almost* everybody has talked about it. "But what is it?" you ask. "Does it do any good?"

Perhaps we had better start out by making it plain that psychoanalysis is a *part* of psychiatry. It is a specialty of its own; but it is a part, a branch, of psychiatry. And before we go on to consider psychoanalysis itself, I think we had better find out something about its history. In order to do this, we must begin with a discussion of psychiatry.

Up to about fifty years ago, all psychiatry was based entirely on *conscious* phenomena like vision, and hearing, and memory, and acting, and so forth. But then along came some people—the great psychologist, William James, was one of them—and these people began to say, "Look, there is more to all this than meets the eye. There is an *unconscious* part of human psychology that has some effect on the conscious part."

They said that hypnosis demonstrated this, and a certain kind of forgetting demonstrated it, and there were other reasons for believing that an *unconscious* influenced the *conscious* mind. Many people knew this, and were thinking about it, but none of it had any application. Then a few of them, like Mesmer, did some amazing things.

A man covered with burns is groaning and gasping in the hospital and someone trained in hypnosis goes in and tells him, "You're on a green lawn looking at the dandelions, and it's April not October. You haven't any pain." This man is then quiet the rest of the day and people think it is a miracle. It *isn't* a miracle; but it does make you realize that there is more to psychological functions than is ordinarily understood.

Back in the time of Mesmer, the psychologists didn't understand this at all. And the doctors didn't understand it. In fact, they all agreed it was a fake, including Benjamin Franklin. But hypnosis wasn't a fake. It was an empirically discovered way of making certain contact with the unconscious.

The trouble with hypnosis, though, is that it is unpredictable. Not everybody can be hypnotized. Nor can everybody hypnotize other people. Some have more ability at it than others. But in spite of its having been labeled a fake, some of the doctors got interested in it. An English doctor—James Braid, an ophthalmologist—picked it up, and worked at it; then two French doctors, Bernheim and Jean Charcot.

Now we are getting closer to psychoanalysis. Charcot was demonstrating some of his hypnosis on patients when Sigmund Freud went to see him. Freud watched and was impressed. If there was only just some way to do this without the unpredictability! He went away pondering it.

About this time an old practitioner in Vienna told Freud about a funny experience he'd had. This doctor had had a talkative patient, and she kept on talking to the doctor until somehow she seemed to talk herself into a state of mind in which she could explain things (symptoms) that she hadn't been able to understand before. When she understood these things, she got well. Freud studied this patient's record, and he began to use this method systematically on a number of similar patients. He found out that he was making a kind of exploration of unconscious areas of the mind. The peculiar thing is that it was the patient herself (or himself) who did the exploring, and that the process of exploration seemed to be accompanied by improvement and even recovery.

Thus a new way of treating patients was born in connection with a new way of examining patients. Even more important was the fact that this laid the foundation for a new kind of psychology.

None of this was in the medical books. It was not in the psychology books. Here was something *new*—and out of this psychoanalysis developed.

I could talk on for a long time about psychoanalysis, but suppose I say, in the most general and primary terms, that it has to do with the unconscious, and with Freud's method of exploring the unconscious, enabling us to obtain a knowledge of the nature of the unseen conflicts of the patient, and organizing and using that knowledge. The doctor doesn't use the knowledge himself;

he helps the patient to acquire that knowledge and do something about it himself—if he wants to. Sometimes it is painful knowledge and requires painful changes. But usually these changes are worth making and the individual gets an entirely new understanding of himself and why he has been tripping himself up and zigging when he should be zagging and having headaches instead of good ideas all these years. That isn't all there is to psychoanalysis, but that is the general principle of the treatment. It takes special training for a doctor to do it and the treatment takes a lot of time and it is expensive. Usually it is worth it.

I expect now that we had better start thinking more specifically about the young people to whom I am talking. They want to know about psychiatry as a career. What training will they need? Where, and how, can they get this training?

To begin with, they must have a medical background. Before a young man can start psychiatric training, he must have completed medical school and had his time as an intern. He comes to us with an M.D. degree and some hospital experience. He knows something about responsibility to patients, his duty in caring for patients, and the objectives of therapy in general. But even after this background and training, when he comes into a mental hospital he will have some difficulties. He enters a world that is strange to him—different terms, different symptoms, attitudes, procedures, treatment methods.

So what happens to him? We teach him in more ways than one, and we keep shifting and rotating his assignments and instructors, seeing that he gets various experiences and different teachers. We guide him in techniques of diagnosis study, case analysis, and case presentation. He finds out about the special kinds of therapy that are used in a mental hospital, and about their techniques. He takes greatest care in learning to work with patients and with their relatives, talking with the relatives and guiding them. He learns what each member on the psychiatric team does, so that he himself can do most of each assignment and later on he can direct all of it.

The training is conducted and carried on under the most intensive supervision. No young doctor treats a patient here without supervision, and that supervision goes on not for a few weeks but for several years. Being a psychiatrist is a difficult and a demanding thing, for you are dealing with people and people are too precious to take chances with.

After three years of training as a resident, a psychiatrist still must have two years of "experience" before he can come before the American Board of Psychiatry to demonstrate his proficiency, and, if successful, receive his certification. So let's add up his time of training. First, there are his years in medical school. Then there are one or two years as an intern. Then three years as a resident. Beyond this, he is still faced with the additional two years of "experience" before he can gain his certification.

Confronted with this extent of time, it is natural that many a young physician who has just finished his internship should look askance at the training period of psychiatry and turn a covetous eye on the shorter period of some other specialty, or even more likely on the immediate role of the general practitioner. General practice can provide continual interest, of course, and it is a rewarding life. What's more, it brings one an income promptly, so that he can get married and have a home and start raising a family. To go into specialty training, regardless of whatever specialty, is a postponement of some of these things and a definite sacrifice. On the other hand, a specialist has some rewards that the general practitioner never gets. This is particularly true in the field of psychiatry.

Psychiatrists have tremendous responsibilities. They are treating some of the most difficult, and often some of the most important, people. The medical student is apt to get the idea that only ne'er-do-wells, and lonely, rich, and bored women, trivial in their interests, come to psychiatrists. As a matter of fact, executives and many others who have heavy tasks and heavy responsibilities are among those who consult psychiatrists and in many instances receive continued psychiatric treatment. Some statistics were recently published showing that more than 75 per cent of the patients now under treatment *by psychoanalysis* are professional people, most of them doctors.

There is undoubtedly a prestige value to psychiatry which does not attach in the same degree to some of the other specialties, or to general practice, yet I know quite well that many psychiatrists earn smaller incomes than do some general practitioners and many surgeons. I doubt, though, if money really determines to any considerable extent what branch of medicine a young physician selects as his lifework—young physicians are idealistic in spite of their elaborate pretense not to be.

It would be hard to generalize with any degree of accuracy what income a young physician might make in psychiatry. Some psychiatrists have very good incomes, or, if they are employed, they make very good salaries. The highest-paid employee in several of the states now is not the governor, or the professor of surgery at the university, but the psychiatrist in charge of the state institutions.

Let us suppose that our young friend has chosen psychiatry and has completed his three-year basic training. He is then faced with the need for two years of "experience." How can he get it? There are a number of ways and for most of them he can get paid. Some of the men get their experience in the Army or the Air Force or the Public Health Service. These two years are not a humdrum time of grubbing at books or at some dull job; they can be a great learning experience. Once they are completed and the physician has gained his specialty certification, his full career as a psychiatrist is ahead of him. What now can he do? Actually, there are all kinds of possibilities open to him.

There are public hospitals and private hospitals. There are public clinics and private clinics. There are medical schools and various institutions. And, of course, there is always private practice. Every one of these fields for young psychiatrists is crying for young men. We who have any responsibility for training psychiatrists get letters almost daily from people around the country wanting us to recommend someone to them, either for a full-time salaried job, or a part-time job, or to begin a private practice.

It may seem hard to believe that many of our young men, despite the openings available to them, and the years they have already spent in training, decide to prolong their training beyond the basic requirements. Psychiatry itself is divided into various specialties and our graduates often stay on for training in child psychiatry, or in criminology, or in industrial psychiatry, or military psychiatry. They may want to specialize in psychoanalysis, which within itself takes several extra years of training. They may want to specialize in administrative psychiatry or community psychiatry. Very few of our graduates go into private practice wholly, and most of them gain additional training in some specialty.

It should be pointed out that while the young men are getting this specialized training, they usually can receive compensation. In other words, once a doctor has received his basic training in psychiatry, he can ordinarily take a specialty within psychiatry, and, at the same time, also fill a salaried position or at least get a fellowship. The pay ranges from $8,000 to $12,000 a year, with annual increases in most instances.

Where can one get basic training and training in the psychiatric specialties? Originally there were very few places in the United States, but today there are hundreds of good ones scattered over the country. We here in Topeka have a rather large training program, not only in basic residency training, but in nearly all the specialties in psychiatry.

What about vacancies at these training centers? Always the young people ask, "Can I get in?" And the answer is: So far as openings are concerned, you can certainly get in. There are always openings but one must remember that for each of them, at most psychiatric centers, there is a very careful screening of applicants. One can quickly see the reason for this. We don't want young fellows getting into this field who in some subtle way are unequipped for it, a fact which previously they have never been told by anyone. Some persons just have no gift for psychiatry, and we try to detect this before they invest their lives in it. That is why here at the Menninger School of Psychiatry we have never filled our quota. Our standards of admittance are not impossibly severe, and we accept over 60 per cent of those who apply, but we always have room for more. I expect that is true of most psychiatric centers.

The applicant for a psychiatric residency must be looked at in a somewhat different light from the applicant for cardiology or surgery, for instance. The basic requirements in psychiatry are not only the usual ones of intelligence and aptitude; a psychiatrist's effectiveness as a clinician and as a therapist relates in a large measure to the stature and breadth of his own personality. What a psychiatrist *is* has effect on his patients as well as what he *does*.

This leads, of course, to the inevitable question that is so often asked: What qualifications does a psychiatrist need? *What makes a good psychiatrist?*

If you will forgive me, I would like to quote something I wrote about this a while back. It was printed in the *Bulletin of the Menninger Clinic* and reprinted in a book called *A Psychiatrist's World*. It is "A Psychiatric Fable" and I wrote it to answer the question: What makes a good psychiatrist? This question had been coming up repeatedly in discussion with students and staff, and I read my answer at one of my Saturday Colloquiums in the Menninger School of Psychiatry.

There was once a psychiatric resident here named John Smith. He was a rather ordinary-looking fellow, a bit self-conscious and perhaps somewhat lacking in social grace, but he was a pleasant, quiet chap. One might not notice him on the first glance around. Even after several months he wasn't very well known. He wasn't very outstanding. Psychological tests didn't rate him as "very superior." He wasn't made chairman of anything or secretary of anything or even sergeant-at-arms.

But gradually this John Smith began to be heard about. His *patients* liked him. They seemed to feel he was their personal doctor. If he was absent for a day they asked, "Where is Dr. Smith?" "Can't I see Dr. Smith today?" New patients were tipped off; they wished he was their doctor, too. He seemed to remember his patients even when he was off duty.

He didn't write easily but he put down his observations simply, clearly, and with conscientious thoroughness. He made no glib references to "adjustment" or "relating" or "identifying" or "acting out." He didn't use "libido," "Oedipus," "psychotic," "syncretistic," or other impressive Greek or Latin words. But he spent his time listening to his patients and then tried to record what he saw happening to them and in them, written in a way that fellow workers could understand, including the aides and nurses. And he got his reports in on time.

He didn't rush to make application for a training analysis for himself, he said he felt there was plenty of time to learn more about his own unconscious after he had studied the multiform behavior of his patients, and had learned from experience his special points of difficulty.

In reading groups and other seminars, he read the assignments— and sometimes more. He spoke up often in the discussion, but only to ask questions, and his colleagues concluded that he really didn't know much about the subject. He took notes in the lectures, so it was concluded by some that he had a poor memory.

Dr. Smith knew all the nurses and all the aides and all the patients on his wards; and they all knew him. "We felt quiet and comfortable and secure when he sat down with us," one of them said. He went with the patients on their picnics; he helped the nurses plan a Christmas party; he sat and talked with the aides at length about their problems.

Then, too, there were a lot of little things. The radiator in the men's toilet stuck one cold morning, and Dr. Smith fixed it before the maintenance men could arrive. When one of the therapists lost his wife, Dr. Smith went to the funeral. He spent an hour (at home) fixing a patient's cigarette lighter and took a patient's mother to the contact office because he was afraid she might lose her way. He listened sympathetically to a social worker tell a long, weary story about her nephew's alcoholism without giving her the impression that he was very busy or bored. He was frequently seen on the wards on Sunday afternoons and holidays.

Toward the end of his third year of residency John Smith was wondering where he should go when he finished his training. He assumed that no prize position would be open to him. Sometimes he doubted, in view of what he realized he didn't know, whether he was competent to go anywhere and take the responsibility of being regarded as a psychiatrist. When he was offered an appointment as an assistant section chief, he felt greatly honored, and he was pleased that he had the opportunity to go on learning and helping others to learn.

Toward the end of the three years, the residents were asked by the faculty to help them decide whether the training they had received seemed to be in the direction of helping them to become the kind of psychiatrists they wanted to be. There was a good deal of discussion among them as to just what constituted a *good* psychiatrist, and how success in professional achievement could be evaluated. As an experiment, they decided to vote on which of them seemed to most nearly typify their conception of a good psychiatrist.

The result in the poll was astonishing. It was almost unanimous. All but one vote was for John Smith.

Now I suppose that there are two or three other questions that I should answer. Some young fellows sometimes ask: Is it depressing to work with mental patients?

No! *It is the most exciting thing in the world.* Psychiatric patients are, in many ways, the most rewarding of all patients to deal with. They come to you and this is the understanding between you and them: "Here are my problems and you are going to listen to me. You are not going to laugh at me, no matter what I tell you. My wife would be ashamed if she knew of the silly or unpleasant symptoms I am going to tell you about. People would be shocked and some people would be hilarious, but you are not going to laugh. You are going to realize that it distresses me to have to get up suddenly and go off and shut the door, and scratch myself. It embarrasses me no end to tell you that I can't be driving down the road and pass a dead dog, or a dead rabbit, or a dead anything lying in the road, without having to lean out of the window and spit. I don't understand why I have to wash my hands twenty times, thirty times a day, or why I wear dark glasses even on a dark day, even inside the house. Most people would laugh about all this and ridicule me, but you are going to give it thought and you are going to see some kind of meaning in it. I don't understand all this, but you are going to make me realize that it has a connection with other things that I never thought of. And you are going to lead me out gradually—mostly by your silence and then maybe with a few questions."

This kind of thing, as the patient has just described it, can be a part of what we call psychotherapy. And psychotherapy can act in many ways. It can be simply a rational explanation of what has been troubling the patient. It can be a pat on the back and approval of what little gain has been accomplished. It can be a scolding for the kind of goings-on that the patient was into last week, and that just aren't going to be tolerated by society, or by the doctor, or anybody else, and they have got to be stopped.

Psychotherapy can be so very many different things. There is one recent form of psychotherapy in which the doctor doesn't do a thing except to say what the patient says. The patient says, "I'm feeling better." And the doctor says, "Hmmmm—so you're feeling better?" "Yes, and I don't exactly know why I'm feeling better. It may be that I understand myself better." "You think you understand yourself better?" "Yes, I believe I do because you see just talking with you has clarified some things." "It's clarified some things, has it?" "Yes, it's clarified my relations with my wife a bit." "Hmmmm—clarified your relations with your wife?" "Yes, I understand our relations better." And so on. All the doctor does is echo what the patient says. I am exaggerating a little, but that's about it. And the remarkable fact is that many patients are definitely benefited by it.

Here at our clinic we don't use this method and I cite it only as an illustration of the way in which just listening to a patient and making even the most banal and noncommittal responses can sometimes enable him to think more clearly and see himself better—and so improve. I myself don't think that psychotherapy should be limited to such echoing as I have just described. I think it should be explanatory or clarifying in various ways, but I wanted to illustrate that listening itself is a part of the therapeutic process. Afterward, what the doctor *does*, in regard to what he has listened to, can indicate his skill and the effectiveness of his training.

Usually psychotherapy is on a one-to-one basis, but it can get away from this usual procedure and in one kind of treatment there may be half a dozen patients in the room at the same time. One patient says he understands himself better, and somebody else says, "Well, I don't know that you understand yourself better. It doesn't show." And the first patient says, "I thought it was showing. Didn't it show yesterday when I was nicer to the group than usual?" "Well, I didn't think you were nicer than usual. You just think you were nicer than usual." By this time maybe you, the doctor, say to the person who has been criticizing, "Well, now is this an objective observation of yours, Mr. Jones?" And he says, "Yes, because I myself am growing more tolerant, but I don't think he was unusually nice to us yesterday." Gradually the members of the group come to understand each other better and themselves better.

You may ask is it healthy for people to go on talking and talking about themselves. Certainly it is healthy. For one thing it helps the doctor to find out *why* they want to talk about themselves. I don't think that ruminations before unskilled people are healthy or helpful, but the skilled psychotherapist knows when all this talk *is* getting somewhere. It's getting around, maybe, to saying, "I don't like myself. People think I do; they think I am vain. Actually, I'm very much concerned about myself—the inner core of rottenness—or something that is in me that I wish wasn't."

In psychotherapy you go with people into unexplored areas of their lives. You don't know where you are going with them, or what you are going to decide, but you manage to help them see criteria for decisions which change things and which they had not thought of. And you encourage people. You do all kinds of things for people without knowing always just how.

A patient told me yesterday that he had come into a hospital with terrible pains. He had a peptic ulcer which had caused two weeks of agony. He had been refused admission at another hospital because he had been there three or four times before with the same complaint—at least this is the reason he said they refused him admission. He said they told him he ought to depend on himself and not on the charity of the government to take care of his ailments.

I don't know why they were so rough on him, but this time he had come to a different hospital and was immediately taken over by the doctors. They were very concerned about his pain, and about the fact that he had had four or five attacks, and about various other things about him. They took a careful case history and gave him some treatment. In a matter of a few weeks he was back on his feet again. They had asked me to see him.

I asked him, "How come you got well so fast?" "Why," he said, "I was treated like a human being." "What do you mean by that?" I asked. He replied, "Listen—I was at that other hospital five times and they got bored with me. They got mad at me. They didn't want me to come back or to see me any more. They never did me much good anyhow." "What do you mean they never did you much good?" I asked. "They never paid any attention to me," he said, "and that's half of it!"

There were some young surgeons and some internists standing around and they needed to hear this, so I said, "What was that you just said?" "Well," he said, "it's hard to explain. But here I am. I pass this blood and I have these terrible pains and everybody knows I have an ulcer, and I know it. I know it can't be cured just by my being treated nice, but it's a fact that I come in here and I'm treated like a gentleman. People are concerned about me and that helps. I begin to get easier. I think to myself —Joe, maybe there's some reason for you to exist, after all. These fellows are for you. They are trying to help you. You'd better get back on your feet and get going again. And, in some way or other, I begin to feel better all over and my stomach is better and I can't explain it."

But you see he did explain it. Here was a relatively ignorant fellow who could make all this pretty clear to the doctors. He wasn't a psychiatric patient in the ordinary sense. But there is a psychiatric element even in these medical cases. In recognized psychiatric cases you get effects that can be even more exciting. People who have been rambunctious, disagreeable, queer, ridiculous, absurd—they come to somebody who doesn't laugh at them and doesn't ridicule them and doesn't scorn them, even when they have been most obnoxious. After a while, and gradually, something happens. "Why have you been that way? How did you get to be so disagreeable, Mr. Jones?" "Gosh, doctor," he says, "I don't know. I guess I just quit trying to please anybody. I didn't think I could."

Pretty soon you begin to find out that Mr. Jones is one of your greatest admirers. And, what is a lot more important, he begins to act like a different person. I can't begin to tell you how exciting this is. You suddenly see people—ugly, unpleasant, aggressive people, and, as they receive the right kind of treatment, they start to change their whole way of living. "I've got to make a little use of the rest of my life," they say. You see these people turn right around. It's like the old-time evangelism. They get converted. And you suddenly think: Look how people change their ways, and change themselves, when the right word is spoken.

"If I become a psychiatrist, do I cease to be a doctor? Am I left outside of the medical world and looked down on as if I were dealing in voodoo?"

Every psychiatrist is familiar with this kind of question, even from his own children. "Dad, why aren't you a *real* doctor like Bobby's dad?" "Well, I am a doctor, son." "I know, but not a real one, Dad, because Bobby's dad takes out people's tonsils and you don't take out tonsils." "I know how to and I've done it, but that's not the thing that interests me. I think that some parts of people are more interesting than their tonsils."

That's all right for you to talk that way, but it doesn't get very far with the kids. "But Helen's dad is a doctor, and he gives medicines. You don't give medicines." "Yes, I do, son, I give medicines." "But you don't go around and see people at their homes like he does." "Sometimes I do."

But the children have got something. They sense that there is a difference. I couldn't deny it. I would like to say that a psychiatrist is just a doctor along with the rest. But he is not. We belong to the medical societies; we go to the hospitals with the other doctors; we have professional dealings with them. But in a general way, psychiatrists tend to get out on the periphery of the medical fraternity.

On the other hand we have a closer association among ourselves than with other doctors. I often say that lawyers fight in public, but they are excellent friends in private; whereas some doctors stick together in public, but seem to do quite a bit of fighting in private. This is less true among psychiatrists. You see, we have been a kind of minority group and to some extent we have stuck together in self-defense.

There is no feeling of the pariah in the psychiatrist. There used to be, but not any more. Psychiatry is now a great growing specialty. Twenty-five years ago there were only a thousand psychiatrists in America. Today there are ten thousand, eleven thousand, twelve thousand. They are growing in numbers and growing in influence. Today, other doctors are more interested in psychiatry than psychiatrists are interested in their fellow doctors.

Let me explain this. Psychiatrists get so fascinated by their work, so wrapped up in it, that they tend to lose interest in the sort of problems that occupy the majority of doctors. But they shouldn't. They should be constantly interested in all of medicine. Yet they are prone to stay so much in their own field that there is a slight tendency to lose touch with the rest of the medical world.

Suppose I put this in a practical way? When I was a young psychiatrist, I joined every medical organization I could. I belonged to the County Medical Society, the State Medical Society, the A.M.A. of course, and a half-dozen district medical societies of various kinds. Furthermore, I never missed a meeting. Do you know why? I wanted to know the doctors and I wanted them to know me. I wanted to be of help if they needed me. And if I helped them, then they would refer patients to me. And that was a matter of bread and butter.

Today the psychiatrists are not so dependent upon the doctors any more, so far as patients are concerned. In the old days if a doctor had a patient for me, he would call up: "Karl, I want you to see a patient." Well, I'd get palpitations, I'd be so pleased. "Why, yes, Dr. Jones, of course. When would it be convenient for you, Dr. Jones?"

They don't talk that way any more. They call up: "Please, Dr. Karl, could you see a patient sometime in the next two or three weeks? I'm awfully worried about her and it would be a great favor to me and to the family. Could you squeeze her in sometime this month?"

The point is that there are now many more psychiatric patients than there are psychiatrists to see them. Patients don't wait for doctors to send them; they come themselves. But doctors, of course, do send some. So do lawyers. So do judges. So do business executives and school boards and church organizations. All kinds of people send patients to us. The reason is that there are many people who need help, and want help, and see some hope for getting help in psychiatry.

I still belong to all the medical associations that I joined through the years—dozens of them. I pay my dues and I go as often as I can. I urge the young doctors to go, but I can't always get them to. They say, "I don't want to go halfway across the state to a meeting to hear about gall-bladder diseases and spend a whole afternoon—when I have fifteen patients waiting to see me because they couldn't sleep last night, or because they are depressed, or because they are afraid they are going to go and get drunk and perhaps kill themselves. I'd like to know more about gallstones, but I haven't time to learn it that way."

No, you don't cease to be a doctor when you become a psychiatrist and you don't lose touch with medical science, and you don't become a second-class citizen in the medical world. Or at least you don't need to. Some psychiatrists have let themselves feel a bit outside the medical world partly because they are a little dissatisfied with the lack of interest on the part of some medical scientists with the intangible. To some people, science means measuring tangible things. To them, things that can't be measured are not scientific data.

But many people do not conceive of science in that way. It is true that in surgery, pediatrics, and obstetrics you can measure, weigh and take pictures. But you can't weigh mother love, and you can't measure resentment. You can't say how many inches of hate. What kind of picture would an X ray show of the suffering and loneliness experienced by a woman drifting away from everyone into a shadowy world of phantasy?

Some psychiatrists in recent years have made definite efforts to get closer to the rest of medicine. I think that this is a good sign, even though I don't agree with some of the assumptions made by some of these doctors. The professor of psychiatry in one of our big medical schools is a man known not for his psychological work, or his work with psychiatric patients, but for his skill as a biochemist. The chemical way of looking at human beings is an important way, of course, just as the anatomical way of looking at human beings is important, but these are not the only ways. The psychological way is also important.

My dear old chief, under whom I studied and worked, and whom I loved so much, Professor Ernest Southard, spent his life looking for spots on the brain that would explain things. But before he died he had seen the futility of this, I believe, and he gave up looking for spots on the brain and began to look for behavior patterns.

Perceptive men know that a behavior pattern of bad habits—repeated truculence, getting oneself fired because of continued lateness—bad habits of all kinds, will, more than likely, bring people to a doctor. A different kind of behavior pattern—good habits—don't bring people to a doctor.

It is curious how some people say that none of this has anything to do with doctors—a person just has "bad habits," that's all. They say that a brain tumor can explain some bad habits; remove the tumor and the habits disappear. And this is true. Bad habits, they say, can be caused by poor education; re-educate, and the bad habits disappear. This, too, is true. Bad habits . . . ? Bad habits can really be bad habits (cigarette smoking, for example). Threaten the smoker, or anyone else who has a bad habit, make the penalty frightening enough, and he may correct himself.

But there are other bad habits that can't be explained simply by brain tumors, or by poor education, and that can't be made to disappear by threats. Some of these habits come about because of conflict. The fellow has a perfectly good brain and has been well and properly educated. Also, he knows this isn't a good thing for him to do. It's silly and it's foolish; it's unsightly and it's aggravating. But, just the same, it seems to him the way to do, and he does it—and this is his solution of conflicting psychological pressures.

None of this would be considered scientific by some scientists. They say you can't *prove* it. Of course you can't prove it in the conventional ways of science. You can't measure it. You can't weigh it. You can't cut it out and put it under a microscope. But there are other kinds of proof than those that science has used up to now. Science is a growing thing. Through the years it has developed various kinds of proofs and it will develop still others. Scientific methods, just the same as scientific products, will go on developing and evolving. Today we rely heavily on the statistical method and on measurement, but they aren't enough.

We have come a long way in the science of psychiatry, and in teaching people to understand what is being done in psychiatry. I remember back more than two decades ago when my brother and I became convinced that we would have to speed up psychiatric training if we were ever to get a substantial supply of good psychiatrists. A friend of ours gave us a few thousand dollars and said, "Go around to the medical schools and talk to the boys and see why they don't have any interest in coming into your field of work." So I did. I visited the chapters of the medical fraternity that I belonged to. They would generally invite me to dinner and afterwards we would sit around—chairs, floor, any- where—and I would ask them why they didn't give a little thought to going into psychiatry. They would act as if they didn't quite hear me. "Psychiatry?" they would ask. "Yes," I would say, "*psychiatry*. Why not?" Then there would be a silence. And then maybe one of them would be brave enough to say, "Oh, what the hell, Dr. Karl, why should we go into psychiatry? Psychiatrists never cure anybody. All they do is use big words and make them- selves look ridiculous. Why, one of our professors . . ."

"Well," I would say, "wait a minute. Haven't you seen any patients treated or cured?"

"Heavens, no. Psychiatrists talk a lot of theories and show off weird people, but around here they either work in an asylum for low pay, or they sit in their offices and do psychoanalysis. Nobody ever gets well as a result of what they do. Instead of that, look what we can do with drugs and ordinary medicine."

So then I would begin to talk with them about my own experiences, some of my own cases. I told them (and I told them this because I believe it) that psychiatry is the most exciting branch of medicine. "We cure more patients than any other branch—except obstetrics, of course. Our patients are getting well all the time, and a lot more would get well if we had more people to treat them.

"As for making a living, there are ten jobs for every available man, and this will be true for years. We want you and we need you. You won't have to push your way into this specialty, as you must do in some of the others. Come on in with us and help us."

That is the way I used to talk to the young men—and I still do! A lot of young doctors have come in, of course, but psychiatry is growing and we are still looking for more doctors of the right kind. As medical science conquers other diseases, the progress seems to leave us with still more problems. We haven't done anything about feeble-mindedness yet. There are five million disabled alcoholics in this country. There are so many juvenile delinquents! And 80 per cent of the state mental hospitals are not giving their patients any treatment.

So we are still looking for young men, the right kind, young men with vision and idealism and zeal. I suspect we will always be looking for them. There will never be enough.

_11_ *You as a*

GENERAL

PRACTITIONER

BY JAMES T. COOK, JR., M.D.

GENERAL PRACTITIONER

Marianna, Florida

DR. JAMES T. COOK, JR.

Born: 1916, Porterdale, Georgia

Covington (Georgia) High School
Emory University: B.A., 1937
Emory University School of Medicine: M.D., 1941

Captain, United States Army: 1942–45

Intern, Emory University Hospital: 1941–42
General practice, Marianna, Florida: 1945—

Medical Director, Charity Heart Clinic

Florida Medical Advisory Committee for State Scholarships
Florida Physician's Placement Committee
State Council on Specialty Medicine
Chief of Medicine, Past Chief of Staff, Jackson Hospital
Jackson-Calhoun County Medical Society: Past president
Director, Florida Heart Association
Member, American Academy of General Practice
Director, Florida Academy: Past president
Medical Advisory Committee, University of Florida College of Medicine
Emory University Medical Alumni, President
Chairman, Florida Board of Parks and Historical Monuments
Director, Blue Shield of Florida

Recipient of the American Medical Association's General Practitioner of
the Year Award, 1960

As THE old Army song goes, "You'll never get rich." But you'll make a good living. You'll never be famous—but you'll be respected. You'll rarely get bored—it's too interesting.

A general practitioner, a generalist, a family doctor—which is the term preferred today—is not as some would have you believe, a Jack-of-all-trades and master of none. He is, indeed, involved in all the many facets of human illness and all the diseases that his patient population is heir to; but he does not know, and does not claim to know, all about every disease he sees or even some of those he treats.

A family doctor is one who offers, through scientific training and skills, continuing medical care for all members of the family.

To me, to many other family doctors, and to many people in these United States who are searching for medical care, this is the logical approach of the physician to the family. To offer this kind of care a doctor must be well-read and must continue his study year after year, always keeping up with the developments and advances in medicine.

He must be able to get along with people, particularly with the families he treats. He must be interested in them and conversant with their ways of living, their pleasures, their hobbies, their problems.

Finally, any good doctor, whether he is a specialist or a generalist, must realize that he has limitations, and recognize them. No man can possibly cope with all the illnesses that people have. If you encounter a patient with a condition beyond your capabilities, send that patient to a person who is expert in that particular field. It will be appreciated and you will not lose patients by doing this; they will come back to you.

My great-grandfather was a Civil War surgeon and his daughter, my grandmother, passed on to me some of his love of medicine. I knew from boyhood that I wanted to be a doctor and I entered the field of general practice because it was what I preferred. I could imagine no other field in which I would not feel myself limited. The only specialty I ever seriously considered was radiology. It is a respected branch of medicine, to be sure, and is scientifically interesting; but it lacks the continuing close contact with people which I find so stimulating in my practice.

I finished high school in Covington, Georgia, then went to Emory University in Atlanta. There I had what I thought was a tough break. At the end of my third academic year I was accepted into medical school, but the family funds were low because there were three of us in college at the same time and this was shortly after the depression.

Unable to see any way of going straight on through medical school, I decided to take my fourth year in college, then I would drop out of school and work for a while. Later I would come back to medical school.

This was a big disappointment to me, but it turned out to be one of the best breaks I ever had. In this fourth year in college I took all kinds of courses that otherwise I would have missed, particularly in the field of fine arts, philosophy, and literature. I wouldn't trade anything for those subjects. They stay with me now more than most of the courses I had before actually beginning medical training. This is particularly true of my special hobby, which is music.

About this time the family finances opened up and I was able to enter medical school immediately after I took my A.B. degree; but I will never regret my fourth year in college. What I learned then, I not only enjoy now, but I am better able to get along with people. I may bore my friends by whistling the major themes of the Beethoven symphonies, or a Mozart concerto, or even the leitmotif from the Nibelungenlied—but at least *I* get something out of it and it gives a kind of lilt to my living. I may sound somewhat sophomoric reciting Shelley, Browning, or Robert W. Service, but at least my patients don't think my head is so engulfed in medical clouds that I am unable to think with them about their illnesses, or talk with them about their problems.

I have worked in cotton mills and in business offices. I have supervised painters and carpenters. And I have my A.B. degree. So I believe I have a well-rounded education, but what I actually learned in all this was to communicate with all kinds of people in all walks of life. No matter how beautifully trained or how skillful a doctor may be, if he cannot communicate with his people, he will have an unsatisfactory practice. I can say from experience that most of my failures as a doctor, especially when the patient or his family got aggravated with me, have been due to failures in communicating properly.

As an example of this, one of the basic difficulties that confronts any physician arises when he cannot assimilate what his patient is telling him. They may have a common language but not a common understanding. It is then that he cannot do his work properly. Furthermore, any time he fails to make his patient understand what he is trying to tell him, either about his care, his diagnosis, his appointments, or anything else, his patient will not be satisfied and this failure in communication may end in the treatment's not being beneficial.

We in the medical world must take into account that we are salesmen, just as in other professions. If we aren't successful salesmen, both of ourselves and of our medical proficiency, people will not come to us. Any salesman who cannot make himself understood is a failure. No matter how good a technical job we as doctors do on our patients, or how much they may want to like us, if there is an undercurrent of misunderstanding, or a continuing lack of communication, then there will be unhappy patients who may not come back to us.

Education, in its broadest meaning, helps in this communicating. Reading, in particular, helps—whether Shakespeare or Perry Mason.

I digressed here to tell you this before we go on to medical problems, because I think the more general education you get, the happier man you will be and also the better doctor.

I am assuming that you who read this chapter have already decided upon one great step—you are going to be a doctor. At least, you *want* to be a doctor and you are now trying to decide what branch of medicine interests you most. I take it that you are considering, either slightly or in a serious way, general practice. Should I encourage you, or should I try to turn you in another direction?

I really don't know because I don't know what you want out of life, or out of the practice of medicine. I can only tell you the kind of life I lead and the kind of problems that general practitioners face, what is good and what is bad. The decision can then logically be yours, as it should be.

Several questions must be answered. First, is there a general need for family doctors? Yes, and a greater need than ever before. In my more-or-less rural community, I am continually faced with people who have moved from, or are moving to, some large city. Those coming here are pleased to find doctors who will treat the whole family, will respond to night emergencies when necessary, and will send them to a specialist when the occasion arises. Conversely, those who are moving away from a small town are worried about finding such doctors available where they are going.

It is curious to me why, with so many people and so many families wanting a family doctor, there has been a marked drop in the number of family physicians trained during the past two decades. This is true despite a steadily growing demand for such doctors. Fortunately this trend is now being reversed and we can look forward to an increasing number of family doctors in the future. Also, in passing it might be noted that the American Medical Association now has a declared policy of encouraging people to have a family doctor. This, of course, is also true of the American Academy of General Practice.

In preparing to be a family doctor, you will need all the graduate training you can possibly get. Exactly what that training should be, I cannot tell you, nor can anyone else give you a detailed answer. However, the demands on you in your training are indicated by the very nature of family practice. You must be competent in many fields and your training, therefore, cannot be limited. If you desire to restrict your training to areas which particularly interest you, then you might as well restrict yourself completely and go directly into the specialty which interests you most. In general practice you will be called upon in many fields and you must be prepared in each of them.

Even as I encourage you to broaden and extend your training, I must warn you about situations you may have to face. In some communities the activities of general practitioners are limited. You must therefore, even during your training, take into account the type of community in which you intend to practice. In some communities, for example, the staff of the community hospital does not allow the general practitioner to do orthopedics. In others he is not allowed to do surgery. In still others, he is permitted to do only simple obstetrics. It would be foolish to spend two years of your time in surgical training, or a prolonged time in orthopedics, then go to some community where you would be prevented from performing these services. This is a handicap that you should take into account during your training.

To realize the full situation, try to understand that even if you took a twelve-year residency, say three years each in surgery, medicine, pediatrics, and obstetrics, some hospitals would still refuse you privileges in the special fields mentioned. You would have to be "Board Certified" to achieve their staff privileges. Your degree of competence would have nothing to do with it, nor would they be willing to help you improve your degree of competence; the door would just be locked to you.

Once you know about these restrictions, you will probably prefer to go to some community where they do not prevail. There are more than enough openings in such places, for they are in the vast majority, and there is where I would go. The present custom in some communities of unduly restricting the privileges in hospitals is about to reverse itself, I believe; but before you go to a community, you should ascertain what staff privileges you can look forward to, and what increase in these privileges you can expect as you gain experience.

This, of course, leaves a question. What if you have no particular community in mind? What about your training? Then go ahead with no thought of restrictions and let your abilities, the services you can adequately perform, influence you later in your selection of a place to practice—after, of course, you have found out what limitations might be placed on you in that community.

I believe it pointless to debate the question of general practice against any of the specialties. Both are necessary and both are good ways to practice medicine. On some occasions the medical student or the intern gets the impression that he cannot practice good medicine as a family doctor. This unfortunate idea is just not true. You can practice the best medicine in the world, and do more good for more people as a family doctor than in any one of the specialties. To merit the title, a family doctor must be a good doctor. We are not only useful; we are essential.

Twenty-five years ago a child who had congenital heart disease, just had it; there was no particular treatment and most of them, perforce, died. Now surgery and antibiotics have made it possible to cure many of these children; but early recognition is important and the cure begins with the family doctor. He looks after these children, examines them regularly, and he must know about heart diseases, recognize them early, and understand the possibility of their correction. He must be a good cardiologist in order to be a good family doctor.

While I am on this subject, I would like to stress it—a good general practitioner *must* be a good cardiologist. When one thinks of the prevalence of cardiovascular disease in the aging population, he can more readily realize this. I have worked hard, and still work hard, on improving myself in this field. I have spent a great deal of time reading, consulting with specialists in cardiology, and more than once I have gone back to my old university for intensive postgraduate study in seminars arranged for practicing physicians.

If you don't know about this subject, and are fond of your patients, you can have some nerve-racking experiences when things go wrong. I remember several years ago when a young woman, a close friend of the family, with known congestive heart failure due to old rheumatic heart disease, had a Stokes-Adams attack, due to ventricular fibrillation. In the first attack I thought she had merely fainted, for she had not been feeling well. With the second—house calls both—I took her to the hospital. There I started her on Quinidine, and she kept passing out and having convulsions. I would pound her on the chest and she would come to, either because of, or in spite of, my treatment.

I called the chief of cardiology at my alma mater to ask his advice, and he told me to keep up what I was doing. This was before the days of defibrillators, and at this time Pronestyl (procaine amide) was a new drug. Actually, one of the main reasons for my calling was to find out if I should use it on her.

That night I sat by her bedside while she had thirty-seven convulsive attacks, and I thought she would die with each one of them. Early the next morning my old chief called to ask how she was getting along—this from two hundred and fifty miles away—and he and I decided to use Pronestyl intravenously under electrocardiographic monitoring. This brought her out of it.

She lived several years before moving to another city, where she subsequently died. I shall never forget the feeling of anguish that night, and the feeling of inadequacy, despite the fact that the consultant and I were doing the best that was known in that era of treatment. You, too, I assure you, will know the same anguish and the same sense of inadequacy.

Now to go ahead: Three decades ago a person with any of the various types of pneumonia was treated in a routine, uncomplicated manner, mostly requiring good nursing care. Today scientific advances have forced the family doctor to be well acquainted with the bacteriology of the disease, and the specific treatment of the various types of pneumonia. The same is true in the forms of cancer; in the multitude of surgically correctible diseases of the chest and abdomen; in the many complications of brain disease, brain tumor, and of brain infection.

I could go on about this, but the point is that any competent family physician must, at the very least, be on the alert for the disease that is curable by specific means. To be alert he must be familiar with its diagnosis. If the occasion arises he can send his patient to a specialist; but before he does this, the family doctor must be able to recognize the problem. Besides being a good cardiologist, he must, therefore, be a good "diagnostician," a good internist.

Then, too, most family doctors want to do obstetrics. It is a good way to build a practice and a good way to make friends with a family, for a healthy baby is welcome. It is sort of fun, too, to be able to walk out of the delivery room and tell a man he is a father, particularly when the man is a friend of yours. So what do you, as a general practitioner, need to know about obstetrics? I will tell you that in order to do OB, you will need to know a lot of OB, and to be able to apply it. In obstetrics, there is never any knowing what situation may confront you.

A few years ago Mrs. T. R. came to the hospital in early labor with her second baby. I had delivered the first a couple of years before, with ease. Now, with no warning, she suddenly began massive vaginal bleeding, so much so that in a few minutes she was in shock. The nearest specialist in obstetrics was over forty miles away and that was too far, not in distance but in time. Of course she had a complete placenta previa, and we gave her blood, did an immediate Caesarean, and saved both mother and baby.

I did nothing marvelous, but I, a family physician, did what had to be done. I could not have sent her to a specialist, she would have died on the way. Had I called a specialist to come to her, she would have been dead before he could get there. In a rural area, such as the one in which we live, all patients cannot travel forty to seventy miles to have their babies—babies sometimes come faster than that—and sometimes, too, a desperate situation arises. The family doctor must be ready to care for it and be capable of doing so.

Naturally you cannot expect to come out, after two or three years of training, and imagine that you can manage all that might come up. You will have to rely on the more experienced physicians in your community to help you when you get into trouble and until you can do better. I believe, though, that in most communities you can look to these senior physicians to abide by the precepts of the Hippocratic oath and do their best to assist you, doing whatever they can to advance your knowledge and training.

I have discussed cardiology, a little medicine, and obstetrics. How about pediatrics? Well, I think, of course, that the family doctor will want to care for his own babies, I mean the ones he has delivered. So he will have to know pediatrics. After all, it is just internal medicine practiced on babies, and if you are going to take care of families you will certainly want to take care of the children. Personally, I like this part of my practice.

You will have to know dermatology, too. You can help your patients a lot by being able to recognize the more common skin ailments. Also you will need to know when one is really an uncommon one, so as to know when to send the patient to a specialist.

Some people are advocating at least six months of psychiatric training for the family doctor. I don't have an opinion. You will certainly, however, have a lot of psychiatry to do. Every illness, from pregnancy to senility, has a psychogenic overlay, either mild or severe. One suggestion for you: be a good listener and don't give too much advice. Better to say nothing than too much.

Everyone expects the general practitioner to engage in a number of medical activities such as the ones I have already mentioned; but there is one that is debated, even argued in some medical circles. Should the general practitioner do surgery?

I think that he should and I do it. I am careful, however, to limit myself to those procedures in which I am competent, and know that I am competent. My graduate surgical training did not prepare me to be a fully competent surgeon in the more intricate procedures, but over a period of years I have acted as first assistant to a number of experienced men who have taken the greatest pains to prepare me for many surgical procedures. These are the procedures that I do, and I undertake no others.

I suggest that you do not hold to the old belief that any man who opens the abdomen must be able to perform any possible operative procedure upon the abdominal cavity. This just does not stand up as a fact. If a doctor is careful about his diagnostic efforts, he can be sure of what he will find—he will find, at most, one of several diseases. If he cannot satisfactorily perform on any of the diseases that he anticipates, he should not tackle the job.

I am in a position to have a strong opinion about what will

happen if a man follows these precepts. In several thousand surgical procedures performed by general practitioners at our local hospital, I have never seen a case that the operating surgeon could not handle satisfactorily. Of course we have referred many patients for surgical procedures that we could not perform, but the referral, in every instance—and I stress *every*—was made *before* the surgery, and not after an unsatisfactory opening and closure.

On many occasions we have referred patients to surgical specialists who have performed simple procedures which we could have performed ourselves; but the referral was because we were not absolutely certain that our diagnosis was correct, and we were concerned that we might encounter something beyond our abilities. Let me say to those young doctors who are going into general practice: If you get a decent amount of surgical training, and have the advantage of associating with senior physicians who will teach you and help you, there is no reason why you cannot learn to do a good amount of surgery. Furthermore, what you do can be done just as well as any other man could perform the same service for the patient.

Up to this point, I have been discussing the fitness of the general practitioner, if properly trained, to perform surgery. Emergency surgery, of course, can be quite a different matter and our rule of diagnostic certainty cannot then apply. In emergencies, I have performed surgery that I should not have had to do, and, except for the demands of the circumstances, I would not have done.

I remember a girl, a schoolteacher, who had been stabbed in the chest and head with an ice pick. She had fallen immediately unconscious and by the time she was brought to the hospital she was deteriorating rapidly, with obvious bleeding in the cranial cavity. Now I am not a neurosurgeon; but we opened her up, found the bleeding point, achieved hemostasis, and that woman is teaching again today. The nearest neurosurgeon, at the time she reached the hospital, was two hundred and fifty miles away. Without immediate surgery she would have been dead in less than an hour.

My confreres and I have done the same kind of emergency

operations on other occasions, and we lost one patient who died as we were opening his skull. The others also would have died if we had not attempted, and achieved, an operation for which, admittedly, we were not specifically trained. However, in such cases you are not tackling something you are sure you can do; you just have no choice.

I suppose that over the years we have saved a good many people by being able to do emergency surgery; I have no idea how many. But if we didn't do ordinary surgery day by day, if we didn't have an operating-room crew, and an anesthetist, we would have lost the majority of these emergency patients. Considering that we have done no people harm, and that we have done a lot of people a lot of good, I don't see how anyone could rightfully say that we general practitioners should not do any surgery.

Every once in a while in surgery, in addition to stimulus and satisfaction, we get a really unusual case. I suppose the most unusual one we have had was the fat man from the side show in our County Fair. He said he weighed 650 pounds (we could not weigh him), and he was brought to the hospital with acute appendicitis. He also had severe diabetes. The diagnosis was largely made on history, for palpating that massive abdomen was a futile procedure.

He wouldn't fit our operating table, for he hung too far over the sides. So we used a hospital bed, head reversed, with three extra mattresses, and we stood on a platform. He couldn't breathe lying flat, so we put him halfway on his left side and this was an added advantage for it allowed a great mass of that fat to fall over out of our way. In spite of this we had to make quite an excavation before we were able to get a very acute appendix out of the poor man. He had an uneventful recovery—and while I don't mean to be immodest, I do challenge anyone to say he has operated on a fatter man.

I have tried to answer the question: Should a general practitioner, if properly trained, do surgery? I believe that he should. Some very able men will disagree with this, but that is my answer and I will stick with it until I am proven wrong.

With what I have said about surgery, and about the other

varieties of practice within general practice, I hope that you have recognized the extent of your responsibility in getting all the training you can possibly get. You will need it.

In selecting the community where you want to practice, you should take into account a great many factors. One, as I have mentioned, is the local hospital. What is its standing, its equipment, its rules and regulations, its possible restrictions on you? What about the other physicians in the community? Will they aid you in times of difficulty and help you to improve your knowledge and abilities?

Beyond these professional questions, I would say that your main consideration is to find someplace where you and your wife would like to live. Some people prefer cities, some prefer the country, and some prefer the small towns in between. Wherever you go, look at the schools, the recreational facilities, the churches, and all the other things that go to make up family living. You needn't bother too much about earning a living. You can earn a living, and a reasonably good one, just about anywhere you want to go provided you are willing to work.

I would like to warn you now about one thing: it takes a very dedicated man to be the only doctor in a community. There are many small communities crying for doctors today. They are even building clinics and offering a lot of fringe benefits to attract physicians. I have been on the Physician Placement Committee of our state organization for many years, and I believe that most of these communities are not satisfactory places for a doctor. There are several reasons.

First, you are by yourself and this is a disadvantage. Second, if there were adequate people and money in that area they would not have to beg for a doctor. I know of several communities today that are trying to get a physician, but none of them could support one if he came. There are enough people, perhaps, but most of the people who could afford to pay if they had a serious illness would go to a larger facility for treatment and the poor local doctor would end up treating bad colds. Then, too, being the only doctor in a community makes it difficult for you to get the necessary time off for vacations, for recreation, and for the postgraduate study which is so important for every doctor.

Furthermore, these above-mentioned small facilities have sometimes caused the practicing of some pretty bad medicine— innocently of course. A community will build a clinic, or even a small hospital, and open it up with one doctor. He begins by being conscientious and doing exactly what he should do, taking care of what patients he is capable of handling and referring others to some larger facility. Before long the local fathers, and especially the hospital administration, start questioning him. What's the matter? The way things are going, what's the point in our having a hospital in our town? How are we going to pay for it if you keep sending patients off somewhere else? Eventually, in some cases, the pressure gets too tough and the physician starts doing things that he is not competent to do. The outcome is obvious, and I am sure that no young graduate wants to be caught in such a situation.

Undoubtedly there are isolated areas in this vast country of ours where the populace is large enough to support one physician, but is not large enough to support two. I believe, though, that such places are rare and that, wherever possible, medicine should be centralized in communities of reasonable size.

People forget that the major factor in the availability of a doctor today is not distance but time. A sick man in an area such as I live in, with good roads and plenty of automobiles, is only fifteen or twenty minutes from medical care no matter where he lives. Sick people within a large city may live within fifteen or twenty blocks of their physician, but they must contend with traffic, parking, et cetera, and the time spent in getting to the physician may be longer than if they lived fifteen miles from him in the country. With this element of time foremost in our minds, we might discount the problem of distance and think of medicine as being centralized in one community, and then another, each reasonably spaced from the next. In such an arrangement, the doctors could care not only for the people in the communities themselves, but all people in between. Such a plan, if carefully thought out and put into effect, would make unnecessary any one doctor's practicing alone in some out-of-the-way place. There may be areas where this could not be done, but they are probably few.

If you intend to practice in a small community where there are several doctors, or in a city where there are many, should you practice in a group or solo? You should first understand that there are various types of groups. One is made up of several physicians, sometimes including a general practitioner and with other doctors representing many specialities. This group is predicated on the idea that the patient can anticipate complete diagnostic and therapeutic covering in one medical organization, at a relatively reasonable cost. I have little knowledge of such groups and cannot advise you concerning them.

A second kind of group is made up of physicians who are all in similar practice—all general practitioners, for example. The idea of this group, I believe, is an ideal of medicine for it is organized so that the patient may have adequate medical coverage at all times, and the participating physicians may also have some free time for themselves, for vacations, study, recreation, and so on. The group may be closely knit, operating in one building and with shared facilities; or it may be more loosely organized. Economically, I understand, the close-knit groups work out well, and they certainly give what they are designed for: constant patient coverage.

Although I am a solo practitioner from most standpoints, I work in a group. The members have separate offices, send separate statements, and are financially independent of each other. However, we have an understanding that if at any time one physician is not available, his patients will be cared for by his confreres. It is understood, too, that these patients will be returned to him immediately on his return to practice, no matter how long he may have been away, whether hours or months.

I would certainly advise any young doctor to go into solo practice to begin with. I would also advise him to make friends with the older doctors in the community, caring for their patients when asked to do so, either when the senior doctor is in some emergency or for whatever reason he is not available. Then, if the young doctor is carefully ethical and returns all patients who have been referred to him in this way, he will breed good will both with the doctor and with the patients. People will begin to talk about him, saying that he is ethical and proficient; and his practice will grow.

At the beginning of your practice make all the house calls that you can. They take time and are unremunerative, but they make people like you.

Also, I would suggest that you be available. The best doctor in the world is no good to people when he can't be reached. Don't get the idea that practicing medicine is easy. A doctor, like a man in any other profession, has to stick to his job.

Now for a detail or two. Don't build an office to begin with. You do not know what kind of office you will eventually want. Rent or lease on a short-term basis, and do with the least possible expenditures until you are well settled. Don't forget that you need to learn about your traffic problems and your business problems.

It is unfortunate that doctors do not have training in the economics of medicine; the chiropractors do. I shudder to look at my original set of books. I set them up myself and this was a foolish thing to do. They proved, of course, to be completely unwieldy.

Many supply firms carry special types of books for physicians, but get an accountant to look these over and advise you how to adapt them to your particular situation. Have him set up your financial system for you. It will pay you in the long run and will also protect you from any potentially embarrassing moments with Uncle Sam who, I can promise you, will have a considerable interest in all that you collect.

A family doctor's standing with his patients is obvious; they have confidence in him and they trust him or they wouldn't come to him. In fact, herein lies the greatest satisfaction in being a family doctor. We have the respect, the love, and the gratitude of our patients. It is fine to deliver a baby for a family and have them happy over it, then a few years later maybe fix the child's collarbone, or perhaps remove his tonsils, or treat his pneumonia. Maybe check him and his little brother for Boy Scout camp. At the same time it is gratifying to have treated the mother during some illness and perhaps father for kidney stones.

So it goes, on and on through the whole family, year in and year out; usually successful, but sometimes not, and then there is the joining with them in some anguish or grief. You, the family doctor, are associated not only with their medical problems, but with their emotional problems as well. I had rather treat a whole family than any one person; it is more involved but it is more rewarding.

There is quite a compliment in being requested to act as the doctor for a family, and with it goes a tremendous responsibility. To agree to care for a family, with all its illnesses, year after year, is taking a serious load on one's shoulders. Some doctors don't like to assume such responsibility, and this has nothing to do with their competence; it is more an indication of their outlook on life and their philosophy of medicine. Such doctors should, and do, enter the various specialties.

We family doctors have to be self-confident, but we must constantly bolster that confidence with study. We must have courage, and implement that courage with self-respect and a faith beyond ourselves. In short, the family doctor must be good at all that is good in medicine. This is a great requirement, but it is possible to the man who is willing to devote himself completely to it.

What is the future of the family doctor? I cannot see how it can be anything but extremely bright. Everyone these days, both lay and medical, stresses the importance of the family doctor. The specialists tell me, and I believe them, that we are the backbone of American medicine. The general public believes in us and a recent survey on a nation wide scale, performed by disinterested survey teams, revealed that the most favorable and pleasant "image" of American medicine, to people at large, is the image of the family doctor. Since this is true, how can anyone possibly imagine that so important a portion of the medical profession can do anything but grow?

To me, being a family doctor is the ideal life. We are well paid financially and further paid in gratitude. We are respected by our medical colleagues and wanted and loved by our patients. Certainly I can be replaced, but my patients—most of them— think I cannot, and this gives a mighty good feeling to any man.

12 *You*

IN PATHOLOGY;
IN CLINICAL IN-
VESTIGATION;
IN CANCER RESEARCH

BY SIDNEY FARBER, M.D.
PROFESSOR OF PATHOLOGY
Harvard Medical School at The Children's Hospital and
DIRECTOR OF RESEARCH
The Children's Cancer Research Foundation

DR. SIDNEY FARBER

Born: 1903, Buffalo, New York

University of Buffalo: B.S., 1923
Harvard Medical School: M.D., 1927
Suffolk University: D.Sc. (Hon.), 1960
Boston University: D.Sc. (Hon.), 1961
Providence College: D.Sc. (Hon.), 1961
University of Ghent: M.D. (Hon. Causa), 1962

Member of the Faculty, Harvard Medical School, and of Staff, The Children's Hospital, 1927—
Chairman, Division of Laboratories and Research, Children's Medical Center, 1946—
Pathologist-In-Chief: The Children's Hospital, 1947—
Director of Research: The Children's Cancer Research Foundation, 1948—
Professor of Pathology, Harvard Medical School at The Children's Hospital, 1948—

Member: National Advisory Cancer Council, 1953–57, 1962—
Chairman: Cancer Chemotherapy National Committee, 1955—

THE PRACTICE of modern medicine and the conduct of medical research both make use of the laboratory. This chapter will be devoted to a consideration of three aspects of the vast pattern formed by the many disciplines and sciences from which the field of medicine is fashioned. These three are Pathology, Clinical Investigation, and Cancer Research. All make fundamental contributions to the care of the patients and to the prevention of disease, and all make use of the laboratory. Here are challenges to meet the desires of the most courageous. Here the young doctor or scientist may find training to prepare him for a lifelong dedication to his chosen work.

Since the laboratory is the seldom-seen part in the practice of medicine, and since its significance is comparatively little realized, let me dwell on its importance for a moment, citing a statement made almost a century ago, in 1878, by Claude Bernard, the great French physiologist: "In my opinion, medicine does not end in hospitals, as is often believed, but merely begins there. In leaving the hospital, a physician, jealous of the title in its scientific sense, must go into the laboratory; and there, by experiments on animals, he will seek to account for what he has observed in his patients, whether about the action of drugs or about the origin of morbid lesions in organs or tissues."

I suggest, therefore, that we now go into the laboratory, and there concern ourselves first with pathology.

Pathology is one of the largest disciplines in all medicine, and still serves as the foundation of clinical medicine and surgery. The word has its derivation from *pathos* (pain, suffering), and *logos* (study). So broad are its interests that it has been described not as a single science, but rather as a mosaic of sciences. It draws freely upon the technics and bodies of knowledge in the sciences of physics, the several kinds of chemistry, and biology.

The pathologist is, first of all, a medical doctor. Ordinarily, though, he does not treat the patient; nor does he operate on the living. His field is concerned, primarily, with diagnosis, research, and teaching. Pathology is important also in fields other than medicine, as in botany, zoology, or parasitology.

It may be of interest to discuss the several careers which may grow out of an initial preparation in pathology. The university or hospital pathologist prepares himself for his task optimally by serving, after graduation from medical school, as an intern for at least a year in either medicine or surgery. He then works in a hospital department of pathology for at least three years. In the hospital he may add another year in the laboratories of clinical pathology, where examinations of many different kinds are made on blood, sputum, urine, spinal fluid, specimens removed from areas of inflammation and other materials removed for the purpose of verifying or ascertaining a diagnosis, or furnishing information which may aid in the making of the correct diagnosis. Here the technics of chemistry, bacteriology and laboratory studies in the blood (hematology) are employed in the making of precise measurements.

The pathologist may choose to spend a part of his professional activity, or all of it, in the clinical laboratories. Most of the time in training, however, is devoted to what was known in the past as "pathologic anatomy," or "morbid anatomy," terms which today are rarely employed. The work of the young pathologist includes the performance of post-mortem examinations, or autopsies, and the examination of all tissues removed from the living patient by the surgeon (surgical pathology).

Modern medicine properly begins with the institution of postmortem examinations systematically performed and characterized for their thoroughness and objectivity in description. Although it was not until the nineteenth century that the autopsy assumed a position of major importance in medicine, postmortem examinations were performed much earlier. It was during a plague in Italy, in 1286, that a physician of Cremona opened many bodies to discover the cause of the epidemic. Autopsies were performed with regularity before anatomic dissection had been instituted, a presumptive interest in the abnormal explained by the opinion, then prevalent, that normal anatomy had been established in the work of Galen, centuries before. (The performance of an autopsy must not be confused with anatomic dissection, which is concerned only with the normal structure and relationships of the various parts, organs, and structures of the body. The technics employed and the purposes are quite different.)

The autopsy is essentially a surgical procedure carried out after death. (The word means literally to view, or examine for oneself.) The autopsy begins with a complete examination of all the organs and structures of the body and the cranial vault, and as much of the skeleton as may be viewed. The immediate purpose is to reveal and demonstrate congenital and acquired abnormalities and gross anatomic changes; to explain mechanical problems noted during life, such as obstruction to the normal functions of the intestine, the lungs, or the kidneys; and to furnish material for further study by microscopic, bacteriologic, or chemical methods. A further aim is the determination of the nature of the disease processes and, if possible, the establishment of the cause or mechanism of death.

The purpose of the autopsy is not achieved until every attempt is made to explain clinical signs and symptoms noted during the last illness, in addition to any deviations from normal noted during the entire life of the patient. The results of all observations, both gross and microscopic, and of further chemical and bacteriologic studies, must be recorded in an accurate and objective manner in permanent form and made available to the attending physicians, to medical students as part of their training, and to other pathologists for the purposes of adding to their total knowledge.

The great Morgagni (1682–1771) wrote a monumental work on the seats and causes of diseases. This marked him the founder of pathologic anatomy. Through the years since that time, the importance of the autopsy has grown. It now includes more than mere dissection of the dead body for the purpose of ascertaining the cause, seat, or nature of a disease. Broader implications lead to a consideration of the information it yields to the relatives of the deceased, and to the state. It was in the late fifteenth century that Bernard Tornius, a physician of Florence, recommended that an autopsy be performed when the son of a high official died. His purpose was to discover if the disease was of hereditary character, so that he might prescribe more intelligently for the other children of the family. Today, this consideration represents one of the most important purposes of the autopsy, particularly because the great advances in genetics justify the hope that inborn errors of metabolism or hereditary disturbances may be one day controlled chemically, or even corrected.

The interest of the state in the post-mortem examination lies in the information given by the autopsy concerning the exact cause of unexpected death, of the mechanism of death by violence or accident, or the precise cause of death when infectious disease of unknown nature may mark the starting point for an epidemic in a community, or the spread to other countries.

The forensic pathologist (medical-legal pathologist, or coroner) is a pathologist whose main responsibilities are concerned with the law. Special technics and fields of knowledge characterize this specialty of pathology, but the expert begins with broad training in pathology after his medical-school studies have been completed. This is a field which combines the talents and training of the physician, the pathologist, the lawyer, and the detective. The demand of the medical-legal pathologist's work takes him from his laboratory and classroom into public life, where he must live under constant public scrutiny. The contributions of such men to the establishment of guilt or innocence and to law enforcement are recognized. They are charged with the responsibility of evaluation of the role of accidents, violence, violations of the law in the causation of death, and must, in addition, attempt to determine the cause of death when no diagnosis has been made during life, or when death is sudden or unexpected.

The place of pathologic anatomy, which is concerned mainly with the post-mortem examination and surgical pathology, remains of *absolute* importance throughout the history of medicine. It can never become obsolete as a field of importance to the advancement of medicine, so long as there are diseases which are manifested by alterations in the structure of the body. Since pathologic anatomy represents but one part of the field of pathology as a whole, its relative position in the medical world may fluctuate, depending upon the discovery through basic sciences of new methods of approach. The application of these new discoveries and technics of research to the problems recognized by the pathologist make constant the progress of the science of pathology.

Now, a word about the hospital pathologist and the practice of pathology. Regulations governing the accreditation of hospitals make mandatory the study of every piece of tissue removed by a surgeon from the human body by a skilled, properly trained pathologist, who has passed the Specialty Board, as well as medical licensure examinations. This regulation is designed primarily for the protection of the patient, and constitutes an independent control of the accuracy of diagnosis and the correctness of treatment.

During the operation, the surgeon leans heavily upon the pathologist before removal of an organ, or a part of the body, such as a limb, for reasons of a suspected cancer. Whenever there is any question of malignancy of the tumor, the pathologist is asked to examine a small representative sample of the tumor, before any part or organ is removed. Such an examination can be performed within a few minutes by the expert pathologist with the aid of rapid technics of freezing the tissue, cutting of thin sections, staining and examination under the microscope. The survival of the patient frequently depends upon his decision. The practicing pathologist also is a valued consultant at the bedside or in the examining room, particularly before operation when the question of cancer is raised, or when a rare disease or bizarre manifestation of a commoner ailment creates problems in diagnosis.

Almost thirty years ago, when I tried to assess the requirements which were then imposed upon the pathologist, I used the following words: "The pathologist of today must be proficient in the various divisions of anatomy and embryology; he must dedicate years of activity to the routine laboratory in the acquisition of an adequate knowledge of pathologic anatomy; he must recognize problems at the autopsy, and investigate them or cause them to be investigated by bacteriologic, physiologic, or chemical means. He must act as guide and as consultant to the clinicians in the solutions of their routine problems; he must maintain a broad view over the whole of medicine, and keep close connection with progress in the basic sciences and in the clinical fields. He must incorporate into his work new methods developed in other disciplines, and collaborate with the specialist in related lines of endeavor when a combined attack is indicated. He must fulfill the final obligation of spreading, by spoken and written word, what he has learned through the privilege of his position."

Ideally, the pathologist is a devoted physician, a scholar whose zest for continuing study is never dulled, and a man whose deep interest in the welfare of the patient is manifested also by his desire to teach not only medical students, but also doctors, throughout their years of medical practice. His range of interests and scientific curiosity may cause him to create research programs of immediate practical importance to the patient; or, at the same time, the extent of his scientific concern may cause him, as a great pathologist of the past once phrased it, "to investigate the reaction of living things—from unicellular to man—to injurious agents."

It may be said that no research today, in any of the many disciplines or subdivisions of medicine, can be carried out without some use of the technics employed and developed by pathologists or their approach to the problems of disease. Certainly, it was not until the autopsy was developed to its full by Rokitansky (1804–1878) in Vienna, and Virchow (1821–1902) in Berlin, that medicine was able to break from the speculative thinking common at the time, from which emanated complex classifications of disease, created in the fertile brains of nonobserving thinkers, and which were wholly without basis in observation or experimental fact.

The pathologist begins his examinations with a careful study of the clinical record, and discussions with the attending doctors concerning the nature of the problems to be solved by further in-

vestigations. With standards of cleanliness and orderly procedures comparable to those in the surgical operating room, he
proceeds to a detailed examination, following the technical
regulations and sequences laid down by Rokitansky and Virchow
in the middle of the last century. With respect for the dead and
in a spirit of scientific objectivity, he conducts his examination of
the body and of its contents in a period from two to four hours.
Study with the aid of bacteriological and chemical technics, and
of microscopic sections especially prepared from every important
organ and tissue in the body may take days and even weeks for
completion. Inoculation of mice, guinea pigs, or rabbits, or utili-
zation of specialized technics of tissue culture or virology, may
convert the initial examination into a valuable piece of laboratory
investigation.

There are no "routine" examinations and in every well-organ-
ized department of pathology there are experiences which could
be used to illustrate the enormous number of contributions to the
saving of life and to medical progress which have emanated from
the deadhouse. From past centuries comes the motto so often
found on the walls of the great post-mortem rooms of Europe:
Mortui vivos docent. (The dead teach the living.) As an example
of this, there are these facts, included in the records of a medical
school hospital department of pathology of twenty-five years ago,
concerning a problem which arose with little warning.

On the Saturday of Labor Day week end in 1938, an unfortunate boy of eight years died after an acute illness of only three
days' duration. This had been characterized by very high fever
and by some form of encephalitis—an involvement of his brain
by an acute infectious disease. Examination of the child and
study of his spinal fluid during his brief stay in the hospital did
not provide a scientific diagnosis. It was known that large numbers of horses had died during the previous month, and their
deaths had taken place just a few miles from the home of this
child. They had died of a disease called equine encephalitis, but
this disease was not known to affect man. At the time, two forms
of this virus disease were recognized and were called, because of
their geographic distribution, the Eastern and the Western forms.

The careful post-mortem examination, made with the usual

precautions to protect the pathologists and their assistants from infections, and to prevent spread of possibly infectious material, revealed a widespread inflammatory destruction of the brain. Pieces of the brain were removed for examination under the microscope, and specimens were taken for study with the aid of many different bacteriological technics, to see whether bacteria might be the cause of the disorder. Tissue was also taken for inoculation into Swiss white mice, which were known to be sensitive to a number of different kinds of viruses.

It is the custom of scientists and doctors to mobilize all knowledge and abilities in behalf of patients. Accordingly, portions from the brain were sent by air mail to a virus laboratory in another city, where scientists were conducting a large-scale investigation of obscure forms of encephalitis. This was done to take advantage of their experience and to furnish independent parallel studies to provide as rapid a diagnosis as possible.

Within three days, the inoculated mice showed signs of the same kind of brain damage found in the child. When autopsies were performed on them, the microscopic changes were identical. The absence of any evidence of bacterial infection, and the nature of the microscopic changes produced in the brains, indicated the probability of a virus infection. Now, because of the suspicion that the horse disease might indeed have been passed in some way to this child, it was decided to make an immediate test of this possibility.

It was known that a scientist in a large pharmaceutical research laboratory some three hundred miles away was perfecting a means of protecting horses against the virus of horse encephalitis. Telephone communication disclosed quickly that he had on hand guinea pigs which had been protected—some against the Eastern form of equine encephalitis, others against the Western form of the disease. Prepared animals of both kinds were sent by air, and these were inoculated with tissue from the brain of the child. Within five days, the animals protected against Western encephalitis were dead. Those protected against the Eastern form of the disease appeared to be perfectly well, and remained so.

Thus, within fifteen days after the death of a child with a disease of unknown causation, post-mortem examination and subsequent laboratory investigations disclosed the exact diagnosis of the Eastern form of equine encephalitis. Proof was thus at hand that a disease, hitherto regarded as occurring only in horses, could affect man as well. The course was now charted for further research by scientists to determine how the disease is spread from horses to humans, and from horse to horse, where the virus resides between epidemics, and how the disease can be eradicated or prevented.

Besides what I have already told you about pathology, it must be understood that the pathologist is concerned with the *science* of pathology, as well as with the *practice* of his specialty. After his years of training, he may decide to devote his major energies to the science rather than to the practice.

In the science of pathology he will make use of exactly the same tools as those used by the research biochemist, or physiologists, since these are derived from the sciences basic to medicine—chemistry, physics, and biology. In his research, the pathologist may become further identified as an expert in any one of many disciplines which fall within the broad definition of a study of disease. Today he may work with chromosomes and define, with the technics of the geneticist, abnormalities in chromosome structure, number, or position. He may employ spectroscopic or chemical technics for the identification of precise nucleic acids, of greatest importance to the nucleus or the cytoplasm of the cell.

He may devise methods of growing virus in tissue culture or in special biological systems. He may attack the age-old problem of cancer by the study of minute chemical and structural changes within the once normal cell grown in tissue culture, when physical or chemical cancer-producing stimuli are brought to bear upon the cell in carefully measured amounts.

He may become expert with various kinds of microscopes which carry the descriptive terms "light," "interference," "electron," "infrared," "ultraviolet," or "phase" microscope. For the solution of his problems he may use the technics of the biophysicist and study the structure of protein within a virus, or of a muscle or any other kind of cell, with the aid of the X-ray diffraction apparatus. He may employ nonharmful bacteria grown in a medium of known composition under constant conditions which will permit the identification and measurement of growth-promoting chemicals, such as vitamins or specific nucleic acids.

He may study disease of trees, grass, birds, or horses. He may even attack problems of phylogenesis, from the viewpoint of a pathologist. My own teacher, the late, great S. Burt Wolbach suggested, for example, that the adaptation of marine creatures to the terrestrial conditions might be regarded as a result of eons of response to nonlethal injuries in myriads of survivors.

As I told you earlier, here are challenges and questions to meet the desires of the most courageous, to test the intellect and try the energy of the most industrious and restless of scientists. Young men and women may find answers, and these answers themselves will ask questions—until the investigator is completely enmeshed in the enthralling science of pathology.

What opportunities for you are there in pathology? There is a notable shortage of competent pathologists and the reason is not so much in the lack of candidates, as in the increasing demand for pathologists. In the rapid improvement of medical care in hospitals in all parts of the country, particularly in the last fifteen years, every hospital now requires the services of a pathologist for the provision of good medical care. Indeed, the Joint Commission on the Accreditation of Hospitals will not accredit any hospital that does not have a pathologist on its staff to provide essential diagnostic services, or an arrangement by which the services of a pathologist are immediately available.

In further regard to the need for pathologists, it should be pointed out that the number of positions open to them in research programs in medical schools, hospitals, and research institutions has increased enormously. There are only some 4,500 pathologists in the United States, and there are a good many more vacancies than this to be filled.

Clinical investigation is the second of the three aspects of medicine, all centered in the laboratory, with which we are concerned in this chapter.

The challenge of investigation, of all medical research, carries special appeal to young men and women who are born with the need to find explanations for poorly understood phenomena. Such people simply cannot accept authority without proof. There is also a kind of doctor who is possessed of this quality, and, in addition, he is so constituted that he cannot use the word *incurable*. It is clear to him that what was incurable yesterday may be curable today, on the basis of the acquisition of new knowledge.

For generations, the doctor faced with the problem of mental retardation, disseminated cancer, or serious congenital malformations, such as those of the great vessels of the heart, found nothing in his armamentarium to alter the prognosis of such "incurable" disease. Malformations of the heart and great vessels have been recognized and described after death for a few hundred years, but were regarded as museum monstrosities and not clinical entities susceptible to adequate treatment. Causative factors were not understood any better than the explanation given in King Lear that "good wombs have borne bad sons." Certainly there was no hope of repairing such abnormalities, even if they could be recognized with accuracy during life.

But all this has been changed in the last twenty-five years, not by one man alone, but rather by doctors and scientists of many different kinds and backgrounds. The story of this tremendous achievement began in the pathology laboratory, with the precise anatomical description of the nature of the abnormality, its exact location, and variations, and the explanations of what went wrong at what stage in the embryological development of these structures. Post-mortem examinations furnished the necessary opportunity for the imaginative surgeon to make the necessary dissection, measurements, and observations. He saw, in these "incurable" conditions, a challenge which needed to yield to skillful and courageous surgical intervention.

Such an accomplishment, however, had to wait for development of several different kinds. The advent of the sulfonamides and, later, the antibiotics, made possible the control and prevention of infection when the thorax was opened. Discoveries in the field of anesthesiology produced anesthetic agents and technics borrowed from the laboratories of chemistry, pharmacology, and experimental physiology. These made it possible safely to open the thorax, and so work directly on the heart. And finally, the skillful introduction of catheters into large blood vessels in the arm or in the neck gave the physician and surgeon the opportunity of examining the heart and great vessels under X ray. Accurate diagnosis of the exact nature of the defect could thus be made before operation.

The first operation of this kind was performed on a child in 1938, and consisted in obliterating a short, thick artery connecting the pulmonary artery and the aorta—the *ductus arteriosus*. This structure is normal in the fetus but is closed, normally, during the act of birth. When it remains open after birth, it constitutes an important hazard to the patient.

The success of this first operation encouraged more daring attempts to correct abnormalities within the heart itself, and there are today teams of surgeons, physicians, radiologists, pathologists, and both laboratory and clinical investigators, who devote their major energies to devising new technics for the diagnosis and correction of congenital malformations of many different kinds. These would have been regarded as incurable just a short time ago. The next step, of course, must be the *prevention* of these abnormalities, since only prevention can make treatment unnecessary. Investigators of totally different backgrounds are at work. Their accomplishments already give promise that this goal one day may be reached.

When I was a second-year medical student, an assistant professor at Harvard Medical School, Dr. George R. Minot, gave my class a clinical demonstration in which he referred to a patient forty-five years of age, whom we had just seen in the patient's room. The man looked healthy and in the prime of life. He has stayed very much in my memory, for he resembled my father. I will never forget Dr. Minot's quiet words: "This man has pernicious anemia. He will not live more than six months."

Nor will I ever forget the lecture given by Dr. Minot, only two years later, when I was a fourth-year student. He took a package of cigarettes from his pocket and said, "A piece of liver no larger than this will keep a patient with pernicious anemia healthy and well, indefinitely."

Dr. Minot's own life had been saved, a short time before, when the first recently discovered insulin had been brought to Boston and administered in time to alter the severe course of his diabetes. While diabetes was not cured by insulin, nor pernicious anemia by the administration of liver, yet in both cases health was restored and survival greatly prolonged by successful treatments, each of which was discovered before the exact cause of the disease was known. Of greatest importance, of course, was the fact that the word "incurable" could then be removed from association with the names of these two disorders. Once the threat to the lives of these patients was removed or postponed, opportunity was afforded clinical investigators and laboratory scientists to determine the precise mechanisms involved in the production of the disorders and to search, too, for means of their prevention.

At this point in our discussion, it should be pointed out that medical research is not limited to research done by medical men alone. One of the most important results of the deep concern of private citizens, voluntary health associations, and the federal government with the advancement of medical research in the past fifteen years has been the attraction of large numbers of Ph.D.'s into this field. Furthermore, there has been an extension of research, which is of great importance to medicine, into the departments and subdivisions of physics, chemistry, and biology, in the colleges, universities, and technical schools throughout the country.

A most valuable partnership has developed between medical doctors and Ph.D.'s who have spent years in special training in the basic sciences. It is not at all unusual to find Ph.D.'s working side by side with medical doctors in the laboratories immediately associated with research wards. Indeed, it is heartening to realize that many of the great medical discoveries in recent years have come from men who hold the Ph.D. degree, such as John F. Enders, who, with Thomas Weller and Frederick Robbins, grew the virus of poliomyelitis in tissue culture. This discovery made possible the well-known polio vaccines of Salk and Sabin. We can mention, too, the discovery of streptomycin, one of the first of the truly important antibiotics, by Selman Waksman when he was Professor of Soil Bacteriology in the Agricultural School of Rutgers University.

It should be further pointed out that support for large numbers of careers in medical research is being provided by both federal and private appropriations for men with either the Ph.D. or M.D. degree. I should mention here that it is not uncommon for a man to take his medical degree and then return to the laboratory, as is the case, for example, with two distinguished professors in the sciences at Harvard College. Their contributions—the one in biology and the other in physical chemistry—have been of real importance in the advancement of medical research, as well as in their own specialties.

The laboratories in a teaching and research hospital, and in a medical school today, are no different from those in a great institute of technology, or in the colleges, universities, or special research institutes. The Ph.D., therefore, finds the hospital or medical school no alien environment and he takes his place with the M.D. as an important and respected colleague in medical research, not only contributing to the advancement of medicine but also finding a very satisfying and rewarding career for himself.

The combined efforts of these doctors and scientists, during the past fifteen to twenty years, have brought about the introduction into clinical medicine of large numbers of chemicals, hormone analogues, antibiotics, and extracts of natural substances, such as those of roots and other botanical substances. This era of clinical pharmacology began with the discovery of the sulfonamides in 1935 by Dogmagk for the control of some of the bacterial diseases.

The previous two decades had been characterized by what was called "therapeutic nihilism," but there now entered into clinical medicine the scientific methodology and critique which caused a revulsion against the long years of treatments of *symptoms* rather than the actual *causes* of disease. Such treatment of symptoms had consisted usually in the use of a number of ingredients in every prescription, some of which were inert, and a great bulk without specific value. The discovery of a chemical treatment for syphilis by Paul Erlich at the turn of the century gave practical meaning to the new term "chemotherapy," which he coined to imply the use of a chemical, not to counteract symptoms, but rather to act against the precise cause of disease within the affected cell. During, and shortly after the Second World War, success in the manufacture of penicillin, along with the discovery of other antibiotics, and the perfection of sulfonamides, produced a great reduction in deaths caused by many infectious diseases. The age of chemotherapy had arrived.

With the discovery that some forms of leukemia and cancer could be controlled by hormones and by chemicals, the hope that chemical agents could be found which could control, destroy, or even prevent the many forms of cancer was given further support. Also, important improvements in the control of some forms of mental disease by chemical agents, and the improvement in health of many patients with high blood pressure by chemical means, intensified research efforts in all fields of medicine for the discovery of specific forms of chemotherapy.

These discoveries of the past, however, all of them vital as they are, are now looked on as only prelude. Infinitely greater discoveries lie waiting in the laboratories today, and will be there tomorrow, for young men and women to come and point them out and name them.

The third subject of our discussion has to do with cancer research.

There are so many kinds of training which a doctor may select, if he intends to devote himself to a career in the field of cancer. He may be a surgeon, a physician, a radiotherapist, a hematologist (who is a physician or pathologist interested particularly in the study of the blood and bone marrow), or a pathologist interested primarily in the rendering of expert diagnostic opinions to help the surgeon.

There is such a vast field of knowledge concerning cancer today that it is impossible for any one man to be an authority on all aspects of the problem. Cancer may involve any organ or tissue of the body and, in its course, mimic most of the known diseases at one time or another. To combat it, there must be specialists of all kinds engaged in research and treatment of its multiple forms.

One of the most rapidly developing fields of clinical cancer research is concerned with the application of chemicals which may either arrest or destroy cancer which has grown beyond the reach of the technics of surgery or radiotherapy. The practice of chemotherapy of cancer calls for men with a knowledge of pathology of tumors and an intelligent understanding of organic chemistry, biochemistry, the mechanism of action of chemical compounds, and the danger and prevention of toxicity produced by the new chemicals. Such men literally must have one foot in the laboratory and one on the ward.

The research programs which make possible the discovery of new anticancer chemicals are in the main, and with good reason, in the hands of men with Ph.D. training. New chemical compounds are synthesized by organic chemists. The mechanism of action in test-tube systems, or in the intact animal in the laboratory, is studied by men with training in physiology, biochemistry, or experimental pathology. Studies on the toxicity and further aspects of mechanism of action are made by pharmacologists who may be Ph.D.'s, or medical doctors with special training in pharmacology or biochemistry.

Other fields of cancer research today are being developed by scientists who may be either M.D.'s or Ph.D.'s with special knowledge of and interest in embryology, in any one of the subdivisions of biology, or in cytology, which is really a branch of experimental pathology. Also, great strides have been made by the application of technics used by virologists in the search for evidence of a possible virus causation of any one of the many forms of cancer in man. The virologists who are making the greatest progress in this field of cancer research are those who are expert in the technics of the experimental pathologist, with ability to manipulate cells in tissue culture and in the experimental animal, and who are able to add to this qualification an expertness in the technics of modern nucleic acid chemistry.

We may say that there is really no single kind of scientist or doctor who conducts cancer research today. A broad training in experimental pathology, which includes the various subdivisions of biology (such as endocrinology, genetics, virology, bacteriology, and cytology), or expertness in pharmacology, or in the various kinds of chemistry including organic, biological or physical chemistry—all of these, or any of them, will open the door to cancer research whether it be conducted in a college, a cancer institute, a medical school, or teaching hospital. Whether such scientists ever see a patient with cancer, or deal with human cancer in any form, or whether they acquire knowledge concerning either clinical or pathological aspects of cancer, their contributions can be of fundamental importance to progress in cancer research.

Now let us consider more specifically some of the programs in which scientists, or properly prepared medical doctors, are working today:

It has been known since the work of Ellerman and Bang in 1908 that a virus was the cause of a cancer of the blood and blood-forming tissues of the chicken, called "leukemia" or "fowl leukosis." Also, somewhat more than fifty years ago, the distinguished scientist, Dr. Peyton Rous, of the Rockefeller Institute, was able to show that a virus was the cause of a form of cancer in the chicken, which bears his name—the Rous sarcoma.

A number of important discoveries concerning the relationship of viruses to animal tumors followed. However, many unsuccessful efforts were devoted to the application of these technics for demonstration of viruses in cancer removed from human beings. It was not until several years after the end of the Second World War that an important forward step was made by Ludwik Gross, a Polish surgeon, who had worked for a time at the Pasteur Institute in Paris. During the war, however, he served in the American Army, and, afterward, remained in the United States. In his laboratories in the Veterans Administration Hospital, in the Bronx, he was able to construct a totally new experimental approach to the relationship of viruses to leukemia in the mouse. By injecting material from the leukemic tumor of one mouse to newborn mice, he was able to show that this form of cancer could be passed from tumor extract from which all cells had been removed.

This notable achievement was followed a few years later by an expansion of the work of Gross, carried out in the National Institutes of Health by two young women, one a pathologist, Dr. S. E. Stewart, and the other a biologist, Dr. B. E. Eddy. Using Gross's technic, with refinements of their own, they were able to show that cell-free material derived from a leukemic mouse, and presumably containing virus, when injected into other mice could produce many different kinds of cancer in many organs. This discovery emphasized the importance of the recipient of the viral infection and raised an important question concerning the possible single identity of the chemical components of the virus which might be responsible for inciting many different forms of cancer under these experimental conditions.

Pathologists now are working actively in many laboratories in the world in an attempt to demonstrate evidence of a relationship between viruses and human cancer. It is probable that such a relationship will be established since it is unlikely that one biological law will operate for animals, and another for man. If this is accomplished, it will be on the basis of a totally new conception of a virus. Converging upon the same question, at the same time, are the research programs of scientists who created them with different goals in mind.

The nucleic acids within the virus are in the center of the problem, and these nucleic acids, known by letters which are familiar to high-school and college students today, DNA and RNA, are the center of attention in the field of chemotherapy of cancer, and also in exciting research in genetics. In this rapidly expanding field of research, attempts are made to construct new chemical compounds which will interfere with the formation of essential nucleic acids in the cancer cell without interfering with the growth of normal cells. It is possible that when sufficient knowledge of the cancer cell, and of the normal cell, and of the virus is at hand, the means of preventing cancer, as well as destroying it, may be found to reside in the identical chemical substance or pathway.

Here is a field worthy of the imagination of the doctor or the scientist. It presents a challenge to his skill in creating research models to test new hypotheses which can be constructed on the basis of new chemical information coming today from research laboratories in medical schools, hospitals, research institutes, and universities in many parts of the world. This is the second direction of important cancer research in *chemotherapy*.

Today the largest program of voluntary co-operative research in the history of medicine is going on in this country, with important communications with all other cancer research programs in other parts of the world. Several different technics are being employed in the initial search for cancer-destroying chemicals. There is the rational approach which underlies the making of new chemical compounds on the basis of still incomplete information concerning the chemical differences between the normal cell and the cancer cell. There is another method which was inspired by finding that antibiotics derived from micro-organisms in the soil, similar to penicillin, could destroy cancer experimentally produced in the mouse and also some forms of cancer in man. No rational approach is possible here, but advantage can be taken of the vast amount of knowledge concerning the biology of these micro-organisms and the chemical technics required to produce antibiotics from them. More than 40,000 of these crude antibiotic filtrates are studied for anticancer effects each year in the national program of the National Cancer Institute. A similar search is being made for the extracts of materials found in nature, such as roots and other botanical materials. And, finally, there is testing of large numbers of known chemical compounds from the shelf of the chemist which are selected, not at random, but in accordance with a technic which has been termed "enlightened empiricism."

From programs such as these some thirty chemical compounds have emerged which are actually in use in the treatment of cancer in the human being. Some of these are of value in prolonging life and relieving pain. In addition, a few forms of cancer actually may be destroyed to an extent that patients are apparently well five years or more after the beginning of the treatment of what was considered an incurable disease. Clinical investigators in numbers far greater than those available today are needed for the precise studies on humans which must be carried out in the evaluation of new anticancer chemicals. Similar needs have been created by this vast program for chemists, biologists, experimental pathologists, pharmacologists, statisticians, and experts in virology.

A third direction of research in cancer concerns the investigation of materials of many different kinds to determine if they cause cancer. Specific concern for public health lies in the materials present in smog, and in the air of any industrial community. We may mention, too, the need for rapid and accurate methods for the demonstration of dangerous products of fall-out. The great increase in one exposure of artificial materials in food and in our daily life makes mandatory the study of such substances for cancer-producing properties. This is a field of experimental pathology, with strong emphasis on chemistry, biology and physics.

Finally, one of the most difficult but essential fields of research in cancer is that concerned with our need for a diagnostic test to disclose the presence of cancer when it is small and before it has damaged important organs or tissues, or spread to other parts of the body. The list of failures in the search for a diagnostic test is long and disheartening.

What is needed is a diagnostic test which can be performed on a small amount of blood or other body fluid, at little expense and with complete accuracy, reliability and simplicity, so that it can be carried out in mass studies on the population as a whole, and repeated at intervals. It may be, however, that many diagnostic tests will be discovered for the many different forms of cancer, which would diminish their value for mass screening of the population. The great success of the Papanicolau cytologic test for cancer of the uterus has encouraged scientists to enter this field. This is an activity, too, for the experimental pathologist in the broadest sense, who either has expert knowledge of biochemistry and endocrinology himself, or who has colleagues who are experts in these disciplines.

Great improvements in the technics of radiotherapy have been made in recent years. One great promise for the future of radiotherapy lies in the discovery of chemical substances, which when administered in conjunction with radiotherapy will increase the effectiveness of the physical modality. Some tumors, such as the cancer of the kidney in children, which may spread to the lung, are now being treated with considerable success by the use of small doses of radiotherapy combined with small doses of an antibiotic. Results are obtained which could be accomplished by neither alone. This opens a new world of radiobiology research.

Discussions with doctors and scientists in cancer research today yields an impression of controlled optimism that the solution or solutions to the problem of cancer can and will be found. This is not wishful thinking, but is based upon awareness of the great advances that have been made in just the last few years. Tools are now available which the investigator can use to great advantage. How different is this point of view from that prevalent in 1927 when I was beginning my own career. It was in that year that we were saddened by the loss of a promising young doctor, a highly respected teacher, who unfortunately took his own life. I well remember the discussion among his friends at his funeral. The fact that he was devoting himself to a search for the cause of cancer was regarded as sufficient evidence of the mental instability which was responsible for his death.

If this chapter has confused you, I am not astonished. The medical disciplines and sciences, and the fields of clinical endeavor, are so intertwined and happily so interdependent that sharp separation would not present a true picture of them.

For those of you who will enter any field of medical science, or of the practice of medicine, opportunities and facilities for work will await you far beyond any imagination of students of my day. Of course there were challenges before us then, and work to be done without end in behalf of the sick, the dying, and those enduring diseases which today are preventable or curable. But the challenges of today, left for those of you who will enter medicine, are of such enormity that it would appear as though only the more simple problems have been solved. To meet these challenges you will have available to you knowledge, technics, and resources commensurate with the magnitude of the task. How fortunate to be young at this time when progress in medical science and practice is so rapid!

You will have the opportunity to participate in the eradication, prevention, or cure of many of the dread diseases which still remain. This will come all the sooner because university scientists have joined with medical scientists and medical practitioners in a rewarding partnership for the good of all.

It is my hope that those who choose medicine, or any branch of medical science as a career, will regard themselves as privileged members of the community. And do not be disturbed if your final choice of discipline or specialty is slow in being recognized by you. Even Hippocrates pointed out that in medicine, experiment is perilous and decision difficult.

13 *You as a*

RADIOLOGIST

BY ALBERT A. RAYLE, JR., M.D.

PRIVATE PRACTICE OF RADIOLOGY

Atlanta, Georgia

DR. ALBERT A. RAYLE, JR.

Born: 1921, Athens, Georgia

Boys High School, Atlanta
Columbia University: A.B., 1941
Emory University School of Medicine: M.D., 1944

Lt. (j.g.), United States Naval Reserve Medical Corps:
Active duty, 1944–47
Interning at United States Naval Hospital, Norfolk, Virginia, 1944–1945
Residency in radiology, Cleveland Clinic Foundation, Cleveland, Ohio:
1947–1950
Diplomate: American Board of Radiology, 1949
Junior staff: Cleveland Clinic, 1950
Private practice of radiology, Atlanta, Georgia, 1950—

Staff appointments: Ponce de Leon Eye, Ear, Nose & Throat Infirmary,
Atlanta, and Newton County Hospital, Covington, Georgia
Volunteer staff: Grady Memorial Hospital, Atlanta
Volunteer faculty: Emory University School of Medicine, Radiology Department
Presently, Assistant Clinical Professor of Radiology

Member:
Radiological Society of North America
American College of Radiology
Georgia and Atlanta radiological societies with offices held in these
societies
American Medical Association
Medical Association of Georgia
Fulton County Medical Society

Author of papers in national radiological literature

SCIENTIFIC "discoveries" so often are called accidents. This is not usually true. More than likely these "accidents" have occurred before, many times before, but there was no prepared, imaginative mind there *to see* them. Today there are innumerable other "discoveries" lying open and exposed before us and surely, for any young man or woman with even a fraction of imagination, there can be no more tantalizing fact than that these discoveries are just waiting for someone to see them.

With such thoughts in our mind we can go back to a Friday evening in 1895. Late on that evening, November 8, a faint glow emanated from an experimental tube in the physics laboratory of Dr. Wilhelm Conrad Roentgen in Wurzburg, Germany. He, and many other scientists before him, had been experimenting with electric discharges through rarified gases, the passage of an electric current in an evacuated tube, and "X rays" undoubtedly had been produced long before Roentgen produced them, probably as early as 1785, more than a century before him. The early investigators, however, did not appreciate what was happening or, for various reasons, were unable to pursue what they had produced. It was left for Roentgen to see, and experiment, and make his magnificent contribution to all science, with its especial benefits to medicine.

For several years Roentgen and other physicists had formed glass tubes of various shapes, some similar to our present light bulbs. They sealed wires into opposite ends of the tubes and pumped the air out of them. They then passed an electric current through the wires at the ends of the evacuated tube and the current jumped the gap, causing a glowing, fluorescent light to occur. These were cathode rays, later proved to be streams of electrons, or negative electrical charges, emitted by the heated wire cathode.

Roentgen at this time in his work was probing, searching, and in the course of his experiments was using various types of tubes. On that evening in 1895 he covered one of them with black paper; but even though the tube was covered, Roentgen soon noted that a few crystals which lay on his table several feet from the tube were brightly fluorescent. These crystals were at much too great a distance to be excited by ordinary cathode rays, and suddenly Roentgen knew that he was dealing with cathode rays of unusual penetrating ability, or that in some way he had discovered a new type of ray. (There is a fine story, of deep scientific significance, told of a conversation that Roentgen had with another scientist years after the night of the discovery. "When you first saw it," the other scientist asked, "what did you think?" "I didn't think," Roentgen replied. "I experimented.")

In the early days after his discovery—or shouldn't we really say "detection" or "recognition," rather than discovery?—Roentgen did not record his experiences in detail and we do not know all that actually happened. We do know, however, that he placed a screen at a greater distance from the tube than known cathode rays could reach, and the screen fluoresced. He put a book in the path of the rays and the fluorescence persisted. He then put heavier—and still heavier—materials in the path of the rays and he found that radiation was absorbed in varying degrees; but with the thickness of metals employed in those first days, platinum and lead were the only materials that would actually stop the rays.

Continuing his experiments, Roentgen went a step further, replacing the absorbing material with his hand, which he thrust into the ray to test it. The fluorescent screen revealed the outline of the bones within the outline of the less-dense flesh. This was the first fluoroscopic study of human material and in this way the medical specialty of radiology, with all its benefits to mankind, was begun.

These rays, however, were unknown to Roentgen and for this reason he called them "X rays." While he could see something of what they did—passing through substance opaque to ordinary light—he did not understand them and he confided to a friend: "I have discovered something interesting, but I do not know whether my observations are correct." His puzzlement and his care were so great that he seldom spoke to anyone during the early days following the discovery and even his two laboratory assistants were unaware of the exact nature of his experiment, learning it only at the time of the formal publication, December 28, 1895.

Soon afterwards, Roentgen gave a demonstration of his rays before Kaiser Wilhelm II in Berlin, but his first public lecture, "On a New Kind of Ray," was before the Wurzburg Physical Medical Society, January 23, 1896. His words epitomize the modesty and integrity of this great scientist: "I found by accident that the rays penetrated black paper. I then used wood, paper, books, but I still believed I was the victim of deception. Finally, I used photography and the experiment was successfully culminated." He demonstrated many of the amazing properties of X rays and among the other radiographs (which is the professional name for X-ray pictures) that he showed was probably one of his wife's hand, the first radiograph of a human part. It was at this meeting, after Roentgen made and exhibited a radiograph of the hand of the anatomist, von Kolliker, that the latter proposed a name for the new rays, suggesting that they be known as "Roentgen's rays," a name by which they are still widely known today, particularly among scientists.

There were skeptics, of course, as there always are, and one of the surgeons at the meeting warned against too much optimism. He particularly doubted that the method would prove to be of value in the diagnosis of internal disturbances. How little did he foresee that these rays would, in fact, deepen our vision into the hitherto concealed parts of the body, enabling us to view and radiograph structures and conditions which previously had been seen only by surgery or at autopsy. Indeed, in later years, with the nature and control of the rays more clearly understood, their use has enabled us to examine the entire skeletal structure and every organ system of the body.

Even at the beginning, however, Roentgen foresaw at least a

part of what was ahead and he answered the skeptics by saying it was not difficult to "photograph" a dog or cat according to his method, and he believed it would be possible in the near future to make X-ray pictures of the larger parts of the human body. His belief has been justified, and far beyond his conception. Indeed, the value of the rays was speedily recognized throughout the world and only four days after the discovery was first made known in America, a bullet embedded in the calf of a patient's leg was located by X ray and was quickly and easily excised.

Here I think that we should continue briefly in the general area in which we have started, staying with the *physicists* and their work before we go on to discuss the medical specialty of radiology. The work of the physicists came first, and all that radiology now means to medicine, developed later from their findings.

Besides Roentgen, other European physicists in the latter part of the century were making important and critical contributions in the area that we are considering. In 1896, one year after Roentgen discovered X rays, a famous French physicist, Henri Becquerel, found that rays coming from *uranium ore* affected a photographic plate in much the same fashion as did Roentgen's X rays. These rays reported by Becquerel were the first recognized evidence of a natural radioactivity that exists in some elements. In these elements, of which uranium is one, the atomic structure is such that a certain type of instability exists, causing the atom to emit one or more types of energy or ray in seeking to stabilize its existence. (It was soon learned that these radioactive elements have a definite and established rate of decay or energy release, an invaluable discovery in regard to their use.)

But back to Becquerel: In his work he had come to realize that the rays from uranium ore are more powerful than those from pure uranium. This observation fascinated two other great French physicists, Marie and Pierre Curie, husband and wife, and they became deeply concerned with radioactive substances. Working with tons of uranium ore, or pitchblende, and using a most laborious process of fractionation, they finally isolated minute amounts of two new and highly radioactive elements which they named *radium* and *polonium.*

One can sense in this the beginning of the nuclear and the atomic age. It was brought even nearer by the daughter and the son-in-law of the Curies when they produced the first artificial radioactive isotope by bombarding boron with alpha rays. This work of the Joliot-Curies paved the way for production of the hundreds of radioactive isotopes which are available today for research and treatment. Joliot's research, furthermore, contributed materially to the achievement of the release of atomic energy.

All the persons we have mentioned so far have been physicists, and their work was so significant that each of them received the Nobel Prize for his or her accomplishments. It is obvious, therefore, that X rays and radioactivity belonged initially to the physicists.

Their discoveries quickly caught the imagination of the public and Roentgen, in particular, was besieged by reporters for stories that were published around the world. The possibility of seeing through the human body so excited the laity that soon it was common for photographers to offer "sittings for your photograph by means of Roentgen's rays." In fact, the whole thing became something of a fad and went so far that circuses and side shows at fairs had booths for demonstration of the phenomenon.

Of course the imagination of the medical profession was stirred and the recognition of Roentgen's discovery was quick and positive. Within weeks after newspapers had spread the story of X rays, many physicians in America and elsewhere were either taking their patients to physics laboratories for radiographs or had purchased equipment for their own offices.

Not a few of these pioneers became martyrs and paid for their scientific devotion with their lives. The inherent danger of excessive radiation was unknown at the time and it was a common practice for the pioneer user, while dealing with the erratic gas tubes of those early days, to place his hand in the beam, viewing the image on a fluoroscopic screen to evaluate the performance of the tubes. This was done to estimate the exposure time needed for the part of the patient to be examined. The repeated use of the hands led to the development of skin cancers which too often spread and penetrated, and, in spite of surgery, resulted in death. One pioneer succumbed to radiation damage after some eighty operations, beginning at his finger tips and continuing up his arms. Injuries of this type need never occur today, partly because of modern equipment and also because the experiences of these early men taught us the inherent dangers of the rays.

Today, in a radiologist's office or hospital department during fluoroscopy, the physician and his technicians wear protective aprons, and gloves if their hands are to be in the beam. (These aprons once were a combination of lead and rubber, but now they can be plastic impregnated with lead or of special fiberglas cloth.) Furthermore, during the actual exposure of the films the technicians are behind protective screens which usually have lead content.

Such measures insure the lowest possible dose of X ray to the workers, but to make protection even more certain they wear "film badges" or other monitoring devices to record the cumulative dose of ionizing radiation. These recorders are read at intervals and if the dose is high, corrective procedures are put into effect and the work habits in that office are changed.

When we think back to the men who began the specialty of radiology, at a time when the exposure of a hand was measured in minutes, we wonder how they achieved so much. We wonder, too, if they could have dreamed of experimental apparatus obtaining a radiograph of even heavier parts of the body in thousandths of a second.

Now let's get more directly to our specialty. How does one become a radiologist? What training must he receive?

He must first undertake the fundamental training common to all doctors, attending a recognized medical school and receiving the M.D. degree. He then spends at least a year as an intern, which is required before beginning training in radiology.

The need for fundamental medical training is plain when one considers the responsibilities of the radiologist. On any day he may be concerned with a simple fracture, a complex heart condition, a suspected cancer, an obstetrical problem. All branches of medicine are his field. The general practitioner will consult him. The surgeon will call on him. Other specialists will require his aid. He must understand the problems of each and assist in making diagnoses, sometimes advising about treatment and the expected outcome or prognosis. After considering the variety of demands made on the radiologist, one can agree with what has been said of him: "He is the general practitioner among the specialists."

It should be remembered, too, that while he is concerned so much with aiding other doctors, he is also concerned with treatment of his own patients. He is both doctor and clinician, whether working in diagnosis and therapy, or in only one of these branches of radiology.

For such a career, he obviously needs all the training he can get in general medicine, surgery, and pathology. After completing his internship, and if possible gaining additional general training, he enters his residency for a minimum period of three years. Some institutions have extended it to four and this is likely soon to become general.

Just what is he training for? What does a radiologist do? The specialty is made up of three parts: *roentgen diagnosis, radiation therapy,* and *nuclear medicine.* What does he do in each part? How does he prepare himself?

Two years of his residency will probably be spent primarily in *diagnostic radiology,* which is concerned with fluoroscopic and radiographic studies. This is the actual photographing of areas of the body that not even the surgeon can see except in the operating room. As for the general practitioner, when using the tools and abilities that are common to him, he cannot possibly look completely into his patient's lungs, or inspect his stomach, or see his colon. Even a simple fracture can only be imagined by the examining physician, since he cannot see the bone and the actual break. But the radiologist can see—the lungs, the stomach, the colon, the fracture—and make a radiograph, and give it to the physician.

Diagnostic radiology is the "bread and butter" work of most radiologists and the resident, therefore, will find that much of his initial training will consist of fluoroscopic procedures. Each morning he will observe fluoroscopy as performed by an experienced radiologist, visualizing the image of small or large areas and radiographing any desired small area as a permanent record on film. In the afternoon he and the radiologist will view the spot films made during fluoroscopy and also the films of the entire area made by a technician. This training will continue for months before the resident is allowed to examine a patient alone.

Along with the morning fluoroscopy and the afternoon viewing of films, there will be training for the resident in other parts of his work. From each patient there must be obtained a short history of his complaint. This will be augmented by information from the patient's referring physician. The radiologist correlates this with his own interpretation of the fluoroscopic and film findings, and offers an opinion as to the illness. He then forwards a written report to the referring physician—and this is roentgen diagnosis, the viewing and radiographing of the inner parts of the body and the report of the interpretation of what is seen.

Examination of the gastrointestinal tract constitutes a considerable part of the work of the radiologist, but practically all other parts of the body are amenable to some type of radiographic procedure—the examination of the skull and skeletal system for fracture, the kidneys and gall bladder for stone formation or other disease, the lungs for tumor or infection, the long bones and trunk for degenerative or destructive disease. The radiologist also carries out certain studies in the operating room as a member of the surgical team. These studies consist of the injection of air into the pathways of the brain, injection of opaque liquids into the blood stream to show the circulation within the brain, within the heart and lungs, or within the blood vessels of the trunk, arms or legs.

Besides the training during residency for *roentgen diagnosis*, there is also training in two other divisions of radiology: *radiation therapy* and *nuclear medicine*. Emphasis will be placed on them for at least one year and the resident will learn to treat cancer and certain other disease conditions with radiation in the form of X rays, radium, cobalt, other natural radioactive materials, or artificial radioisotopes. This penetrating, ionizing radiation will be employed chiefly for malignant growths, their palliation or cure.

During the time of therapy, the radiologist is closest to his patients. He sees some of them almost daily for four to six weeks, some even longer. Many will be seriously ill, some hopelessly ill, but they all look to him for help. Fortunately, most of them can be helped by skillful therapy and a reasonable number can be cured. This is one of the greatest of all satisfactions, and an endless source of interest. Before becoming a radiologist, I could envision the surgical removal of cancer; but even today, after years of experience, I still am amazed as I see the shrinking and final disappearance of sensitive types of cancer as the result of radiation therapy. This phenomenon is even more astounding to me than the ability to "photograph" with X rays.

Along with years of training in diagnostic radiology, and in the various forms of therapy, the resident will spend months in the pathology department. Here he learns to differentiate the various types of diseased tissues, recognizing them from both their gross and their microscopic appearance. During this period he will also learn to evaluate the other procedures performed in the pathology laboratory.

During all his years of training, the resident will be concerned with that portion of physics which deals with radiation. This instruction often is given by members of the physics department of a university and one learns exactly how the laws of physics are related to the work of the radiologist and to his continuing use of radiant energies.

After completing three or four years as a resident, the candidate must wait still another year before taking the examination of the American Board of Radiology. He may spend this year as he desires, in additional training, research, private practice, or military service; but a year of experience is required.

The Board examination has to do with film interpretation; clinical application of roentgen rays, radium, and radioisotopes; pathology, physiology, radiobiology, and radiophysics. The taking of the examination is voluntary, but one must pass it before he can receive a certificate from the Board. Such a certificate is almost a requisite to the fulfillment of anyone's desires as a radiologist.

No particular qualifications are essential in a radiologist beyond those of any good doctor. However, interest and training in mathematics and physics will help, since radiology has technical aspects not found in other medical practices. Also, the radiologst, because of the machines he works with, will probably have more interest in mechanics than the ordinary practitioner; but let there be no misunderstanding about the radiologist, or about his duties and responsibilities. While he requires the utmost in mechanical precision, he must also accept the obligation, common to all doctors, of making critical judgments and offering opinions. He must be a good doctor first, and then, by adding the technicalities and precisions of his specialty, he may be a good radiologist as well.

Because of the lack of radiologists in some parts of the country, and the demand for them, there are numerous residencies open to suitable candidates.

In 1949, the number of residencies was 970. There were 897 men in training. Seventy-three residences were vacant.

In 1960, residencies had increased to 1,883. Men in training were 1,537. Three hundred and forty-six residences were unfilled.

In 1962, the number of radiologists needed in the United States was estimated at 7,000. Only about 6,000 diplomates of the American Board of Radiology were in practice, and a number of these were in government service, research, or teaching.

The need for radiologists grows a good deal more rapidly than the supply. From 1946 to 1961, the *physician* population of the United States increased by 40 per cent. The *radiologist* population went up by 170 per cent, but even this did not keep up with the demand. It should be mentioned that radiology is one of the medical specialties that welcomes women; there are a number of wonderful and competent women in it.

Despite the attraction of radiology there is one worry for almost any young man or young woman considering it: How much will all that equipment cost? How can I pay for it?

The following figures (as of 1962) are closely accurate:

Diagnostic equipment	$10,000–$15,000
Darkroom equipment	1,000– 2,500
Therapy machines	10,000– 16,000
Taxes	700– 1,000
	$21,700–$34,500

Such initial expense might turn some young people away if it were not, as Dr. John McClenehan of Philadelphia has stated, that most companies supplying X-ray equipment are very human: "Those worth dealing with will adapt their financing to suit the prospective purchaser if he is well trained, well recommended, willing to work, and with wit enough to pitch his tent in a community that needs him. He can count on generous terms and special help in many ways." So the initial cost need not be a barrier, or deter anyone from going into radiology as a career.

In this brief mention of economics, I should make it clear that the person who enters this specialty cannot aim primarily at money and should expect no more than a comfortable income, sufficient to satisfy reasonable wants, but with no thought of wealth. For most men this is probably enough, particularly when it is joined with the realization that he is of some use in the world, and of help to people.

It is relatively easy for the young radiologist to find a niche that will satisfy him, and there are three ways open: hospital practice, teaching, private practice.

The smaller hospitals (twenty-five or fifty beds) do not need the full-time service of a radiologist. He can visit them weekly or come in an emergency. A hospital of seventy-five to one hundred beds will need one or more radiologists.

In a hospital, the radiologist will see a larger number of acutely ill patients and more with unusual diseases. He will be in daily consultation with physicians and will be able to keep abreast of medical knowledge as he correlates his radiographic findings with the clinical and laboratory reports. This correlated information is usually more readily available in a hospital setting, thereby aiding in establishing an early diagnosis.

The X-ray department of any large hospital, in addition to being equipped for routine radiological procedures, is ordinarily prepared for more complicated diagnostic studies. In order to participate in these complicated procedures—granted that there is a particular interest in them—a radiologist will find that hospital practice is mandatory.

For the young radiologist planning his career there is another advantage in a hospital. For him to contribute to medical and radiological literature may be important, both for his immediate advancement and his later standing. His opportunity to make such a contribution is usually greater if he is in hospital practice.

For those who teach, there will be lectures, demonstrations, and various administrative responsibilities. There will be daily discussions with other members of the radiology department. There will be instruction not only for the students but also for the house staff, interns, and residents in departments other than radiology.

In addition, most teaching departments have one or more research projects that the professor of radiology must direct. There are also postgraduate courses for radiologists already in practice, designed to help them increase their skill in diagnosis and therapy through newer techniques. All this work requires that he who teaches shall be a truly dedicated individual.

The private practice of radiology may not offer the glamour or challenge of a hospital or teaching appointment, yet for many doctors it is more satisfying.

One is captain of his ship and may proceed at his own pace, unhampered by organizational requirements or administrative decisions handed down from above. Private practice is more like ordinary medical practice, a doctor seeing his patients in his own office, with an opportunity to know them better than if he were at a hospital or on a teaching staff.

Whichever way one decides to go—hospital, teaching, private practice, or a combination of these—he will find much to do, almost all of it interesting, almost all worth while. The radiologist can always know that he is playing a useful part—indeed, an essential part—in the world of medicine.

14   *You in*

PUBLIC HEALTH

BY LUTHER L. TERRY, M.D.

SURGEON GENERAL, PUBLIC HEALTH SERVICE

*United States Department of
Health, Education, and Welfare*

DR. LUTHER L. TERRY

Born: 1911, Red Level, Alabama

Public Schools, Red Level
Birmingham-Southern College: B.S., 1931
                             D.Sc., 1961
Tulane University: M.D., 1935

Instructor and Research Fellow in Pneumonia: Washington University, 1939–40
Instructor, Assistant Professor, Associate Professor: Preventive Medicine and Public Health, University of Texas, 1940–46
Instructor and Assistant Professor in Medicine: Johns Hopkins University School of Medicine, 1944–61
United States Public Health Hospital, Baltimore:
  Member of the Staff, 1942–43
  Chief of Medical Services, 1943–53
National Heart Institute, Bethesda:
  Chief of General Medicine and Experimental Therapeutics Branch, 1950–58
  Assistant Director, 1958–61
Surgeon General: United States Public Health Service, 1961—

Cardiovascular Study Section, National Institute of Health: 1950–55
Chairman, Medical Board, Clinical Center: 1953–55 (Member 1955–58)
Director Residency Training Program: National Heart Institute, 1953–58
Chairman: Cardiovascular Research Training Committee, 1957–61
Member Medical Division: Strategic Bombing Survey, Japan, 1945–46
Chairman, Civilian Health Requirements: United States Public Health Service, 1955–58
Member Advisory Committee on Nutrition: Indian Health Service, 1957–58
Director: Tuberculosis Association, Washington, D. C.
Past President: Washington Trudeau Society
Past President: Public Health Clinical Society
Governor, American College of Physicians
Member, American Heart Association
Member, American Medical Association
Diplomat, American Board of Internal Medicine
Member, National Board of Medical Examiners
Member, Advisory Board, Leonard Wood Memorial
Member, Committee of Board of Overseers of Harvard College, School of Public Health
Honorary Member, American Hospital Association

Author: Numerous papers on professional subjects

EVERY physician is "in public health." When the doctor of medicine receives his license to practice, he takes on responsibilities to the public as well as to his patients and his profession. The quality of public-health services in his community, and throughout the country, is just as much the concern of the private practitioner as it is of the men and women who choose public health as a career.

You, as a physician, will soon realize that the well-being of your patients depends to a large extent upon the protection that public health affords your community. You will realize, too, that the resources offered the private physician by good public-health services are essential in medical practice.

I first became aware of this close relationship between medical practice and public health when I was an intern at Hillman Hospital in Birmingham, Alabama. Nowadays, most physicians practicing in the United States will never see a case of typhoid fever. I saw plenty of them as an intern, twenty-five years ago. Every one of our patients had acquired the disease outside the city of Birmingham. Inside the city, a well-staffed health department ensured safe water and milk supplies. It maintained close surveillance over restaurants and other food-serving establishments. It conducted vaccination campaigns to make sure that a high proportion of the city population was protected against typhoid fever. The state health department supplied private physicians and hospitals with typhoid vaccine free of charge.

Whenever a private physician vaccinates a patient against an infectious disease, he is "in public health." He is helping to protect the community, as well as his patient. When he signs a birth or a death certificate, or reports a case of disease to the health department, he is "in public health." He is contributing to the nation's health intelligence which, like military intelligence, gives up-to-date information on the location and strength of the enemy. Health intelligence seeks such information on diseases and accidents, environmental hazards, and other conditions that are the enemies of human life and health.

In return, the health department is "in practice" with the private physician on many occasions. When the health laboratory performs diagnostic tests on a specimen taken from a patient, it answers the physician's question, "Is such-and-such a disease present?" When a public-health nurse gives nursing care in the home, she carries out the physician's instructions. In both these cases, the health department is "in practice" with the physician.

These examples of the relationship between public health and clinical medicine indicate the mutual interests of the private practitioner and the public-health physician. However, they are only clues to the role of public health in the life of the modern community. The scope of public health is much wider than these few activities suggest.

Public health is a function of government. The history of civilization from remotest times shows that governments have exercised this function to enable human beings to live in communities. Many of the laws attributed to Moses, for example, were public-health laws to protect a nomadic community moving from Egypt to Israel. The tribal chiefs were given specific responsibilities for camp sanitation, protection of water and foods, the services of midwives, and so on. The control of epidemics also is an age-old responsibility of government.

From ancient times, governments have set standards for the practice of medicine and taken responsibility for the medical care of some groups. In Imperial Rome, soldiers, sailors, and other employees of the state—such as temple attendants and gladiators—were the only recipients of such care. In modern times, governments began to provide care for other groups, such as the destitute and the mentally ill. Until the twentieth century, however, this care was crude and often cruel. Medicine had little to offer for the treatment of disease, while the "insane" and the destitute were regarded more as criminals than as helpless people.

It is not possible to define the function of public health precisely because the required services vary from place to place and from time to time. The growth of science is a powerful force in changing the precise functions of public health. When the Black Death swept through Europe in the fourteenth century, destroying perhaps one-fourth of the population, there were no effective measures to halt its spread. Frightened people fled from their stricken cities and carried the plague with them. Today, governments can prevent bubonic plague or halt its spread by the use of vaccines and antibiotic drugs, and by the eradication of plague-infected rats. A world-wide health intelligence system also gives warning to all governments of outbreaks of bubonic plague so that preventive measures may be applied in advance. Governments also have responsibilities for the quality of the vaccines and drugs that physicians use in the prevention and treatment of plague.

Industrial development and population growth also bring about changes in public health. In highly industrialized civilizations, people are exposed to a wider variety of hazards than confronted our forefathers in the pioneer days. For example, dangerous fumes and gases from industrial plants, motor vehicles, and incinerators were unknown in most of our cities a hundred years ago. Radiation from artificial sources affected only a few hundred medical and industrial workers fifty years ago. Today, these hazards are serious public-health problems affecting all parts of the country. Governments also have heavier responsibilities for the promotion of research and education in the life sciences, as well as for services affecting the health of the people.

No two governments employ precisely the same methods in carrying out their public-health responsibilities. However, it can be said that modern governments are involved in the following wide range of health and medical activities:

Scientific research on threats to human life and health, including the means to prevent or alleviate diseases and injuries

Education of health and medical personnel

Licensure of practitioners of the healing arts and of other occupations affecting health and safety

Licensure of hospitals, nursing homes and other institutions

Prevention of disease and epidemic control

Safe public water supplies and community waste disposal

Control of environmental hazards, such as: water and air pollution and radiation exposure

Control of drugs, vaccines, foods, and other products to ensure the maintenance of standards in their production and marketing

Protection of workers from occupational hazards

Special services for mothers and infants, school children and the physically handicapped

Institutional care of the mentally ill, the mentally retarded, and persons with tuberculosis and certain other infectious diseases

Medical care of certain other groups, or, in some countries—the United Kingdom, the Scandinavian countries—of the entire population.

Despite the medical activities in which all governments are involved, the federal, state, and local governments in this country provide only a part of the numerous services and facilities required for the health and safety of the people. Our great national research effort, for example, involves not only public institutions but also private medical schools and hospitals, philanthropic foundations, voluntary health agencies, and industrial laboratories, all of which play a major role in the nation's health research. The same wide range of public and private resources is involved in the education of the nation's health personnel: physicians, dentists, nurses, scientists, and many other groups.

While there is this interplay of public and private effort in regard to our national health, it should be understood that the American people rely chiefly on private practitioners, voluntary hospitals, and the commercial sources of drugs and appliances for the health care of individuals. Of the many billions of dollars spent annually for personal health care in the United States ($26 billion in 1960), less than one-fourth is spent by federal, state and local governments. Furthermore, of all the public funds spent by governments for personal care, a considerable portion goes for the purchase of services from private individuals and institutions.

There are health and medical activities, however, that are the exclusive responsibility of governments, and some of these responsibilities belong solely to the states. For example, the states alone grant licenses to practice medicine and other healing arts. They alone license hospitals and related institutions. Private institutions and voluntary health agencies receive their charters to operate as corporations exclusively from state governments. (A Congressional charter is required in the District of Columbia, which is a federal territory.) State governments alone can grant authority to their counties and cities to make local health regulations and provide local services.

The United States government also has some exclusive responsibilities in health and medical fields. The armed forces and their families, other federal employees, veterans, seamen of our country's merchant ships, American Indians and Alaskan Natives depend on the action of Congress and the federal agencies for all or most of their medical care.

Health problems involving foreign and interstate commerce also are federal responsibilities. For example, my own organization, the Public Health Service, administers the government's programs to prevent the introduction of epidemics from abroad and the interstate spread of infectious diseases. The Service also represents the government in the world-wide network of health intelligence, operated by the World Health Organization of the United Nations.

In these programs, we rely heavily on state and local health departments, private physicians, and hospitals, throughout the country. Let me give you a "case history" of that partnership in action.

Between December, 1960, and February, 1961, physicians in Jackson County, Mississippi, reported to their state health department thirty to forty cases of infectious hepatitis. This disease is caused by a virus about which little is known except that it produces an acute illness with symptoms of jaundice and that it is transmitted from person to person in various ways. The US

Navy operates a shipyard at the mouth of Pascagoula River in Jackson County, at that time with a contingent of 600 naval personnel and their families and a work force of some 2,500 persons. Naval medical officers were concerned lest the hepatitis outbreak in the civilian population spread to the military community. They requested the Public Health Service to investigate the outbreak, and if possible, locate the source of infection.

To make a long story short, physicians of the Public Health Service, working with state health officers, traced the source to infected oysters harvested by poachers in polluted waters off the coast of Mississippi. Hepatitis patients had eaten raw oysters from this source. The same source was involved in twenty-eight additional cases in nearby communities of Alabama. State authorities in Mississippi and Alabama took prompt action. Shellfish collected in the polluted area were destroyed; the polluted waters were more closely patrolled; and the discharge of raw sewage into affected waters was stopped.

This episode was the second in medical history in which shellfish were implicated in the spread of infectious hepatitis, and the first involving oysters. In 1955, Swedish public health physicians had traced an outbreak in their country to infected clams. In our country, if private physicians had not reported their cases, if Navy physicians had not been alert to the threat, the outbreak would have been much more severe. Most important of all, medical officers and private physicians throughout the country were alerted to the possibility of shellfish as sources of hepatitis infection. Pollution controls were tightened in all shellfish growing areas.

The pattern of governmental health and medical activities varies from state to state. No one agency can deal efficiently with the many official duties required to protect and improve the health of the people in a state's communities. In the fifty states and four dependencies of our country, no two have precisely the same method of distributing these responsibilities. So if you asked me, "Who is responsible for the state mental health program?" I would have to know which state you have in mind before giving an answer.

All states concentrate responsibility for many of their health services in their departments of health. *Every* state health agency, for example, has responsibility for disease control, health statistics, environmental health, development of local public-health services, and maternal and child-health services. *Most* of the states place the responsibility for diagnostic laboratory services, food and drug control, tuberculosis sanatoria, the planning of hospital and medical facilities construction, and licensure of hospitals in their health departments. These activities do not comprise an inclusive list of all the functions that have been, or may be assigned to state health departments. Among state administrative organizations, the health department usually has the largest contingent of full-time professional health personnel. As an integral part of its activities, the health department conducts research and provides for the training of state and local public-health personnel.

There is a tendency to group certain other major services directly affecting human health in particular state agencies. For example, school medical services and school-lunch programs are responsibilities of state departments of education. Medical care of welfare clients and services to crippled children are administered by departments of welfare in all but a few instances. Vocational rehabilitation of the handicapped is a responsibility of the state department of welfare or of education. Mental hospitals and schools for the mentally retarded are most frequently administered by an independent department or a special commission. Labor departments or industrial boards are responsible for industrial safety. Workmen's compensation laws, which ensure the payment of medical expenses, disability and death benefits, associated with occupational injuries and diseases, are administered by special boards. Private-health insurance carriers, such as Blue Cross and Blue Shield, operate under the regulations of state insurance commissions.

Most state health and medical services reach the people through their local governments, which usually have counterpart agencies: the local health department, the local schools, the local welfare department. In some instances, however, the county court may be the channel through which state services reach the local community. For example, the county court may have exclusive authority to place a mentally ill person or a crippled child in a state hospital for care.

The combined resources of state and local governments are only a small part of the great wealth of organized health and medical services available to communities in the United States. Voluntary health and welfare agencies play a vital role in providing such services. There are 100,000 national, regional, and local "voluntaries" with a primary interest in health and welfare. Another 100,000 voluntary organizations, such as veterans' associations, business clubs, and parent-teacher associations, and 300,000 churches support or provide some community health and medical services.

The nation's hospital and medical facilities are an unusually interesting composite of public and private effort. These institutions are costly, not only in construction but also in equipment and operation. All but a few of our mental institutions and tuberculosis santatoria are government owned and operated, chiefly by state governments. On the other hand, 80 per cent of the nation's general hospitals are owned and operated by voluntary nonprofit organizations: religious groups, private medical schools, civic groups banded together to provide their communities with modern hospital services. Practically all of the nation's nursing homes are privately owned; three-fourths of these are operated for profit.

You, as a physician, will have hard going at first to find your way through the maze of official and voluntary organizations that affect the care of your patients. It will pay you to provide yourself with some up-to-date road maps.

For instance, you will need to know something about the laws affecting each of the services I have discussed. Your patient wishes a certificate signed by you which he must have in order to claim insurance benefits due to disability. Is this a workmen's compensation case? Or is it a claim for Social Security benefits? Who will pay you for the examination? What procedures must you follow?

Your patient wishes to take a trip around the world. What

vaccinations are required by your government and the countries he will visit?

Your patient should be hospitalized for mental illness. How do you go about helping the family in committal procedures? If he is a veteran, can he receive care without formal committal?

More frequently, you will need to know about the local community's services for patient care of a type which neither you nor the family can provide. If your community has a well-staffed health department, the physician in charge will know the answers to your questions. Another valuable help will be the social worker in your community hospital—if it has one on its staff.

Here is an instance of many organizations, many people, working together to help one patient:

Mrs. X, forty-five years of age, lived with her husband and two teen-age children in a suburban community. She had cancer and had undergone surgery at a large teaching hospital in a nearby city, where her family physician lived and practiced. The patient, her family, and her physicians agreed that she would be better off in convalescence if she could be cared for at home, returning to the hospital for observation and treatment.

Her husband and children would, of course, do all they could to make her comfortable and happy at home; but the family doctor knew that her care was more than they could shoulder alone. He knew also that her welfare depended on keeping family life as close to normal as possible. The patient at this stage of her illness did not need full-time nursing. She would need a visiting nurse—every day for a while: later on, several times a week. The family needed a housekeeper to be with the mother while the father was at work and the children were at school. Also, arrangements had to be made to drive the patient into the city for her hospital appointments. She could not drive herself, and her husband would have to take a full day off the job each time he was called upon to take her to the hospital.

The family physician did not know where these needed aids could be found in the suburban community. He felt sure that the city health officer—*his* local health officer—would know. As it turned out, the city health department had assigned a social worker to help solve just such problems, and arrangements were made to meet the family's needs.

The county health department serving the suburban community was prepared to send a public-health nurse to give Mrs. X the nursing care her physician recommended. The local cancer society, a voluntary agency with many volunteer workers eager to do something more than raise funds, took full responsibility for Mrs. X's trips to and from the hospital. Another voluntary agency, located in the city, was able to provide homemaker service, for which the husband would pay the agency at a rate adjusted to the family's financial situation. This meant that a well-trained responsible woman would work in the home as long as necessary, taking over the patient's household tasks and being there to help her in other ways. With these *community health services*, the family physician could be confident that the patient would have satisfactory care; that she would continue her treatments at the hospital; and that the whole family would be spared much of the unavoidable strain of serious illness in the home.

I wish I could tell you that Mrs. X recovered and lived many more years with her family. But like many other adults in the prime of life, she had waited too long to consult her physician about signs of cancer. She received the maximum of high quality cancer treatment possible in her case, but she died within a year. She died at home in the peace and quiet and loving solicitude which hospitals cannot always provide. Her physician told me that the family insisted on writing to each of the groups that helped, thanking them and him for "letting Mother be with us at home right to the end."

This case teaches us much about public-health action in our communities. It shows us that public and private organizations provide a variety of needed facilities and services for the care of the sick, supplementing the physician's services to his patients. It shows us, too, that the co-ordination of these community services is an important part of public-health action.

If the community is to use its services efficiently and fully, it must have a community-wide organization which acts as an information center on all the available services and which can make arrangements for the particular services required in each case. In some communities, the local health department may play the role of co-ordinator; in others, a community council of health and welfare agencies (official and voluntary) may provide the co-ordinating service. In still other communities, the citizens, whose taxes and personal donations support the official and voluntary agencies, may decide on a different way of co-ordinating their services.

In all these instances, community health action is a joint enterprise involving the practicing physicians, the official and voluntary agencies, and the citizens. The quantity and quality of community health services are as good as the physicians and the citizens-at-large want them to be, and are willing to make them.

Only a small proportion of the physicians in our country adopt public health as a lifetime career. At present, there are no meaningful statistics on the number of physicians in public health and related types of practice. One reason for this lack of information is that neither the medical profession nor the community-at-large has agreed on a satisfactory definition of public-health practice.

I will take the risk of giving you an "educated guess" that 10,000 to 15,000 physicians are employed full time in public health and closely related fields. That range would account for considerably less than 10 per cent of our country's active physicians; but it would include many thousands more physicians than are employed in state and local health departments. These physicians in public health and related fields have certain responsibilities and methods which distinguish their work from that of the clinician, the medical scientist, and the medical teacher.

The public health physician is responsible for a community: that is, for *a human population and its environment.* The size and characteristics of communities vary widely; but if a physician is given responsibility to act for any community in solving its medical and environmental problems affecting health, he is serving as a public-health physician. His primary concern is that the interplay of population and environment works toward better health for all the people.

A clinician may observe the effects of environment on the

health of his patients and he may be concerned to protect them from environmental hazards. He is responsible for giving them the best possible medical care and sound advice about the environments in which they live, work, and play; but it is the public-health physician who has been given responsibility to act for the community in coping with environmental problems.

Dr. N had a number of patients who suffered acutely from hay fever each year during the ragweed-pollen season. He diagnosed their illness accurately, treated them for their allergy, and advised them to install air filters in their homes. But Dr. T, the city health officer, was the one who could, and did, see to it that the ragweed was cut down in public and private lots throughout the city before the pollen season, thus reducing the exposure of all persons allergic to ragweed pollen.

In modern medical ecology, communities are differentiated as natural and artificial. Your home town is a natural community because the population includes persons of all age groups and both sexes, living predominantly as families, and representing a wide range of occupations, educational, social, and economic levels. Their environment includes not only the natural factors of earth, air, water, vegetation, animals, and climate, but also the man-made habitations, work places, schools, hospitals, trade and other facilities, as well as the services necessary for life in a natural community. In the broadest sense, the environment also includes the community's cultural patterns: the types of food consumed by the people; the patterns of family and community life; the ways people go about their daily tasks; their recreation, conditions of work, and methods of caring for the sick. Each member of the community is affected by these environmental factors, according to age, sex, and biological inheritance.

A natural community in our country may be a rural area with less than 10,000 inhabitants, a limited range of occupations, facilities, and services, and relatively simple cultural patterns. Or it may be a great metropolitan center with a population of seven million, a tremendous range of occupations, facilities, and services, and highly complex cultural patterns. In any case, the community physician must have an intimate knowledge of the population and the environment; and he must take appropriate action to help the community meet its medical and environmental needs for better health.

Although the health needs of all natural communities are fundamentally the same, each community has some distinctive problems or some distinctive ways of solving them. The status of a community physician depends on his ability to detect and solve these distinctive problems.

Hence in a rural area, the public-health physician may need to develop an area-wide plan whereby all members of his scattered community may promptly receive the services of physicians and hospitals. There are many rural areas in our country where the doctor shortage is severe. The people have not learned the benefits of modern medical care. Except in dire emergencies, they tend to rely even more than do urban groups on folk remedies and medicines bought across the counter in their trade centers. Rural inability to obtain and use medical services can be overcome to a considerable extent if the public-health physician works with local medical societies, hospitals, and farm groups to solve the problem.

The mechanization of agriculture has introduced many new high-powered machines which farm workers have not learned to operate safely. As a result farm accident rates are very high in many rural areas. The community physician may need to attack this problem through a thorough study of the types and causes of accidents, followed by an educational program on means of prevention. Poor nutrition is a community-wide problem in many rural areas, due in part to poverty among agricultural labor groups and in part to regional preferences of the whole population for diets deficient in essential vitamins, minerals, and proteins. The rural community physician will need to combat both aspects of this problem, working through school-lunch programs, welfare agencies, and farm home services. He will frequently be concerned with the provision of health and medical services for migratory farm labor families.

In a large urban area, all of the medical and environmental problems related to the health of a natural community are compounded by the high density of population, the wide range of industrial and residential areas, public utilities, and the complexity of cultural patterns. The city health officer, however, has more local facilities and services, as well as a larger staff, to assist in meeting the needs of his community than does his rural colleague.

Some of the distinctive urban health problems of the present period are community air pollution, water supply and pollution control, higher rates of chronic disease, alcoholism, drug addiction, mental illness, and accidental poisoning. The urban community physician thus will be concerned about the association of high levels of air pollution with increased illness due to such respiratory diseases as asthma, emphysema, and pneumonia. Community mental-health services will be of major concern to him for more effective care of the mentally ill, together with an attack on associated problems such as alcoholism, drug addiction, and suicide. He may be responsible for a community poison-control center, providing round-the-clock information on toxic substances in household and medical products so that private physicians and hospital staffs may promptly apply the proper treatment to accidental poisoning cases. He will be working with all concerned institutions and agencies for the co-ordination of community health services and facilities.

In contrast with a natural community, an artificial community is composed of a select population in a restricted environment. The students of an undergraduate college may be regarded as an artificial community. The age groups are limited to persons approximately eighteen to twenty-five years old, and in some instances only one sex is represented. Despite the increased rate of marriage among college students, this select population does not live predominantly as families. The educational and occupational levels are highly selective. The college campus with its facilities and services comprises the artificial "collegiate environment." The college physician acts for this community, as does the public-health physician, in meeting its medical and environmental needs.

An automobile factory with its workers; a ship at sea and the men who operate it; a military post with its soldiers—all these are artificial communities from the public-health point of view. In each instance, some physician has the *community responsibility* of a public-health physician. The industrial physician advises workers in the plant on personal health maintenance and treats them for illnesses and injuries incurred on the job. He constantly studies the work environment, for it is his responsibility to detect and correct health hazards. The medical officer of a ship or a military post has much the same responsibilities. Other physicians may serve as clinicians in these artificial communities; but some one of them has the community responsibility for the health of the people and the environment.

In recent years, aviation medicine and space medicine have been developed to serve new artificial communities of the twentieth century: planes in flight with their crews and passengers; space probes and astronauts. These artificial environments do not carry physicians with them; but on the ground, flight surgeons and space physicians are working to solve the biological and environmental problems of their "communities." In these settings, as in natural and other artificial communities, some physician with community responsibility makes the decisions concerning the conditions under which population and environment may interact with minimum threat to, and maximum protection of, human life.

The public-health physician is concerned primarily with prevention. Today his preventive goals are broader than those of public health fifty years ago. At that time the public-health physician was content if he could reduce the transmission of infectious diseases in his community. Now he seeks to avert the occurrence of illnesses and accidents insofar as possible; also to prevent their serious consequences, in terms of prolonged disability and premature death due to all causes in all age groups.

The preventive methods of the public-health physician differ from those of the clinician chiefly in scope and timing. They include the preventive measures the clinician applies in the care of his patients, but the community physician can also manipulate the environment through measures not available to the clinician. Further, the community physician cannot wait until patients present themselves for his attention as does the clinician; he must anticipate the problems and take action even before the community is aware of its needs.

A community survey conducted by a health department to detect heart disease, cancer, or diabetes, for example, invariably brings to light cases hitherto unknown to practicing clinicians. The control of these and other chronic diseases depends on early diagnosis, curative treatment, and restorative care of the patient. The use of community surveys to combat such diseases requires diagnostic tests that can be applied easily to large groups of people and that can be relied upon to reveal evidence of disease in early as well as advanced stages. These so-called "screening" tests do not take the place of a complete diagnostic work-up; that is, careful study of the individual patient accompanied by more definitive tests to guide the physician in his diagnosis and choice of treatment. In a community survey, persons who test positive for a particular disease are referred to their personal physicians or to a hospital for diagnosis and care.

In a recent community survey, the heart sounds of thousands of school children were recorded on tape and "played back" to cardiologists. Children whose heart sounds revealed a suspicious murmur or other evidence of defect were then "re-taped" and given a careful physical examination. Sixty-four children were found to have heart disease; half of them were not under medical care. Ten of the young patients needed heart surgery, and received it. This treatment undoubtedly prevented their untimely deaths. Nine had rheumatic heart disease. They are receiving treatment which will prevent further rheumatic attacks, and probably will allow them to lead normal, active lives. The remaining forty-five were placed under medical supervision to determine the best course of treatment for them.

Education of the professions and the public in subjects related to community health is a major responsibility of public-health physicians. The community health officer and his staff are usually the first to learn about emerging health problems and new techniques for coping with old and new problems. In consequence, the public-health physician takes leadership in bringing new concepts to the attention of medical, dental, nursing, and other professional groups. Frequently he draws on resources inside and outside the community to conduct short courses of instruction and training in the performance of new techniques. Community health education is also necessary to prepare the population for the acceptance of new concepts.

Since 1950, for example, medical scientists have developed the Papanicolau cytologic test to the point where it can be easily and effectively applied in the early diagnosis of cancer of the uterine cervix. Prompt and thorough treatment of early cervical cancer will result in a cure in most cases, hence early diagnosis could lead to drastic reduction of cancer deaths among women. Relatively few physicians apply cytology routinely in their care of women patients; and relatively few patients request the test. Public-health physicians engaged in cancer-control work, therefore, have been in the front line of professional education on the cytologic test. They have co-operated with voluntary agencies in public education on the subject. The goal is to extend cancer cytology particularly through general practitioners in the hope that more cases will be brought to treatment when the chances of a cure are greatest.

Many thousands of physicians serve full time as clinicians, scientific investigators, and teachers in medical organizations throughout the country. All of them share in and benefit from medical administration. This may be defined as the application of medical judgment to the management of manpower, materials, and money in health and medical affairs.

The medical-school graduate usually enters practice without realizing how much medical administration has contributed to his professional education and to patient care in the hospitals where he served as an intern. If he chooses public health as a career, he finds that administration is one of his major responsibilities.

Someone with professional knowledge of *medical* needs and methods was responsible for the organization and smooth operation of every one of the activities I have described in foregoing sections. Administration is not an exclusive function of public-health physicians. It is, however, a major responsibility in health and medical affairs, under both private and public auspices, which involve organization. As an *organized activity,* public health shares with medical research and education, hospital services, aviation and occupational medicine, group practice, and medical societies the need for efficient administration.

The medical administrator plans his activity; calculates the personnel, facilities, supplies, and funds he will need to carry out his plan; and is responsible for the proper use of those resources, as well as for the efficient performance of the personnel under his supervision. These duties apply in every organized medical activity, from an individual research project or a community health survey to the large-scale operations of a national health service.

The medical administrator is employed for a particular purpose, of course. His activity must fit in with the mission and objectives of his organization. It is a common mistake on the part of many young physicians, however, to assume that organization and administration mean regimentation. A few years ago, medical school seniors were queried about their career preferences. As might be expected, private practice in a particular specialty was the choice of a large majority. Most of those who rejected public health and other organized activities gave as a reason that they would be regimented in the management of their patients or in the conduct of research.

No doubt some of those students changed their minds during their internship and residency training. For they could not have escaped eyewitness evidence that the full-time hospital physician and medical scientists are as unrestricted in their professional judgments and actions as the "solo" physician in private practice. I do not know of a single research institution, medical school, hospital, governmental agency, or industrial medical service in the United States that puts professional fetters on the physicians in their employ. They *do* set high standards and they *do* expect their medical personnel to maintain those standards.

The American Board of Preventive Medicine was organized in 1947 to certify specialists in public health (including military medicine), aviation medicine, and occupational medicine. This Board functions in the same manner as those which certify physicians in the various clinical specialties described in foregoing chapters.

A public-health specialist is, first of all, a fully qualified graduate of an approved medical school with at least a one-year internship in an approved hospital and a license to practice in a state, territory, or possession of the United States. What he learns and does in his chosen field builds on his basic medical education.

The candidate for a Diploma in Preventive Medicine must complete three years of special training, some of which is in graduate academic study. He may receive credit for experience —which is comparable with residency training in clinical specialties—for two of the required three years. He must then pass an examination in his specialty.

There are twelve approved graduate schools or departments of public health in universities of the United States and Canada. When a physician chooses a career in public health or one of the other options in preventive medicine, he usually plans to obtain advanced training in one of these institutions as soon as possible.

Financing this training is often a problem for the young physician, but there are many sources of help for the competent young man or woman who has serious designs on a public-health career. A number of private foundations and voluntary agencies award fellowships, paying tuition and a living stipend, for one year's training at a graduate school of public health. The Public Health Service also allots funds to the schools for aid to their students and awards a limited number of fellowships to individuals who have been accepted as students in these schools.

The Public Health Service and other agencies of the United States government select a few of their physicians for advanced public-health training, on full salary and with tuition paid. Some state and city health departments make equally generous provisions for the training of selected numbers of their staffs.

Such opportunities are reserved for physicians who have demonstrated their potential talents, as well as a firm purpose to make public health a lifetime career.

The usual course of advanced academic training required by the Board of Preventive Medicine leads to a degree of Master of Public Health, or Master of Science in the case of students who wish to qualify for aviation medicine. The required courses in the program leading to the degree of M.P.H. include: biostatistics, epidemiology, environmental health, and organization and administration. A fifth course is required, but the student is allowed to choose it in a subject related to his intended career. Some schools, however, do not permit this choice and prescribe the entire program.

The graduate school of public health provides advanced training for a wide variety of professional personnel. Hence the physician as a graduate student may find among his classmates: dentists, nurses, engineers, health statisticians, bacteriologists, hospital administrators, social psychologists, and health educators. This experience is valuable for all the students, since it frequently gives them their first acquaintance of teamwork with many of the specialized groups in modern health and medical services.

The Board of Preventive Medicine has approved a number of state and local health departments as residency training organizations for the two additional years of training for candidates with the Master of Public Health degree. The resident may be an employee of those departments, or he may be an employee of some other organization. As a rule, the resident in public health is a full-time employee receiving special training with full salary.

There are other approved residency centers suited to the option in preventive medicine selected by the candidate. The United States Air Force, for example, operates a school of aviation medicine for its physicians and other flight surgeons. Some industrial medical services are approved for residencies in occupational medicine. Some programs of the Army, Navy, and Public Health Service are approved for residency training in

preventive medicine. In all instances, the Board must be assured
that the resident is under the supervision of competent teachers
in his specialty.

Like other doctors employed full time in organized medical
activities, the public-health physician depends on a salary for
his income, instead of on fees paid by patients or by others on
behalf of the patient. Although the salaried physician is not
likely to earn as large a gross income as the physician in private
practice, there are compensations in most salaried positions that
offset this difference to a considerable extent. For one thing, the
salaried physician incurs no business expenses. The supporting
staff, the facilities, equipment, and supplies required in his work
are provided by his employer.

Salaries in governmental agencies—federal, state, and local—
range from about $5,000 a year in junior positions to $25,000 or
more in top administrative posts. In the federal agencies, regular
promotion is assured, as well as liberal provisions for retirement.

In the Public Health Service, our assistant surgeons are actually
first-year interns. If they remain in the service they are promoted
in the second year, at which time they also receive "incentive
pay"—$100 a month in addition to their base pay and allowances.
Physicians in other federal medical services also receive "incentive pay." Commissioned officers of the Army, Navy, Air Force
and Public Health Service pay federal income taxes only on their
base pay. Since allowances and "incentive pay" account for 35 to
40 per cent of a medical officer's total salary, this benefit permits
a considerable saving.

Most medical positions in *state health departments* are protected by some type of merit system which provides for tenure,
promotion, and retirement pay. Some city health departments
have such provisions.

The federal agencies and some state and local official agencies
make generous provisions for medical and hospital care of employees and their families. Commissioned officers in the Army,
Navy, Air Force, and Public Health Service, for example, as well
as their families, receive medical, dental, and hospital services
without contributing to a health insurance plan. For physicians

employed under Civil Service, the government pays one-half of the health-insurance premiums, covering dependents as well. Group health insurance is the usual method adopted by state and local agencies, with or without an employer contribution.

Public-health physicians are "on call" at all times and they often work longer than the stipulated hours on duty. However, their workweek normally makes less demands on them and their families than that of the average private physician. Their organizations anticiptate a normal workweek of forty to forty-four hours and are closed on Sundays and national holidays. In governmental clinical services, of course, provisions are made for rotation of duty, so that there is no cessation of service but that personnel have equivalent time off. Travel expenses, sick leave, and vacations with pay are allowed.

Medical science today makes possible almost miraculous improvement in the health of mankind. But this knowledge is being applied to human needs only in part. In our own country, the largest gaps between medical science and application are in care of the very young and the aged, care of the mentally ill, and care of long-term illness in all age groups. Often this is due to the lack of adequate community health services and facilities which, in effect, strengthen and multiply the hands of the practicing physician.

Modern medical care is more effective, but it is more complicated and prolonged than in earlier periods. In many parts of our country, there simply are not enough physicians to provide this type of care for all who need it. Also, in some parts of the country and some population groups, such well-known preventive care as immunization of young children against diphtheria, whooping cough, tetanus, and poliomyelitis is not fully applied.

Throughout the world, particularly in Asia, Africa, and Latin America, millions of people suffer and die before their time of diseases that could have been prevented or cured. The World Health Organization, the United States, and other Western nations have helped those countries make striking improvements in health conditions since World War II. What has been done is only a beginning. Our government has a heavy responsibility to help improve health and medical services in those countries— for their benefit and our own protection. We can do this best by exporting our medical skills, in the form of competent health personnel who can teach these skills and demonstrate modern methods.

You, as a physician, will have many choices of the role you play in public health. If you adopt private practice, you can support the efforts of your community, your state, your government. You can use your leadership as a physician and citizen to raise the quality and quantity of health services in your community. You can help to create new services that will benefit your patients and the community as a whole. Your advice is needed and sought in all organized medical activities at community, state, and national levels.

If you choose public health as a career you will have opportunities in each of your profession's three great functions: teaching, research, and service—for the public-health physician, like his colleagues in private practice, has the threefold obligation to teach, to study, and to serve. He shares his specialized knowledge with his professional co-workers and the people of his community. And he serves as physician to his community, whatever its size and composition.

There is a place for you in public health, whatever may be your special field of interest in medicine. My own organization, for example, operates programs requiring the services of physicians qualified in every medical specialty. They are engaged in medical research, hospital and clinical practice, environmental health, mental health, occupational medicine, international health, community health services. As I write, some Public Health Service physicians are located in each of the fifty states and in upwards of twenty foreign countries. Some of them are at sea with Coast Guard cutters. Some are working with their colleagues in aviation and space medicine. I believe all of them agree, as I do, that public health has rewards far beyond the not-inconsiderable benefits our government provides its physicians.

Public health can promise you a lively career in stimulating environments, a satisfying career in close association with your co-workers and your community, an inspiring career in service to mankind. For the young physician, its opportunities are unlimited.

15

THE WOMAN DOCTOR

BY MARION FAY, PH.D.

PRESIDENT AND DEAN
Woman's Medical College of Pennsylvania

DR. MARION FAY

Born: 1896, New Orleans, Louisiana

Newcomb College: A.B., 1915
University of Colorado: A.M., 1922
Yale: Ph.D., 1925
Temple University: LL.D., 1951
Moravian College: D.Sc., 1960
Woman's Medical College: D.Sc., 1950
Beaver College: D.Sc., 1957
Elmira College: D.Sc., 1958

University of Colorado: Instructor of Physiological Chemistry, 1920–22
University of Texas: Associate Professor of Physiological Chemistry,
    1925–35
Woman's Medical College of Pennsylvania:
    Professor of Physiological Chemistry, 1935—
    Acting Dean, 1943–46
    Dean, 1946—
    President, 1959—

American Society of Biological Chemists
American Chemical Society
Physiological Society of Philadelphia

Author:
    "Galactose in the Thoracic Lymph of the Dog"
    "The Effects of Acid Denaturation upon the Combining Power of
        Fibrinogen"
    "The Parathyroids and the Clearance of Inorganic Phosphate"

A LITTLE over a century ago, when Elizabeth Blackwell applied for entrance to the Philadelphia medical schools and to many others, the idea of a woman doctor was strange and outlandish and immodest. When she was admitted to the medical college at Geneva, New York, it was considered a joke by the student body who voted to let her try it. But when she graduated in 1849 at the head of her class, she had established her position as an excellent student and as a lady. Today women are accepted in medicine if they are well trained, ask for no favors, and work as hard as their masculine colleagues.

There are still a few areas—geographical and in certain specialties—where women physicians have some difficulty. These difficulties are few and are disappearing. The letters that come to my desk asking for women physicians show the need and the acceptance of the woman doctor.

Here is one request from a group of doctors in a Midwestern town who need a woman pediatrician to join their group. Here is another from one of my former students who with two other women has a busy group practice. She wants a well-trained young doctor to help her now, and to take over her practice when she retires. The Chamber of Commerce in a small upstate community writes to say that they need a woman to practice there. A graduate of a year ago tells me of the successful completion of a busy internship, and the opening of her office, where she had three appointments for her first day of practice. A graduate of thirty-five years ago writes of her experiences in Nepal in a mission hospital. She and her husband retired from a busy practice in Wilmington and went together to Nepal where doctors are desperately needed.

There are telephone calls, too, asking me to recommend a doctor for an apprehensive elderly patient, or for work in a clinic, or in a school health department.

If you are interested in medicine, there is a place for you and you are needed to take care of sick people. If you are interested in science, then you should certainly consider medicine. This mixture of biological and physical sciences in a developing field has all too few well-trained people, men and women, to carry on the interesting investigations on the living organism that new techniques make possible today. Medicine needs biologists, chemists, physicists, and mathematicians, as well as practicing physicians. This combination of service with science has a great fascination for many young people and they will find challenge and opportunity if they enter medical science.

Each year at the Woman's Medical College there are some forty to fifty graduates. They go to internships and then to residencies and they practice in most of our states—including Hawaii and Alaska—and some of them go to far-off places like India or Nigeria or Angola. Some of them stay in Pennsylvania and some are very welcome when they come back to their college to teach, and do research, and to practice.

But there aren't enough in any of our classes, or in the graduating classes of the other eighty-five medical schools, to meet the need. In all these schools, women make up about 6 per cent of the students and there is about the same percentage of women in practice. This figure has remained remarkably constant for fifty years except for an increase of women students up to 11 per cent at the time of the Second World War.

Why are there so few women in medicine in this country when in Russia over 80 per cent, and in some of the European countries more than 30 per cent, of the practicing physicians are women?

Because the figure has been so constant some people think that there must be a quota for women in most medical schools. Once that was true and prejudice died hard. A small number of brilliant women were admitted, but the good solid student with a B average was passed over for a man who might not be so good a student and might not make so good a physician. However, the last school has now capitulated and in September, 1962, Jefferson Medical College in Philadelphia admitted women for the first time. A few schools still admit women reluctantly and some men still magnify the number of women who accept a place in a limited class and then don't go on with medicine. (There are some men graduates who don't use their training either!)

Medicine is a long and costly four years followed by graduate study and some lean years in getting started. But when a woman goes into medicine, she had better decide not to play Mrs. Lot and look back. When she enlists, it ought to be for the duration. About three-fourths of the cost of those four years is paid by the medical school, not by the student, and there ought to be a return to society for that expensive investment supported by private and public funds.

If I am right in saying that today women have the opportunity of entering medical schools and of getting good hospital appointments and research fellowships, why aren't more of them entering medicine? We need doctors now; and we are going to have a critical shortage of doctors if we don't have more good students hammering at our doors and forcing the public and the legislators and the Congress to help the existing medical schools and to begin new ones. Why don't more women enter this profession which gives such great personal satisfaction and offers such opportunities for a busy, a useful—and to be practical about it—a remunerative life?

One reason, I think, is that the difficulties have been stressed and the rewards have not been explained to interested young women. I know some high-school counselors and some in college, too, who encourage the boys to go into medicine, but who refuse to take seriously the ambitious girl who is interested. Some advisers are still convinced that going into medicine is not ladylike —though they accept shorts and other less ladylike advances with tolerance. They talk about the long and expensive years of training, but they don't mention the sources of scholarship support that are available, and they forget the tuition loans that banks are offering. There is no reason why a girl shouldn't finance herself through medical school by borrowing; after a few years in practice as a doctor she will be able to pay back the loans. When my students are fearful about taking out loans, I tell them if we are willing to bet on them by letting them have loans they ought to have enough self-confidence to bet on themselves. I realize that taking out a loan is a bit more difficult for a woman than for a man. If she thinks about the future and possible marriage, does she want to present her young man instead of a dowry a debt complete with interest and principal payments coming inexorably due on the first of the month—even on the honeymoon? Well, if she is really going into medicine, she can pay it off and get the young man, too; he probably has some loans of his own if he has studied medicine!

This brings us to one of the fundamental questions for any girl —do medicine and matrimony mix? Does the study and practice of medicine by a woman require a vow of celibacy? I usually ask applicants this question and it is interesting to see how they answer it. Some of them strike a pose and state that they will be wedded to medicine only. I always say that I don't believe it. I said that to one pretty, attractive girl of nineteen. She replied quietly, "But I am going to enter a religious order next year." So I had to believe her!

For a woman who wants a satisfying career and a husband and family and home, medicine can be the answer. Medicine and matrimony can mix successfully and many women doctors are demonstrating this fact every day. It takes careful planning, but for those girls whose mothers or mothers-in-law can take care of the small children, the planning is not too difficult. For those who can afford good servants, it isn't too difficult, either. Of course, once women are out in practice, the whole matter is simpler because good organization of their homes and their work can accomplish wonders; it is during medical school and hospital training that the problems are greater. These are full-time jobs in themselves and their requirements cannot be controlled by the individual girl; she must be where the lecture is delivered and the demonstration given, and at the time specified.

A good day nursery is very helpful. I know a group of young people—medical students, residents, graduate nurses—who organized their own day nursery on a co-operative basis and made medical education possible for a number of women students. Life is simpler, of course, if matrimony and a family are postponed until after graduation, but marriage is occurring earlier in our time. Many medical schools accept the married woman student as a fact of modern life and try to help her work out her academic and personal problems together. They expect her to work at her problems, of course, and work at them hard, arranging to do the double job competently. Nobody should be asked to have any sentimental ideas about lowering academic standards because the woman student has chosen to undertake two major responsibilities. A woman who glories in disorganization—and unfortunately there are some "helpless females" who do just that—shouldn't be allowed to try medicine by itself, let alone two jobs.

I do not wish to belittle the complexities and problems of a life divided between medicine and the responsibilities of a husband and family and home. There are many sensible, ambitious, married women who hesitate about assuming the double responsibility, yet they will never be really satisfied until they do. An increasing number of these women have a strong desire to develop for themselves an identity and a career which is their own, and which will continue after their children no longer need their constant care and supervision.

There are benefits for more than the individual woman in this. The need to develop and make use of the skills of our women is a necessary advance in our civilization. As the masculine dean of one of our women's colleges has said, the greatest undeveloped natural resource of our country is the manpower of our women.

The combination of medicine and marriage began early for women of the United States. In the first class to graduate from the first woman's medical college in 1852, there were three married women in a total of eight. This group included Hannah Myers Longshore whose husband and doctor brother-in-law generously encouraged her to study medicine. She was the first woman to begin the practice of medicine in Philadelphia and, indeed, in the United States. I remember meeting her daughter, Mrs. Blankenburg, as a handsome and vigorous old lady of eighty-odd, and hearing her introduce herself at a meeting at the College: "Look at me as the example of a neglected child of a woman doctor!" She was very proud of her mother's career and very interested in the college which furnished women the opportunity of studying medicine in 1850. Graduating in this same class of 1852 was Martha Hayden Sawin, also married, who was the first woman to practice medicine in Boston.

These pioneer women combined caring for their families and their homes with their medical practice. They had to drive a horse and buggy to visit their patients and they didn't have dishwashers and clotheswashers and driers and automobiles. Some of our modern girls are more timid than they were, in spite of all the mechanical aids they now can take advantage of, and in spite of the "emancipation of women."

One high-school student came to me to discuss her ambition to be a doctor. She seemed to be more starry-eyed than practical, and of all professions that have to be practical, medicine is the one. When I told her to realize that medicine was hard work and had its unhappy moments, she replied rather patronizingly: "Oh, I'm going to be a very successful doctor just until I'm thirty, and then I'm going to get married." I sent her to spend the day with some of my students—in the anatomy laboratory, the clinics, the hospital—to see some of the disagreeable things that one encounters when only beginning the study of medicine. She was genuinely interested and enjoyed the day. She went on into medicine, married a doctor, and they have successfully practiced together and have established a home and have a nice family.

A young woman doctor applied to a famous professor of surgery for a residency in his department. She was intelligent and able, with a good record and pleasant personality and she had married one of her classmates. Her husband was also applying for this coveted appointment! The surgeon evaluated each of them and decided to accept them both, but with the warning that she was the first woman resident in the department and that unless she made good use of her training she would be the last. She worked very hard, completed her training, and with her husband is today practicing her specialty. She has organized her household and her career so that her children and her patients are all well cared for.

Actually medicine lends itself to a married woman's life very well. Time out for having babies and for getting them through infancy does not take away that cherished M.D. or annul the license to practice. There can be refresher courses to brush up on new ideas, and part-time medical service can be arranged— in clinics, school-health positions, public-health or research posts, teaching in a medical school. Then, too, some women physicians have their offices in their homes and carry on a private practice without being away from home and family. The schedule is not an easy one—but what is easy that is really worth doing?

Not all women doctors marry, of course, though an increasing number do marry during medical school or shortly after graduation. There are many women who find the practice of medicine so rewarding in itself—the close relationship with patients; the participation in the most important events in a family's life, birth and death; or the thrills of discovery in the research laboratory— that their personal affections and needs are met by their professional lives.

Today there is another factor which must be considered: group practice is making it easier for physicians, both men and women, to fulfill their personal commitments and still do a good job in medicine. The old days when the general practitioner was on call twenty-four hours a day, seven days a week, are over. While this is nostalgically considered a great loss, let's examine the facts. Can anyone do consistently good work on such a schedule? Can he keep up with modern methods and ideas in addition to carrying such a load? Development of group practice increases the possibility of the practice of medicine by married women.

Now let me tell you about some of the women doctors, married and unmarried, whom I have known over many years.

One woman with excellent training in ophthalmology was practicing in a large city where there were a number of good eye specialists. Although she had a good practice, she became convinced that her career was settling into a routine and that other doctors could care for her patients. Two doctor friends agreed that she might be of greater service elsewhere and they urged her to move to a community, the center of three counties, where there were no eye doctors. The local hospital welcomed her, fitted up an operating room and obtained the necessary instruments for eye surgery. She visited the town, went to see the local industries to find out at first hand what types of industrial accidents were likely to involve the eye. She opened her office and is now so busy that she will soon need an assistant (I hope that we can send her a well-trained woman). She holds clinics and operates at the hospitals in the three counties, serves on the state commission for the blind, and has a most satisfying and useful life.

Another doctor came originally from a small town in farming country. After her internship and residency training, she and her husband, who also came from a rural community, went to a small town to practice together. They serve a large population scattered over a wide area; they know the country and the families and they derive enormous satisfaction from giving excellent medical care to a rural community.

Many women like the life of a large city, the hospital type of medicine, the feeling that they are part of a medical community. They enjoy the opportunities for constant training, medical meetings, lectures, and consultations with their colleagues. Then, too, a teaching connection with a medical school in a large community can give greater satisfaction, for medical students by their curiosity and interest stimulate their teachers. Many women hold important faculty appointments—Dr. Connie Guion in Medicine at Cornell for whom the new outpatient clinic is named; Dr. Edith Potter at Chicago; Dr. Helen Taussig in Johns Hopkins, and many others in a long list who have won academic recognition.

There are not as many women in high academic posts as I should like to see. Some women hesitate to assume a top administrative post because of family duties. Some are passed over for fear they cannot give undivided attention to their professional jobs. This is a problem that women face and some of them cannot find a solution. Since this is true, it is not fair always to blame prejudice as the reason for the lack of women in high posts.

In the early days of medical training for women, many applicants were interested in the foreign-mission field. They still are. In 1869, Clara Swain, the first woman medical missionary in the world, received her M.D. and went to the East to practice medicine. She was the first of a group who went to many countries to found mission hospitals, to work in them, and to train the native women in medicine and in nursing. Rosetta Sherwood Hall, who completed her medical training in 1889, went to Korea, founded a woman's medical college, and received from the Emperor three tribute cups and other honors in recognition of the medical care and the education that she gave to his subjects. Her son and his wife, both doctors, have carried on a fine medical program in India for many years. The famous Dr. Ida Scudder founded Vellore Medical College for Indian women. Dr. Edith Brown, a British physician, began Ludhiana Medical College for women in the north of India. Both of these colleges have become coeducational, but the Lady Harding in New Delhi still admits women only. The Indian Congress of Women has petitioned the government to continue it that way, fearing that many high-caste women would not be permitted by their families to study at a coeducational school.

There are many other medical schools for women in countries around the world—in Japan, China, Pakistan. A new one is in Afghanistan where a young graduate of the school in Pakistan, after coming to the United States for three years of graduate training, returned to her native city of Kabul. She went back to teach gynecology and obstetrics to a class of women students who only yesterday were wearing veils. This young doctor herself was veiled when her father put her on a plane for the United States, and, at the time, she said very solemnly that she would never wear a veil again. She is one of those who has helped to emancipate the women of her country from the long and enveloping symbol of seclusion.

In Africa, there are many women missionary doctors and the number of African women practicing medicine is growing. One girl who took her medical degree in the United States and is now teaching and practicing in her own country, Nigeria, is planning to return to the United States for further study in pediatrics. She feels that if Africa is to develop as it should, then the children of that continent must have good medical care and good health education.

To render medical service abroad it is not necessary, of course, to be a missionary. Dr. Louise Pearce, a graduate of Johns Hopkins, had worked with a team of men scientists at the Rockefeller Institute, testing various drugs for their effect against sleeping sickness, and then, about 1919, the group went to the Belgian Congo to carry out field trials of the drug tryparsamide. Working with the local officials, Dr. Pearce went from village to village for the extensive experiments that proved the efficacy of the drug for humans as well as for laboratory animals. The history of Africa has been greatly influenced by this work, for the death rate on the continent was markedly reduced by the drug, thereby bringing on some of the pressing problems of population in Africa.

In the public-health field many women have made significant contributions. One was the health commissioner of New York, Dr. Leona Baumgartner, an able administrator with extensive training in medicine and public health. While she was in office, before resigning to take up official duties in Washington, she greatly improved health conditions in New York. Moreover, she showed her interest in medical students by finding summer work for them so that they could see at first hand some of the problems and the challenge in the work of a metropolitan health department. There are many women in city, state, and federal health positions. This is a field of wide scope and responsibility and yet the possibility of regular hours makes it a practical type of medicine for a woman with duties in her home.

In the laboratory, women have made outstanding contributions to medical science. Dr. Florence Sabin was the first woman to be made a staff member of the Rockefeller Institute where she carried out extensive and valuable laboratory studies on the cell. After retiring from the Institute, she went back to her native Colorado and was alarmed and shocked at the low level of public health in that state. So, after one brilliant career, she began another in an entirely different field and started a campaign for better health laws and programs. She tackled the politicians, the apathetic public, and the medical men—she made history by her vigorous and able battle for better health in Colorado.

I could go on to describe other interesting women physicians in many different types of medical service. There are biographies about them, and autobiographies. Their scientific papers, too, have been published. A great part of this material would interest you, both in the women themselves and in their work. There is always pleasure and excitement in reading a true story of great human achievement. (I have listed some of these books at the end of this chapter.)

There are now questions to be asked and answered, and perhaps advice to be given. Some of it will apply to men and women; some will concern women only.

Certain qualities all men and women deciding on medicine as a career must seek and determine within themselves. The first in importance is integrity. This may seem trite and some will say that it should be taken for granted, but I do not agree that it should. Of all professional people, a doctor has the most responsibility in dealing with human beings and the most independent influence on them. Although we talk a lot about "team effort" of general practitioners and specialists in medicine today, the final responsibility for the diagnosis and treatment is the individual doctor's and he cannot shirk it or delegate it to anyone else. In certain aspects his position approaches that of a person in highest administrative position—even the President of the United States must, after evaluating the information his advisers have given him, come to his own decision and take the responsibility for the outcome. A similar responsibility for the doctor emphasizes his first obligation: absolute honesty in obtaining all necessary information, in studying it, and in arriving at the best possible solution. That, of course, is the key to the approach to any scientific problem; but the doctor is dealing with human life, which places his problem beyond the demands of ordinary scientific problems.

I remember one student who showed a singular lack of the requisite integrity, and she showed it in a most peculiar way. Her defect had not been obvious until she began examining patients and had to report what she found with no help from book or laboratory instructor or partner. Every time she listened to a patient's heart—and she was given the opportunity to practice and to learn over and over again—she reported a weird list of sounds that no one else could hear. She had the queer notion that she should report some kind of abnormality, and she did so on every patient. We tested this girl in every way and her instructors all reported the same result—that she gave the answer she thought was interesting and the one she thought was wanted, not the one actually derived from what she could really hear or see. Obviously this was a personality defect that unfitted her for medicine, or for any other scientific career where complete honesty is always essential.

Another unusual instance—fortunately with a happier ending —involved an Oriental student, who, in studying the pathological slides for an interesting case, persistently disagreed with the diagnosis made by the staff. After repeated study of the slides, she felt that a rare finding—something she had read about—had been missed. It took great courage for her, whose Oriental training had instilled a deep reverence for her teachers, to bring this disagreement to her professor.

In the beginning, this professor was interested in her findings because of the young woman herself; later, he was even more pleased that one of his students had the ability and the courage to find all her instructors mistaken. It is a fine illustration of two points that teachers in a medical school are constantly trying to make, and that students so often find hard to accept. First, a professional school faculty and students are colleagues. Second, the acknowledging of a mistake easily and gracefully is a necessary characteristic of the good doctor. This willingness to say "I'm wrong" is of particular importance to the physician, for so often he is the only person who knows whether he is right or wrong. If he hides his mistakes, medical knowledge is very poorly served. He should learn from his mistakes and teach others from them.

Another trait to be looked for in any person—man or woman— considering medicine, is energy. A doctor has to keep going when he is tired; he can't beg off for some minor complaint and, above all, a woman can never make being a member of "the weaker sex" an excuse for shirking her job. I have never met a more unpopular human being than the woman intern who tried to work off her night calls on her masculine colleagues by posing as a poor weak woman. She could dance vigorously half the night, play a good fast game of tennis or do anything else strenuous that she wanted to do, but night calls were something else again. I have known men who shirked, too, with imaginary complaints; but a woman in competition with men and with other able women just cannot afford this pose.

It should be understood, however, that a doctor's own health is an important consideration. Physical stamina is necessary to tackle a doctor's average day's work, and, while mental stamina and courage can sometimes take the place of physical strength, there comes a time when the needs of the doctor's health must be considered. Indeed, a person's own health can be a determining factor in a decision about a medical career, and the health of various well-known physicians has influenced this decision for them.

One woman, ill with tuberculosis in her student days, studied the disease after her own treatment and became a distinguished specialist in chest diseases. She learned to take care of herself and used common sense to limit her activities when she needed to. The famous Dr. Chevalier Jackson tells, in his autobiography, of his many bouts with illness and of what he did to regain his own health so that he could be of use to his patients and to medical science. Crippled children sometimes become interested in medicine and grow up to be orthopedic specialists. Good judgment, however, must always play its part about any decision concerning a medical career and one must decide whether, in spite of a physical handicap, he can plan a busy and active life. If experienced doctors and medical educators advise against the studying of medicine, then a person should settle for a less taxing substitute—and there are many satisfactory ones. On the other hand, anyone planning a medical career who has good health should be very thankful for it and keep well—an ill doctor cannot take care of his patients.

Here is a question I often ask applicants: Do you want to study medicine or do you want to be a doctor? It is deceptively simple and many applicants rush in to answer. I was talking to a pre-

medical group the other night and posed the question, leaving it
to them to decide. After the talk was over several of the group
came up to me, and one boy sidled over and said, "In case I am
asked that question when I am interviewed, what is the right
answer?" I told him, "Young man, you have missed the point of
the question—the answer must be yours."

If you don't like to study and read, if you avoid the library, if
you don't thrill over the news of scientific discoveries, and have
to be prodded by a deadline to finish your assigned reading,
then I don't think you will have a very good time in medical
school. You will probably forget that graduation is not called
"commencement" because of some old, quaint academic mistake; instead, it really means what it says and you are "commenc-
ing."

Speaking of reading, have you been tested for reading speed
and comprehension? There are ways that can help you if you
have difficulty. If you need help, get it from a reading teacher.
In any learned profession, such as medicine, the amount of reading necessary has always been great, but it grows continuously.
After a long day, some people just give up and read a whodunit
before switching off the light; others find the account of a new
drug or medical theory as fascinating as a thriller. It is really a
matter of habit, which reading you prefer, and you can take yourself in hand and establish one or the other as routine.

Colleges today are getting concerned about their graduates
who are neither interested in, nor capable of, continuing their
worth-while reading and their own education. I remember a
man who graduated at one of the large and famous universities
saying to me, "I haven't read a book since I got out of college"—
and he said it with a curious kind of pride. Colleges are trying to
stimulate their alumni in various ways, one being the new style
of alumni reunion—seminars, workshops, brief lecture courses
aimed at alumni and their wives—instead of the two or three
days of high jinks and nostalgic sentimentality that were the
custom. Some colleges send groups of professors to give conferences to alumni groups, keeping them informed of what is
happening in the educational world. Medical schools are particularly active in planning refresher courses and helping their
busy graduates keep up with recent advances in their specialties.

All these ideas are fine, some even filled with inspiration; but none is a substitute for sitting down to read or really to study on your own.

Once a student came to me and said, "I am bored to death studying medicine. Everything I do is an effort. I work hard and work all the time, and I just don't like to study that hard." I asked her what she was interested in and she said, "Painting." But I found that she had not been to a museum since she came to Philadelphia, and had not listened to any music, and she was, in fact, really bored. I suggested that she take the week end off, go to the art museum, hear some music, and forget about studying. At the beginning of the next week she dropped in to see me —a different girl entirely. She was ready to take my advice and give medical school a real try until midyears, and then make her decision. When that time came, she was calmer, less tired, and could make a more measured choice. She still did not want to study enough to do her work and she decided to withdraw, but she was better satisfied that her decision was right. This girl's experience is one to take into account—if studying bores you, you probably won't like medicine or medical school.

There are rare cases where a young person has not yet had the maturity to find reason for study. Such a person needs a definite goal before she can really work, or even know the meaning of hard study. These are the "late bloomers" who may not do well in high school or even in college, but who blossom out later in studying for a profession. Admission committees are on the lookout for them and take into consideration their total record and progress. Human beings rarely fit hard-and-fast rules and there are always "sports" in biological development.

One earnest applicant had pretty good grades except for a D in freshman biology. When I visited her college, her premedical adviser was very dubious about her having an appointment with me. He kept referring to the D as if it were the only grade on her transcript. The rest of her marks were perfectly respectable and I thought that her third- and fourth-year grades were more important than one she had made as a freshman. (Most of us have dark passages in our first year that we would like to forget.) In talking to the girl I learned that, in spite of the very deep discouragement which so much harping on the D had produced in her, she was genuinely interested in the study of medicine. It was obvious that she was sincere and, while she would never lead her class, she would probably do creditable work and become a useful doctor. We accepted her and I was happy when she completed her four years successfully and went on to make a good record as an intern. She had come from a large family in a small town, and when she entered a large university, she had had many adjustments to make; it was surprising that she had only one D in her first year. However, she did make the adjustments and had completed her work satisfactorily for the remainder of her college course. She is now a good doctor and I am proud of her.

Usually admission committees look with suspicion at an applicant who has too many low grades, or who started out well and then began to do poorly. After all, medical school courses are a continuation of what has gone before and certain tools are needed for use in medical courses. Committees do not believe a student who says, "But my grades will be better in medical school." If you do not have a good foundation in chemistry and biology, you are going to miss a good deal of the joy and wonder when, with the marvelous techniques that biochemistry can furnish today, you begin to study what goes on inside the cell. Only a few years ago the biochemist had to be content with guessing what went on after the products of digestion reached the cells. He could study the end products, but he lacked definite information about the chemical changes occurring in the intermediate steps. Now he can follow many of the reactions that he had to guess at before; also, now he can see where the guesses were right and where they were wrong. The whole story of the production of energy is unfolding before us, and by the time the beginning student of today is ready for biochemistry he will need an even better foundation of organic and physical chemistry than is required of the medical student now in his studies. Furthermore, when this student later finishes his medical school studies, he will know many more of the "why's" than the graduate of today.

There are numerous other advantages for today's beginner and one in particular should be mentioned. In the past, medicine worked by the rule of thumb—certain drugs and certain treatment were successful. This had been discovered by trial and error, but a good rational explanation was hard to come by. Today, many explanations can be worked out and this adds to the interest, even excitement, of those who are beginning their medical studies.

Another qualification that is very important for a physician has not been mentioned. It is compassion. I just looked up that word in the dictionary and it says: "Literally, suffering with another; fellowship in feeling." The example of usage that is cited is "womanly compassion." Now, since this is supposed to be a womanly trait, it should be one advantage that a woman physician has over a man. (This is not necessarily true, for I have known men as sympathetic and tender as any woman.)

True compassion is a wonderful characteristic, and, when one is dealing with cross and cranky patients, who may be ugly and quarrelsome with everyone, it is a wonderful protection both for the doctor and the patient. Unfortunately some people, and in particular some women, confuse this attribute with sentimentality. No doctor can afford to share the suffering of his patient to such an extent that he cannot use a painful treatment when necessary, or be so sympathetic that he produces self-pity in the patient. It is a difficult tightrope to walk, the middle ground between cruel indifference and maudlin sentimentality. Skill is required in making one's way, and this skill comes from experience —but it has to be founded on a real concern for human beings.

For a young person trying to decide whether he or she belongs in medicine, there are many ways of testing interest. A large number of our applicants work as volunteers in a neighborhood hospital, seeing for themselves whether they really want to undertake the day-by-day care of sick people. The volunteer can be a very valuable member of a hospital staff and there are all sorts of places where she can be useful. The Candy Stripers, for instance, help the busy nursing and medical staff and they also help the patients in many ways. Some help in the operating room; some act as receptionists or information clerks in the clinics or in a doctor's office. Some girls, interested in science, work in the laboratory, and when they are skillful enough, they may earn something to save for their future college and medical-school expenses. There are many places where they can find out what goes into a doctor's day and so see for themselves if they would like to spend their future as he does.

In planning a medical career, what preparation is needed? To find out the courses actually required, one would be well advised to see a copy of the Admission Requirements published each year by the Association of American Medical Colleges. A copy almost surely will be in the nearest college library and it will give, for each medical school in the country, the list of college courses required for entrance, the estimated expenses, and so on. It also gives something about the history of each medical school and its philosophy—as much as can be contained in a brief paragraph. You will find very little difference in the science courses required for entrance to the eighty-six schools, but you will find differences in the size of the classes, the number of women in the entering class, the tuition, the estimated expenses, and scholarship policies.

If you are fortunate in having funds, either personal or from your family, then expense need not concern you. You can choose for other reasons—size and reputation of school, location, whether private or public, with glances at the curriculum as outlined in the school's bulletin. Be sure to find out if a school means that a minimum of science courses is acceptable, and if they actually want you to know your own language and have a broad general education that will make you a more interesting person to your patients, your colleagues, and yourself. Many medical faculties really mean this, but some still stress science at the sacrifice of the humanities. Then, too, some colleges themselves make it difficult for the premedical student to obtain a broad background, because, in order to satisfy requirements, a very large number of hours in the sciences must be taken. This poses a real problem for the student who wants to take a bachelor's degree, remaining as an undergraduate in college for four years and extending her education, instead of breaking off at the end of the third year to enter medical school—which, of course, can be done. Always remember, though, that it is done at the loss of a year—25 per cent—of your college education, and, as a Southern dean once told me: "That's a pretty good chunk of anybody's education, man or woman."

Is the degree necessary, the full four years of undergraduate study? The answer to that depends on the individual. If you have come from a home where books and ideas are discussed, if you have some knowledge of literature and language and the arts, and if you are mature, then the extra year may not make such a difference. But if you come from a home where you haven't learned bookish things, then you had better take the extra year and better use it for courses other than science; or if you are "young for your age," then grow up in the fourth year of college. You will need maturity to face the independent atmosphere of the medical school and to handle the human relationships that make up such an important part of medical care. (Perhaps I should mention that students who have had to drop out of college to earn money in order to continue their education often are mature enough to make the extra year more of a luxury than a necessity.)

In planning for expenses at medical school, don't try to get by on a shoestring. One place where medical students tend to cut corners is textbooks. In the first place, you need the books for your immediate studies and later you will need them in a scientific and medical library of your own. I hope that you do not sell or give away your textbooks as soon as you are through with a course. Some of them will grow outdated, but they can be replaced with newer editions.

If you have a good high-school text with your own notes, it will help you in college; the same holds true for college textbooks in medical school. I am always appalled at the many students who arrive at medical school without a single book, though they will need to review chemistry, physics, mathematics, and biology as they go along. Also, I hope that there is a book of poetry or something of literature that you just couldn't leave behind. Books are a bother and expense to move, but every time I have had to move mine I have thought of what Rebecca of Sunnybrook Farm said about her pink parasol: "You are the dearest thing in life to me but you are an awful care." Save on something else if you must, but not on books.

This is an interesting time we are living in. It is no time to choose to be a spectator instead of a participant. It is no time to waste intelligence which might help solve some of the problems, some of the shortages, some of the needs. If you are interested in medicine as a career, find out about it; visit medical schools, ask questions, and don't be discouraged. At the age of eighty-five, Dr. Catharine Macfarlane, who has had a long and inspiring life practicing, teaching, and studying to detect cancer, says: "It doesn't take unusual intelligence and brilliance to be a doctor. It does take common sense and hard work." If you are serious about a medical ambition, you can succeed. You can open doors, you can find funds, you can study medicine—and practice it—for all your active life!

Here are some books I have found interesting, and I suggest that you read them. They have to do mainly with women doctors and, therefore, will be of particular concern to women; but they will be of value to men readers as well.

ALSOP, GULIELMA FELL, *History of the Woman's Medical College of Pennsylvania*, 1850–1950. Philadelphia, J. B. Lippincott, 1950. 256 pp.

BAKER, RACHEL M., *The First Woman Doctor:* the Story of Elizabeth Blackwell, M.D. New York, J. Messner, Inc., 1944. 246 pp.

BAKER, SARA JOSEPHINE, *Fighting for Life*. New York, Macmillan, 1939. 264 pp.

BARRINGER, EMILY DUNNING, *Bowery to Bellevue:* the Story of New York's First Woman Ambulance Surgeon. New York, Norton, 1950. 262 pp.

BLUEMEL, ELINOR, *Florence Sabin, Colorado Woman of the Century*. Boulder, University of Colorado Press, 1959. 238 pp.

FLOYD, OLIVE B., *Doctora in Mexico:* The Life of Dr. Katherine Neel Dale. New York, G. P. Putnam's Sons, 1944. 270 pp.

HAMILTON, ALICE, *Exploring the Dangerous Trades*. Boston, Little, Brown, 1943. 433 pp.

JACKSON, CHEVALIER, *The Life of Chevalier Jackson:* An Autobiography. New York, Macmillan, 1938. 229 pp.

LOVEJOY, ESTHER C. P., *Women Doctors of the World*. New York, Macmillan, 1957. 413 pp.

MORTON, ROSALIE SLAUGHTER, *A Woman Surgeon*. Philadelphia, F. A. Stokes Co., 1937. 399 pp.

TRUAX, RHODA, *The Doctors Jacobi*. Boston, Little, Brown, 1952. 270 pp.

VAN HOOSEN, BERTHA, *Petticoat Surgeon*. Chicago, Pellegrini & Cudahy, 1947. 324 pp.

WILSON, DOROTHY CLARKE, *Dr. Ida:* the Story of Dr. Ida Scudder of Vellore. New York, McGraw-Hill, 1959. 358 pp.

16 _New Opportunities_

IN MEDICINE

BY IRVINE H. PAGE, M.D.

DIRECTOR OF RESEARCH
Cleveland Clinic Foundation

DR. IRVINE H. PAGE

Born: 1901, Indianapolis, Indiana

Cornell University: A.B., 1921
Cornell Medical College: M.D., 1926
John Carroll University: LL.D., 1956
Union University: D.Sc., 1957
Boston University: D.Sc., 1957
Ohio State University: D.Sc., 1960
University of Brazil: D.Sc., 1961

Director, Chemical Division: Kaiser Wilhelm Institute, Munich, Germany,
1928–31
Associate Member: Rockefeller Institute for Medical Research, 1931–37
Director: Lilly Laboratory for Clinical Research, 1937–45
Director of Research and Member of the Governing Board: Cleveland
Clinic Foundation, 1945—

American Society for the Study of Arteriosclerosis: Past President
American Heart Association: Past President
American Medical Association, Section on Experimental Medicine: Past
Chairman
Council for High Blood Pressure Research: Executive Committee
Sociedad Inter-Americana de Cardiologia: Secretario-Tesorero Adjunto
"Methods in Medical Research": Chairman Governing Board
American Association for Advancement of Science: Former Vice-presi-
dent
World Health Organization: Expert Advisory Board

Author:
  Chemistry of the Brain
  Neurochemistry
  Hypertension: A Manual for Patients
  Arterial Hypertension: Its Diagnosis and Treatment
  Experimental Renal Hypertension
  Chemistry of Lipids as Related to Arteriosclerosis
  Connective Tissue, Thrombosis and Arteriosclerosis
Editor-in-Chief: Modern Medicine

I SHALL TRY to present to you only two facets of the very fascinating profession called medicine. One concerns the fun of it and the other its deeper significance which, for lack of a better word, I shall call its dignity. My purpose is to give you some insight into how to pick your career. I do not intend to try to persuade you into medicine, only to give some background which may be useful to you in making your decision.

I have personally experienced medicine in a number of its different forms: in private practice, working full time in hospitals, and doing full-time research in research institutes. I have enjoyed them all.

It seems to me that I might best begin this chapter by telling you something of the way in which I got into medicine, for the paths that lead to a medical career are many and varied and I think that you should recognize at once that there is no set entry into the world of medicine.

I graduated in chemistry, chiefly organic and physical. Since we had been given little or no biochemistry (this was forty-two years ago) I decided to have a look at the so-called "life sciences," physiology and physiological chemistry. My interest proved my undoing from the point of view of continuing as a professional chemist, for I changed from that and entered medical school.

Medical school then was quite different from what it is today. The buildings were old-fashioned and uncomfortable. Student dormitories did not exist. Not even a lunchroom was available. Laboratories were ill-equipped compared with the present. Of course, too, there were far fewer specialties at that time. For example, the study of the blood, called "hematology," was only beginning. Infectious diseases, such as typhoid fever and erysipelas, were of great significance. In fact, typhoid fever was the first disease discussed in Osler's *Textbook of Medicine*. Pneumonia was one of the most dreaded diseases. All this, of course, has been changed by the antibiotics.

There is one other difference between the medical schools of those early days and now. I suggest that our professors then were much less inclined to be the "good fellows" of the present. They were gentlemen and were friendly enough, but they did not welcome being called by their first names.

After finishing my internship at a large New York hospital, a curious pattern of events led me to be called to the Kaiser Wilhelm Institute in Munich, Germany. I was to initiate a department of "brain chemistry," which is a study concerned with the chemical reactions that go on inside your head.

At that time, we American people were not so much concerned with learning a language properly. We had no competition with Russian Foreign Language Institutes, and I, like many other young physicians, believed that English was enough. I had only a smattering of the language when I went to Germany, but after four years I had partially learned German and had come to realize what a powerful tool language can be in creating understanding among people. Given language and a subject of common interest, human beings seem to be able to get along with one another. I wonder if the world outside medicine and the arts will ever understand this.

It was 1928 when I went to Munich. By that time, the predominant position of Germany in medicine, which once had been recognized throughout the medical world, was slipping rapidly. Despite this decline, however, and despite the fact that German schools were no longer up to the quality of ours, there was, and still is, much to be learned by a couple of years in a foreign school. Subtly, and in many ways, one broadens his outlook and finds that having to battle to talk to people, to make himself understood in another language, leads to some degree of sophistication and even wisdom. Then, too, their ways of teaching and their understanding of people are different from ours. Who knows which is right?

After three years in Germany, I returned to the United States and spent seven years at the Rockefeller Institute for Medical Research in New York doing "clinical research." Clinical research begins with problems at the bedside, which are then channeled into the laboratory for solution. Frequently attempts are made to reproduce the patient's disease in animals so that it may be more intensively studied, and this combined care of patients with experimentation on animals can be a very satisfying activity. Also, research in the laboratory can be of special interest when its benefits go back to the patient. As one well-known example of this: it was in the laboratory that liver was shown to be a highly effective source of some substance necessary for blood regeneration, extremely helpful to patients with anemia.

At the Rockefeller Institute, I studied patients with high blood pressure (hypertension), kidney disease (nephritis), and hardening of the arteries (arteriosclerosis). It was an ambitious program —a good deal more ambitious than we doctors, with our limited knowledge, knew at the time—but I would not have missed it for the world.

In 1937, I joined the clinical research hospital and laboratories of a large pharmaceutical firm and stayed there for seven years. The work itself was not very different from that in academic institutions, but the pay was much better. With this pay, however, there came serious disadvantages in the form of constant pressure from the sales force and the business management of the firm. It is questionable whether fundamental research, which has no other object than to contribute to knowledge, can be successfully prosecuted in such an atmosphere. It is necessary, of course, that such firms make money, and there is much that I liked in their developmental research and in the industrial environment; undoubtedly, too, there are great opportunities in these surroundings and in this work, but the physician who contemplates such a job should look into the company and look into himself and at his family with more than usual penetration and understanding before he takes the jump.

One thing that has struck me most forcibly during my thirty-seven years as a physician is the remarkable change occurring in medicine during that time. Infectious diseases such as typhoid fever, erysipelas, syphilis, and pneumonia once dominated the scene. When I was an intern at Bellevue Hospital, there were often dozens of patients with typhoid fever on our wards. There was almost nothing specific available with which to treat these afflictions. Today, the old hospitals devoted to contagious disease have largely disappeared. Young doctors call almost anything wrong with the chest "pneumonitis" (inflammation of the lungs) chiefly because they do not see the point in trying to separate a whole variety of diseases—most of which can be cured by giving penicillin.

Perhaps my most vivid recollection of the period was having to stand by and watch youngsters die from pneumonia, knowing there was really nothing to do for them. When one could see in his mind's eye the lives of these young ones, and what the future might have held for them, the tragedy was all too evident.

Every physician has had experiences which don't fit into the usual textbook idea of the way things are. I have often felt that many patients know when death will occur. They do not fear it in the least. I recall a neighbor, suffering from cancer, whom I visited nightly for nearly a year. He never called me after I had gone home because he did not want to bother me. But about two o'clock one morning the telephone rang and it was my friend's wife, telling me that he wanted to see me right away. I hurried over just in time to have him say, "You are right." His pulse weakened and stopped within a few minutes. His remark referred to his decision in a debate concerning immortality which we had been carrying on for some months.

I also remember a wonderful boy named Tommy. He had rheumatic fever, but he seemed in reasonably good shape. One night as I passed his bed, he said to me, "I am going to die to-night." Quite naturally I tried to talk him out of what seemed a morbid idea, and gave no more thought to it. Early in the morning my phone rang and the nurse told me that Tommy had stopped breathing.

Heart attack, or "coronary thrombosis," apparently did not exist when I was a medical student. That is to say, we did not make the diagnosis because we did not recognize the disease.

Today, heart disorders constitute the major threat to civilized man. Most heart diseases, such as those resulting from high blood pressure or coronary artery disease, have no single cause such as an infecting organism, *i.e.*, the typhoid bacillus or the pneumococcus. Heart diseases have multiple causes—heredity, diet, environment, occupation, and a number of others.

The new era of medicine has brought in its wake a great interest in what is known as "epidemiology," an important aspect of disease too long neglected. As an illustration of the changing face of medicine, we now no longer look only at sick people, but also at well people to determine what keeps them from getting sick. This requires study of people in all parts of the globe, and particularly in those countries and lands where epidemics are more common than in ours.

There is also, here at home, an extending of medical practice into areas where there was comparatively little practice in earlier times, so that now we have "occupational" or "industrial medicine." Even this is not enough, and medicine has gone on into areas that are new to man himself, so that there is now "aviation medicine" and "space medicine," both concerned with environments into which man is entering with greater or lesser success.

In the new era of medicine, there have been many changes in its study and practice. Forty years ago physicians might seem to be reasonably expert in a great variety of diseases such as diseases of the blood, heart disease, kidney disease, and so on, but compared with today they had neither the preparation nor the understanding to deal with these diseases properly. I recall that, when I was a medical student, we students spent no more than a total of twelve hours studying blood diseases. Later, after we were in practice, trying to care for patients with pernicious anemia was terribly discouraging, especially since we knew only too well the outcome.

And yet even at that time, an attending physician in our hospital was puzzled by the fact that one of his patients always seemed to be better during the winter season when he ate a good deal of meat, and especially liver and brain. The significance of the observation, however, was not recognized until Minot showed that there is in liver a substance that cures the symptoms of pernicious anemia. I would like to suggest that this story be taken deep into the thinking of all young men and women in the study or the practice of medicine, for sometimes a simple bed-side observation can be transmitted into a great discovery—*provided* there is someone with the essential imagination to see and comprehend its meaning. The same observation can amount to nothing, and its benefits be delayed, when imagination is lacking.

Most interns today have far fewer patients to care for than we did, simply because now there is so much more to be done for each patient. Today's added knowledge requires that more examinations be given, more tests be carried out, more questions be asked. With all these requirements, the number of patients to each intern is necessarily limited. I recall so well the quiet nights at Bellevue Hospital when I would look down the long rows of beds with patients for whom I was responsible. Often there were a hundred or more, people with every sort of ailment and most of them very sick. Furthermore, each had his own story to tell, and many of them wanted someone to sit and listen.

Some of the stories were unbelievable and I remember one, in particular, that was told me by a quiet and obviously well-educated man of about forty who had a kidney infection and was slowly dying. I got to know him well during his several months' stay and learned that he had been an officer in the Czar's army. His stories of his contacts with the Czar and his family were fascinating, but I was frankly a little dubious. He asked me to return his effects to his wife in Russia if he died. When it became necessary to do so, I had to look over what should be sent. To my amazement, there in his shabby room was one of the most extraordinary collections of documents and photographs one could imagine, convincing anyone of the important part my patient had played during his life in Russia. With today's antibiotics we could have cured that man—and I would never have had the opportunity, or have taken the time, to know him.

It is strange that in our rapid advance there is, occasionally, an accusation that medicine has lost its warm and intimate regard for the individual and has become heartless, cold, and "scientific." I don't believe this for a minute; but even if it were true, let us have it that way. Treatment has vastly improved, regardless of what we may have lost in personal contact, and our time now is taken up with many tools which return people to health. Just think of being able to open a human heart, repair it, and start it off again. In my days as a student, even to have expressed the thought of such a thing would have been grounds for certification for restraint in an asylum.

One more example of change must be cited. In Russia, 80 per cent of the physicians are women and I can see no valid reason why women should not, as a group, do just as well in medicine as men. The change from the early prejudice against women to a time when a woman could be physician to the President of the United States has occurred so fast it is hard to believe. (Here I would like to take a step outside of medicine and say that in another generation or two I believe there will be nearly as many women as men employed in industry. I think we might as well get used to the idea that "occupation housewife" is a dying symbol; the "battle of the sexes" as visualized by Thurber has been lost. A good thing, too!)

Change has not been limited to medicine itself; there have been considerable changes in medical practice also—among them the introduction of group practice and the growth of the great medical clinics. In my youth only the Mayo Clinic was well known and even twenty years ago there was still a good deal of grumbling from private practitioners about clinics, accusations that they were big, impersonal institutions run by businessmen in competition with the private doctor. To an extent, this is true, but actually both can and should co-exist without difficulty.

Clinics are really a form of group practice—on a very large scale, of course—and they are far from being the impersonal organizations that they are sometimes painted. Most of the staff are full time, are salaried, and work exclusively at the clinic. They collect no fees except through the clinic. Their offices and all equipment and services are provided for them. Clinic practice is much better adapted to patients with complicated medical problems where a variety of specialists may be involved in solving them.

I have been at the Cleveland Clinic since 1945—now as Director of Research—but all through that time I have never for a moment lost sight of the value of the private practitioner. I know so well how true it is that often the neighborhood physician can give an understanding and friendship that is difficult to find in large institutions. Yet, as I say, the two should co-exist, and, in reality, they need each other. I recall a patient who illustrates the value of both the large clinic and the family physician.

She was a girl of about twenty who had high blood pressure. There seemed nothing exceptional about her disease until the laboratory at the clinic reported that a most unusual pigment had been found in her urine. This was the sort of observation that only a very alert laboratory could make; but without information supplied by the home physician, who had been attending the girl, the laboratory observation might not have led to a diagnosis. The patient's home physician told us that this girl's social behavior was extraordinary indeed. During some times she was vigorous, athletic, and a very attractive young lady. During other periods, she became irritable, demanding, and infantile. Her mother had to feed her with a spoon. She claimed she was too weak to eat. All this information was put together and a diagnosis of porphyria made. It was a combined diagnosis, the physician and the laboratory working together, helping each other and needing each other.

It has been my observation that those who like working in teams, like working with a group of physicians, for example, do best in clinic practice. Those who like complete independence should not try it. Neither of these forms of practice is necessarily better than the other; they are just different.

While discussing some of the different areas in which one can work in medicine, we must, of course, speak of teaching. It is common to both university and clinic hospitals, though undergraduate teaching is largely limited to the university. I think it is wise for those who wish to spend a considerable time in teaching to seek the university atmosphere.

So we can see that there are many paths which the young physician may follow—private, university, clinic, or industrial practice. They all have their advantages and disadvantages. I have tried them all and, frankly, I don't know which I prefer.

Medicine is a learned profession concerned with all phases of human life—birth, life itself, and death. No other profession penetrates so deeply and consistently into human existence. There has been an impression created in the past several years that the white armor of medical knighthood has become slightly tarnished. This impression has been created chiefly by the clash between government and the American Medical Association over a variety of subjects, but especially over who controls the physician. Many physicians are firm in resenting even the smallest interference with what is called "the doctor-patient relationship," and they strongly oppose the efforts of government to supervise and pay for the care of the elderly. They fear this is an opening wedge to "take medicine over" by controlling the purse strings.

Medicine is not a commodity with a fixed supply and demand and a fixed price. Some people, however, would make it so and they ridicule the unbusinesslike arrangements of the doctors. They do this until they become sick themselves. Human beings are very different when they are well and when they are seriously ill. That is often the reason that a child, after a long illness in a hospital, is more perceptive and more tolerant of other human beings. Sickness helps man look inward, it helps him destroy pride and understand his frailty.

I would like to offer a word of advice to medicine's critics. Before changing one of the fundamentals of medicine, there should be the greatest consideration and care because they have been elaborated over the centuries to fit the needs of people. The fundamentals are not sacrosanct, or above criticism and alteration, but they are not so much in error as some critics would make them. Medicine is now under political attack and its "old-fashioned" honesty is occasionally being questioned. Of course medicine is not infallible and some of these accusations have merit and should not be swept under the rug. But I can say, and say with full "old-fashioned" honesty, that thirty-six years of intimate contact with medicine and science have not dimmed the respect and affection I bear for my colleagues. Medicine, in some ways, may have lost some of its dignity, but that which is left is more firmly based on reality than ever before, and what remains is worth cherishing.

Many physicians will agree with me that the spiritual values of medicine equal or transcend the material values. This may not be the place for a discussion of man's nature, but I would like the thoughtful among the younger generation not to discard those values that are indissolubly associated with man's spirit. The spirit and the soul are hard to define, and they are concepts often encrusted with theology which is confusing to the average person. I personally happen to find a certain logic, compatible with my own feelings, in the view that life has a purpose, which purpose is eternal, and that the individual has an eternal life, and, correspondingly, an eternal responsibility. The inequities of our life on earth, which at times may seem difficult, cannot seem unjust to a person living eternally. Christ taught this and died for it. Have we proof that this is not so? I know of none. Such views may not necessarily be a part of the dignity and the deeper meaning of medicine, but to me they have given satisfaction.

There is another aspect of medicine I consider currently of supreme importance. All of you know of the medical mission of Albert Schweitzer, the Mellons, Tom Dooley and the ship, *Hope*. There are others, but these will serve to illustrate the thesis that the great mass of mankind desperately needs food and medical care. Many men may be momentarily curious about astronauts, men on the moon, and thermonuclear war, but an infinitely greater number of men are concerned with a day-by-day need of food and some form of medical care. This is a great and exciting challenge to the practitioners of medicine and I would confidently anticipate that, probably within fifty years, most of our young physicians will have had experience in giving help, in the forms of food and medical care, to the less privileged peoples of the earth.

Why does medicine occupy such an important place in the hearts as well as the heads of mankind? Quite simply because it deals with the inner secrets, as well as the bodies, of individuals. Each of us thinks of himself as unique, with problems, physical and spiritual, not shared by others. Some of these problems can be dealt with by physicians, but only if they themselves are men of sufficient stature to do so, of superior knowledge and wisdom. This aspect of medicine has always been important and always will be; it gives medicine its true dignity. In dealing with both the material and the spiritual aspects of man, a physician is not a minister, a priest or theologian; but he, like them, must have sympathy and understanding and the union of these with his patient.

There is one last aspect of the dignity of medicine that I have personally much enjoyed; medicine and science provide a universal language. You can travel almost anywhere in the world and find people who will welcome you, and with whom you can have an immediate bond of friendship and common interest. I have found that the brotherhood of medicine is heart-warming.

Sometime ago, a small group of us went to Russia for a three-week visit. I was naturally a bit excited about what would happen. Actually, when we were met at the airport by a charming and smiling professor of cardiology, I came back to earth with the feeling that doctors are awfully nice people. Nothing during our stay altered that feeling.

Moreover, wherever I go, I have the belief that somehow medicine is a great universal solvent which can help amalgamate people. This would appear self-evident, but it needs re-emphasizing today lest we forget. At the moment we are so busy trying to put people on the moon, giving away large sums of money, and building up our armaments, that the simple truths of what men want and live by are being slowly lost.

I don't think I would have stayed in medicine if it hadn't been fun—great fun. It is really an exciting profession—not overpaid, and often grossly underpaid if one is salaried. It requires far more time than most other human endeavors, but I have thoroughly enjoyed it.

The most gratifying aspect to me has been in seeing and participating in the enormous growth of the medical sciences. When I graduated from medical school, serious dealing with mechanisms hardly existed. People were more interested in observing and describing diseases than in trying to find out what causes them, but to get a true understanding of disease one must learn how each step comes about. For example a pneumococcus starts to multiply in your lungs. The lungs begin to react against it, and then the whole body mobilizes its resources to enter the fight. This involves countless physical and chemical phenomena which must be understood. These are the mechanisms of disease and it is appreciation of them by the physician that gives depth and understanding to medicine. I have had the fun of seeing the study of mechanisms of all diseases burgeon in my time, and it has been my privilege to be actively engaged in the development of three great fields—brain chemistry, hypertension, and arteriosclerosis.

In discussing this burgeoning of medical science, it might be of interest, and also encouraging, to mention how swiftly the growth has come about. I remember vividly, back in earlier days, trying to persuade the then editor of the *American Heart Journal* to publish one of our articles on kidney function. He refused on the basis that the kidneys had nothing to do with heart disease. Today, the kidneys seem as busy with the problem of controlling the body's blood pressure as they are with forming urine.

The development of the chemistry of the brain is a good example of the opportunities that lie in medicine. In 1928, when I had finished my internship, I was invited, as I have mentioned, to form a department of brain chemistry in Munich, Germany, and I accepted. To my astonishment I found that there was no such department anywhere in the whole world. Two years later, I discovered that a J. L. W. Thudichum had worked on the subject, but he had done his work in the last century. Physicians and scientists had, of course, done occasional pieces of work on the brain; but none of this work had been formulated into a distinctive body of knowledge.

I realized how true this was when, in 1931, my wife and I returned to the United States—but not to study the chemistry of the brain; instead, to work on heart disease. There simply was no research in brain chemistry anywhere in the United States at that time. Yet when you think about it, what could be more important than the chemical reactions that go on in your head? However, early in the 1930's, it was hard to persuade anyone that this was true. I know because I tried and tried hard. Today, of course, the field is a big one, employing many hundreds of able scientists, and some persons take for granted that there has always been such a field.

Still another example of the unlimited opportunities constantly with us in medicine is the development of knowledge of arterio-sclerosis, or hardening of the arteries. Today, it is almost in-conceivable that so-called heart attacks were not recognized by most good physicians until about 1928. Actually, they were de-scribed some years before that time; but the idea that a blood vessel which nourished the muscle of the heart could get plugged up, thereby slowing down the flow of blood into the heart and causing a "heart attack," had not caught on. Now we know that coronary thrombosis, or "myocardial infarction," is one of the most common diseases among civilized man. "Heart attack" and "cholesterol" are on everybody's lips today.

The mention of cholesterol reminds me that until about 1932 little was heard about cholesterol or steroids. Cholesterol itself had been known for many years, and a few knew that it possibly had something to do with hardening of the arteries. I recall its being mentioned to me as a senior medical student in 1925; but I had already separated, in 1922, a new cholesterol-like substance from, of all things, starfish eggs. I gave it the beautiful name "asteriasterol." The medical world couldn't have cared less!

Little by little more was discovered about cholesterol, but no real attention was paid it until the discovery that one of the hormones in the cortex of the adrenal glands had a similar chemi-cal structure; and that if impure cholesterol was irradiated, the material became active as vitamin D, the bone-calcifying vitamin.

Immediately began a furious activity in both industrial and university laboratories, and, by 1936, so much information had been collected that we were justified in calling it a "field" of work. Indeed, even the name was changed from "sterol" to "steroid" simply to indicate that there were many substances which were like but not identical with cholesterol. A great variety of steroid hormones began appearing on the market, especially those that were related to the adrenal and sex glands. Think today of the great market for these hormones in the treat-ment of arthritis, rheumatic fever, lupus, skin conditions, etc. It is almost a whole industry in itself.

There is another even more important aspect of the once-lonely cholesterol. Now it is suspected of being at the bottom of the problem of arteriosclerosis. In 1911, a Russian scientist fed cholesterol to rabbits and found that some of it was deposited in the blood vessels and caused them to harden. Then it was found that in arteriosclerotic human blood vessels there was also a lot of cholesterol. Still the problem somehow didn't seem important. In 1930, I started work on it; but it was far from an all-consuming problem for me, and had no real urgency in it. I recall giving a talk on it in 1932 at the Philadelphia Metabolic Society. The talk was doubtless a poor one, but one thing was sure—there was little interest in it.

Compare that with the interest in cholesterol today. Most laymen not only know the term, but are greatly concerned with both the fat and cholesterol content of their food.

It is easier, of course, to recognize opportunities in retrospect; yet it must be obvious to anyone that opportunities in medicine today are far greater than the ones I faced, for the simple reason that we now start from a much broader base of knowledge. I have told you so much about the past, stressing it, because what I have described has all been accomplished in the *immediate* past, in one lifetime. I have done this in the hope that it will suggest to you what can lie directly ahead of you, in your lifetime.

No one can know what awaits any man or woman in medicine, and it may be pointless to try to foretell the discoveries that are at our finger tips; but surely no crystal ball is required to see that heart disease, the number one killer, will be "on the run" during the next generation and probably many forms of cancer as well. Also, the treatment of virus infections and their prevention almost surely will be found.

The coming generation will participate in so much that is exciting. The groundwork has been laid and methods of discovery are known. The will to engage in research is being nurtured by an aroused government and people, and in the wake of discovery will inevitably come the better understanding and the better practice of medicine. There are unlimited opportunities ahead.

When I think back to changes in my own time, one of the most satisfying to me has been the gradual development of more and more effective treatment for hypertension. When I started in this field, the treatment available could not be taken seriously. Many quackish remedies were being peddled, ranging from water-melon seeds to garlic, and even "whiffless garlic." Then there were extract of mistletoe, diets low in red meat, and also static electricity.

Many of my elders were completely set against lowering blood pressure in patients with hypertension. They held the view that blood pressure was raised by the body in order to pump blood through blood vessels that had been narrowed until they did not let blood through easily. Lowering blood pressure, they argued, would only deprive tissue of blood and so make matters worse. However, once we learned how to lower blood pressure, this notion turned out to be untrue. It is a great source of pleasure to see a disease, which at first seems hopeless, gradually come under control.

The subject of hypertension has now become a specialty in itself because so many different causes have been found for it. Unlike infectious disease, some diseases, such as hypertension, seem to have many causes. With them, it is not "one to the customer," as, for example, when a strepococcus finds you a hospitable host.

In this time of medical advance, few young people can understand how each patient is an actual area of study, and how stimulating it is to see a new patient with all his particular problems. The notion that medicine is full of dreary routine could not possibly be more false. (The only boredom I ever experienced in medicine was sewing up wounds after a senior surgeon had done the important work.)

It is true that every patient, in a sense, is a research problem and the really alert clinician, by sharp observation of only one patient, and by logical thinking, may solve some important medical problem. The opportunity to describe a new disease may come at any time to any physician, and his bringing out of hitherto unnoted relationships, his defining of new problems, which later may be solved in the laboratory, are limited only by his ability.

Besides the fun of medical practice, in any of its various forms, there is also enjoyment in teaching medicine, whether to undergraduates or on the postgraduate level to other physicians. I am not a teacher by profession or experience, but I have seen a good deal of it, and, in a small way can appreciate the satisfaction that comes from it.

If you do a good job in medicine, you will receive some respect, some money, and some position. Most of all you will know a satisfaction from within and receive affection from others. Experiencing these two will help you, perhaps, to penetrate those bounds which shut off and obscure the deeper meanings and purposes of life.

Beyond the dignity and the fun of medicine there is another aspect that interests me and that I greatly enjoy, even though it is avocational and I consider myself only the rankest amateur in it. This deals with the relationships of medicine that border on the philosophical disciplines.

It is supposed, by some, that a person becomes interested in these disciplines only when he begins to show his age, and this supposition I am willing to accept; but outside the limits of age, young or old, medicine provides a window through which the physician can see into the inner meaning of man's being. If he will but look with care, he will see the core of man's existence, and will wonder at it even though he will not understand. But the sense of wonderment is enough, for this is the beginning of rational thought. And rational thought is what God gave us to make us human.

THE HIPPOCRATIC

OATH

B<small>Y</small> *the middle of the Fourth Century,* B.C., *there had been put together in Greece a remarkable assemblage of scientific writings which has come down to us as the* H<small>IPPOCRATIC</small> C<small>OLLECTION</small>. *The books in the* C<small>OLLECTION</small> *number about one hundred and they were written by many men of varying experience and differing opinions; but throughout the books there is a consistent observance of the ideals and the teachings of Hippocrates, and his name identifies the* C<small>OLLECTION</small>.

The single most famous passage is the Hippocratic Oath. This oath is repeated today by students at the time of their receiving the M.D. degree, and its ideals are continued by physicians throughout the years of their practice.

One should note, however, that the oath has a number of versions, and, indeed, it is changed even today at schools where swearing by pagan gods may not be regarded as a proper oath. The version given here is perhaps the oldest and possibly the one most often accepted.

The Hippocratic Oath

I SWEAR BY APOLLO THE PHYSICIAN, AESCULAPIUS, HYGEIA, AND PANACEA, AND I TAKE TO WITNESS ALL THE GODS, ALL THE GODDESSES, TO KEEP ACCORDING TO MY ABILITY AND MY JUDGMENT THE FOLLOWING OATH:

TO CONSIDER DEAR TO ME AS MY PARENTS HIM WHO TAUGHT ME THIS ART; TO LIVE IN COMMON WITH HIM AND, IF NECESSARY, TO SHARE MY GOODS WITH HIM; TO LOOK UPON HIS CHILDREN AS MY OWN BROTHERS, TO TEACH THEM THIS ART IF THEY SO DESIRE WITHOUT FEE OR WRITTEN PROMISE; TO IMPART TO MY SONS AND THE SONS OF THE MASTER WHO TAUGHT ME AND THE DISCIPLES WHO HAVE ENROLLED THEMSELVES AND HAVE AGREED TO THE RULES OF THE PROFESSION, BUT TO THESE ALONE, THE PRECEPTS AND THE INSTRUCTION.   I WILL PRESCRIBE REGIMEN FOR THE GOOD OF MY PATIENTS ACCORDING TO MY ABILITY AND MY JUDGMENT AND NEVER DO HARM TO ANYONE.   TO PLEASE NO ONE WILL I PRESCRIBE A DEADLY DRUG, NOR GIVE ADVICE WHICH MAY CAUSE HIS DEATH.   NOR WILL I GIVE A WOMAN A PESSARY TO PROCURE ABORTION.   BUT I WILL PRESERVE THE PURITY OF MY LIFE AND MY ART.   I WILL NOT CUT FOR STONE, EVEN FOR PATIENTS IN WHOM THE DISEASE IS MANIFEST; I WILL LEAVE THIS OPERATION TO BE PERFORMED BY PRACTITIONERS (SPECIALISTS IN THIS ART).

IN EVERY HOUSE WHERE I COME I WILL ENTER ONLY FOR THE GOOD OF MY PATIENTS, KEEPING MYSELF FAR FROM ALL INTENTIONAL ILL-DOING AND ALL SEDUCTION, AND ESPECIALLY FROM THE PLEASURES OF LOVE WITH WOMEN OR WITH MEN, BE THEY FREE OR SLAVES.   ALL THAT MAY COME TO MY KNOWLEDGE IN THE EXERCISE OF MY PROFESSION OR OUTSIDE OF MY PROFESSION OR IN DAILY COMMERCE WITH MEN, WHICH OUGHT NOT TO BE SPREAD ABROAD, I WILL KEEP SECRET AND WILL NEVER REVEAL.

IF I KEEP THIS OATH FAITHFULLY, MAY I ENJOY MY LIFE AND PRACTICE MY ART, RESPECTED BY ALL MEN AND IN ALL TIMES; BUT IF I SWERVE FROM IT OR VIOLATE IT, MAY THE REVERSE BE MY LOT.